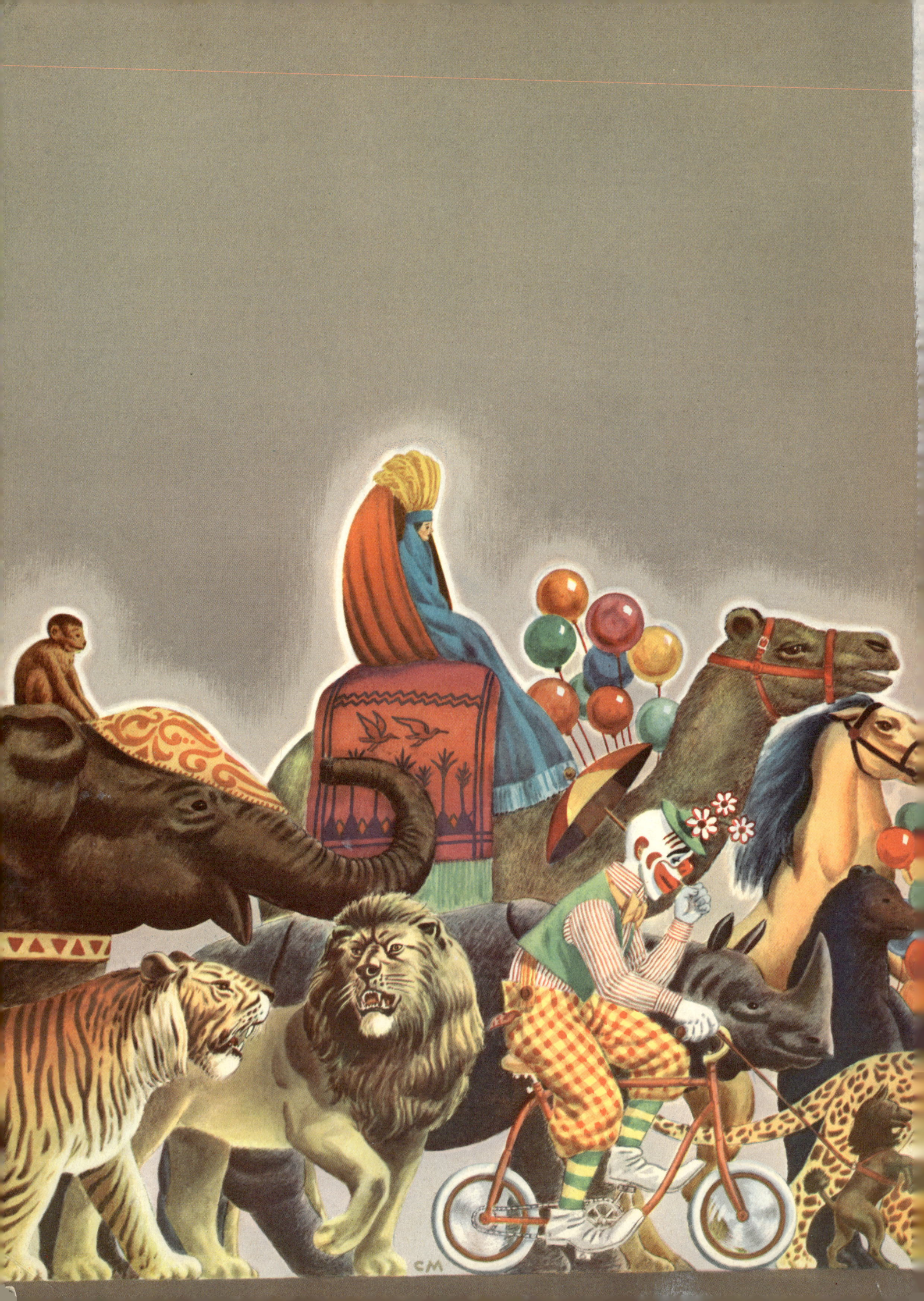

FACTS and FUN

A Treasure House of Adventure for Boys and Girls

The Junior Instructor

IN TWO BOOKS

The United Educators, Lake Bluff, Illinois

From The TANGLEY OAKS EDUCATIONAL CENTER

1

BOOK ONE

Edgar Owl says—
IT'S FUN TO LEARN!

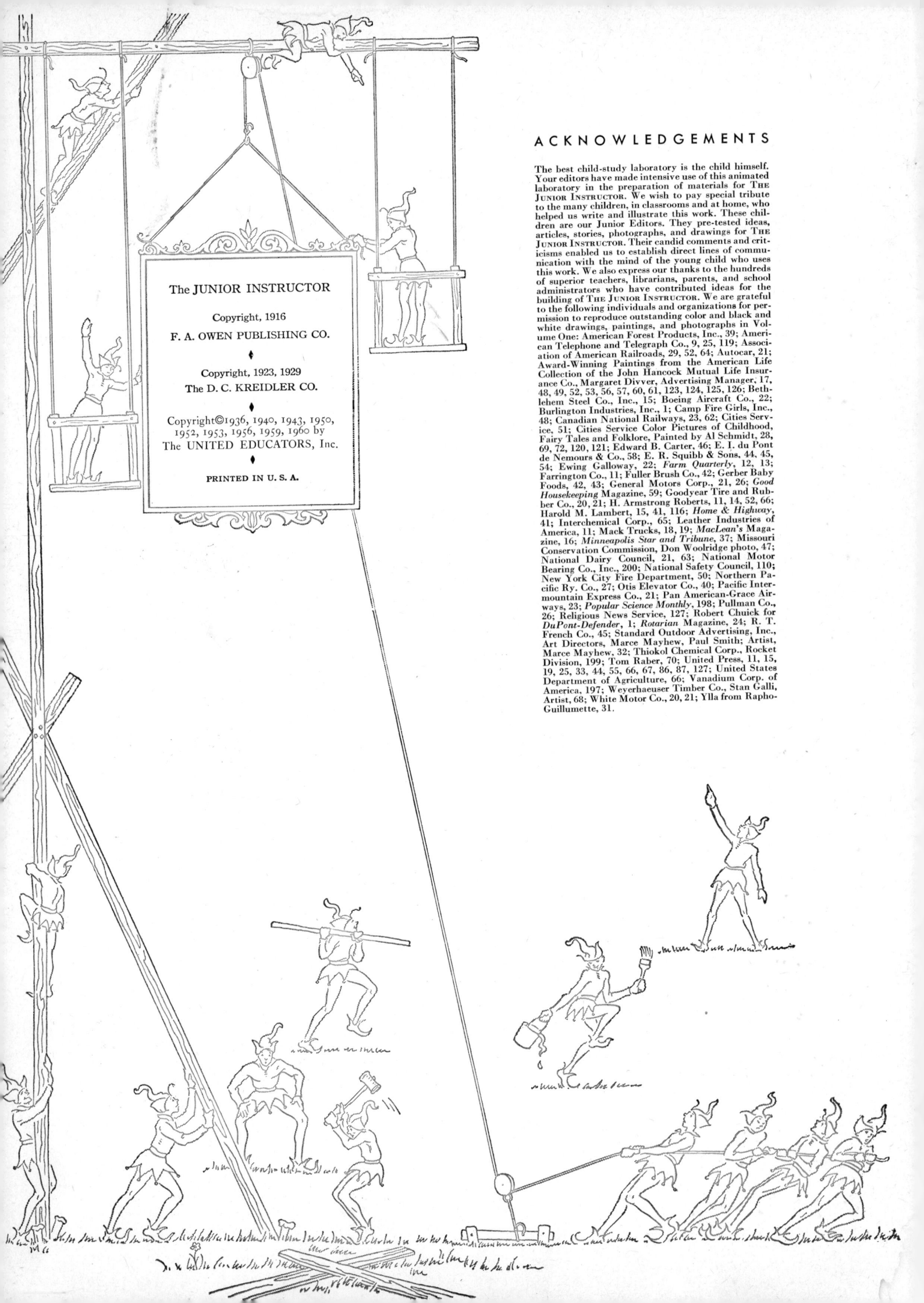

The JUNIOR INSTRUCTOR

Copyright, 1916
F. A. OWEN PUBLISHING CO.

Copyright, 1923, 1929
The D. C. KREIDLER CO.

Copyright © 1936, 1940, 1943, 1950,
1952, 1953, 1956, 1959, 1960 by
The UNITED EDUCATORS, Inc.

PRINTED IN U. S. A.

ACKNOWLEDGEMENTS

The best child-study laboratory is the child himself. Your editors have made intensive use of this animated laboratory in the preparation of materials for THE JUNIOR INSTRUCTOR. We wish to pay special tribute to the many children, in classrooms and at home, who helped us write and illustrate this work. These children are our Junior Editors. They pre-tested ideas, articles, stories, photographs, and drawings for THE JUNIOR INSTRUCTOR. Their candid comments and criticisms enabled us to establish direct lines of communication with the mind of the young child who uses this work. We also express our thanks to the hundreds of superior teachers, librarians, parents, and school administrators who have contributed ideas for the building of THE JUNIOR INSTRUCTOR. We are grateful to the following individuals and organizations for permission to reproduce outstanding color and black and white drawings, paintings, and photographs in Volume One: American Forest Products, Inc., 39; American Telephone and Telegraph Co., 9, 25, 119; Association of American Railroads, 29, 52, 64; Autocar, 21; Award-Winning Paintings from the American Life Collection of the John Hancock Mutual Life Insurance Co., Margaret Divver, Advertising Manager, 17, 48, 49, 52, 53, 56, 57, 60, 61, 123, 124, 125, 126; Bethlehem Steel Co., Inc., 15; Boeing Aircraft Co., 22; Burlington Industries, Inc., 1; Camp Fire Girls, Inc., 48; Canadian National Railways, 23, 62; Cities Service, 51; Cities Service Color Pictures of Childhood, Fairy Tales and Folklore, Painted by Al Schmidt, 28, 69, 72, 120, 121; Edward B. Carter, 46; E. I. du Pont de Nemours & Co., 58; E. R. Squibb & Sons, 44, 45, 54; Ewing Galloway, 22; *Farm Quarterly*, 12, 13; Farrington Co., 11; Fuller Brush Co., 42; Gerber Baby Foods, 42, 43; General Motors Corp., 21, 26; *Good Housekeeping* Magazine, 59; Goodyear Tire and Rubber Co., 20, 21; H. Armstrong Roberts, 11, 14, 52, 66; Harold M. Lambert, 15, 41, 116; *Home & Highway*, 41; Interchemical Corp., 65; Leather Industries of America, 11; Mack Trucks, 18, 19; *MacLean's* Magazine, 16; *Minneapolis Star and Tribune*, 37; Missouri Conservation Commission, Don Woolridge photo, 47; National Dairy Council, 21, 63; National Motor Bearing Co., Inc., 200; National Safety Council, 110; New York City Fire Department, 50; Northern Pacific Ry. Co., 27; Otis Elevator Co., 40; Pacific Intermountain Express Co., 21; Pan American-Grace Airways, 23; *Popular Science Monthly*, 198; Pullman Co., 26; Religious News Service, 127; Robert Chuick for *DuPont-Defender*, 1; *Rotarian* Magazine, 24; R. T. French Co., 45; Standard Outdoor Advertising, Inc., Art Directors, Marce Mayhew, Paul Smith; Artist, Marce Mayhew, 32; Thiokol Chemical Corp., Rocket Division, 199; Tom Raber, 70; United Press, 11, 15, 19, 25, 33, 44, 55, 66, 67, 86, 87, 127; United States Department of Agriculture, 66; Vanadium Corp. of America, 197; Weyerhaeuser Timber Co., Stan Galli, Artist, 68; White Motor Co., 20, 21; Ylla from Rapho-Guillumette, 31.

YOUR CHILD'S ADVENTURES WITH FACTS AND FUN
A Foreword to Parents and Teachers

There is no task in the world more important than yours. One who shapes the mind of a child shapes the future. The quality of training that you give your child will largely determine the degree of success with which he applies his natural gifts throughout life.

Priceless Experiences. THE JUNIOR INSTRUCTOR has been specially planned to make your task easier and more successful. It is designed to serve the child in his early years, when proper training is not merely important but imperative to his future happiness. The child, before he goes to school and in his early years of schooling, has an almost miraculous ability to absorb new experiences. He has a healthy curiosity and a desire to explore, to find out more about the world. These early experiences help to determine the directions of his development, which once started tend to persist. Both parents and teachers find THE JUNIOR INSTRUCTOR a treasure house of beneficial experiences for the young child and a limitless source of ideas for use in directing his interests.

THE JUNIOR INSTRUCTOR has been planned on the premise that every child has an individual personality. No parent or teacher ever denied this fact. Yet many times it is taken as a matter of course rather than as a challenge to provide the learner with those experiences which will develop in him a cultivated, well-balanced, and individualized personality.

A Plan for Successful Living. The child requires many selected experiences and the concentrated guidance of both parent and teacher, if he is to start on the high road to a happy, successful, and useful adulthood. The mental and emotional attitudes which your child will develop as he matures have their roots in the thousands of impressions and experiences of early childhood. His use of THE JUNIOR INSTRUCTOR will broaden and enrich this world of experiences. It will stimulate wholesome, creative, positive attitudes.

The child must learn to cope with his environment, an environment dominated by people bigger and more powerful than he is. For best results, the child's introductory experiences with his environment must be carefully planned. His world must be made understandable and meaningful to him. His environment must be "just his size" at every stage of his mental and emotional growth, as his clothing is just his size at every stage of his physical growth. Gradually he learns simple and unsophisticated facts about the world—his family, his community, the peoples of the world, and living things in it. He learns a little about science, though he may not know it is science he is learning. His mind and heart are stimulated by experiences in art and music and literature. He learns skills such as writing and reading and making rhythm.

It is essential that the child find enjoyment in his acquisition of experiences and skills. That is why the "FACTS AND FUN" approach of THE JUNIOR INSTRUCTOR has proved so successful with generations of eager young minds. These books demonstrate that the process of learning is fun, and that the possession of the learned facts makes life richer and more pleasant. A fact is of value to the child only if he can use it. What a great thrill the child feels in putting a newly acquired fact to use! THE JUNIOR INSTRUCTOR books are filled with down-to-earth, useful, *usable* information, which is unlocked with the golden key of the child's own interest.

Pre-tested for Interest and Comprehension. Who knows what interests a child? Adults can make educated guesses, but the legitimate answer can be given only by the child himself. *The children themselves* helped to form the blueprint for the revised edition of THE JUNIOR INSTRUCTOR. The editors and their advisers first obtained clues to child interests from thousands of parents and teachers of young children, then went to the children themselves for the final answers. With the assistance of outstanding kindergarten and primary-grade teachers, the editors pre-tested JUNIOR INSTRUCTOR materials in classrooms and with individual children. Ideas, pictures, stories, even colors of bindings were presented to the children, revised or replaced and presented again, painstakingly tested until our Junior Editors gave their enthusiastic approval.

The "Lifelike" Way to Learn. The young child has no conception of adult ways of organizing knowledge. "Science" and "Literature" and "Fine Arts," with all their many internal classifications and subclassifications, are purely arbitrary divisions for convenience in study. The natural world has no such pigeonholes into which to cram knowledge. The child knows no such divisions. He has his experiences in thoroughly unclassified order. After breakfast today he may ride his tricycle, observe a butterfly, come in for a drink of milk, hear a song, bounce a ball, come in to have the ball retrieved from the street, visit the neighbors, and watch the fire engine go by. The subject matter of his morning could be classified into at least eight categories, and three times that if his conversations and fantasies were included. But he would not understand or care if you told him he was learning hand-and-eye co-ordination, engaging in nature study, developing sociality, getting a safety lesson, and so on.

The editors have assiduously refrained from "logical" classification of the contents of THE JUNIOR INSTRUCTOR. These books have been planned as "fun" books. In their pages are unexpected doorways to fresh adventures, yet every section has been carefully planned to teach worthwhile facts.

Suggestions for Using The Junior Instructor

Very young children like to identify familiar things in pictures. They point to them and say "Horse" or "Cow" or "Truck" or "Plant." THE JUNIOR INSTRUCTOR contains a wealth of material for this simple and instructive type of observation and vocabulary experience. A little help from parent or teacher soon leads the child from merely identifying the subject to learning more about it in the accompanying text. Virtually every page in these books has been designed on two levels, so that it is equally useful to the pre-school child and the more advanced pupil.

There are countless ways in which THE JUNIOR INSTRUCTOR can enrich the curriculum at school and the child's learning experiences at home. Some of these are suggested in the following guide to JUNIOR INSTRUCTOR subject matter:

Animals. JUNIOR INSTRUCTOR interest surveys of children 3-10 years old show that the most powerful learning motivation in this group is aroused by animals, children, and characters of fantasy (fairy tales and folklore). For animal pictures and information, see **Vol. 1,** pages 10, 11, 12, 13, 14, 15, 16, 17, 31, 32, 33, 34, 35, 36, 37, 44, 45, 47, 62, 65–68, 82–83, 84–85, 86–91, 92–103, 125; **Vol. 2,** pages 7, 8, 9–51 (Birds), 57, 59, 62, 63, 71, 73–76, 78, 79, 86, 87, 96, 98, 99.

Arithmetic. See **Vol. 2,** pages 103-112.

Art Education. An important early lesson in art for the child is that artists, like children, sometimes draw something "just for fun." Freedom of expression in the child is encouraged by CRAZY-QUILT ANIMALS, **Vol. 2,** pages 73–76 and **Vol. 1,** page 32. Imagination is stimulated and the perception and identification of color are given impetus by the magnificent full-color illustrations throughout the volumes. Outstanding color reproductions of MASTERPIECES IN ART, **Vol. 2,** pages 127–157, provide the beginning of lifelong appreciation and enjoyment of great paintings. The necessary skills of drawing are set forth in **Vol. 2,** pages 113–126.

Attitudes Toward the Family. Healthful emotional attitudes toward parents, brothers, and sisters are encouraged by materials in **Vol. 1,** pages 29, 58, 59.

Attitudes Toward Learning. This entire work is designed to promote healthful attitudes toward learning. See especially **Vol. 1,** pages 9, 46, 61, 111–114.

Attitudes Toward Work. See **Vol. 1,** pages 9–48, 49–64.

Babies. At the age of three or four the child develops an intense and continuing interest in babies, both human and animal. This is nature's way of laying the groundwork for healthful adult attitudes toward family life. See **Vol. 1,** pages 14, 33, 42, 43, 55, 58, 59, 65–68, 95; **Vol. 2,** page 139.

Bird Friends. See **Vol. 1,** pages 15, 32, 33, 34, 45; **Vol. 2,** pages 9–51.

Birthdays. See *Parties* on this page.

Character Education. Little boys who want to be cowboys often see their heroes portrayed on television and in movies as cruel, vengeful, irresponsible gun slingers. In **Vol. 1,** pages 86–91 you will find an accurate and more healthful characterization of the cowboy as a worker on ranches, a community helper in the same class with the druggist, the grocer, the postman. See also character education material in **Vol. 1,** pages 28, 41–48, 49–64, 127–128, and **Vol. 2,** pages 162–176.

Children. Children are intensely interested in other children. See **Vol. 1,** pages 9, 11, 16, 18, 19, 23, 25, 26, 27, 29, 31, 39, 41–48, 52, 53, 55, 57, 58, 59, 61, 70, 111–114, 116, 119, 127–128; **Vol. 2,** pages 6, 8, 55, 57–67, 68, 70, 81, 86–88, 133–134, 135–136.

Community Helpers. See **Vol. 1,** pages 11, 16, 18, 19, 20, 23, 26, 27, 49–64, 111–114; **Vol. 2,** pages 92–96, 97–102.

Cowboy and Indian Lore. See **Vol. 1,** pages 24, 86–91, 163; **Vol. 2,** pages 77–91.

Creative Dramatics. THE JUNIOR INSTRUCTOR contains hundreds of different subjects which children may use in dramatic play. For example, the section on GROWNUPS AT WORK AND PLAY, **Vol. 1,** pages 49–64, is rich with ideas for creative dramatics. See also **Vol. 1,** pages 69–78, 86–91, 117–118, 120–126; **Vol. 2,** pages 77–91, 162–176.

Creative Handwork. See **Vol. 1,** pages 149–180.

Finger Plays. See **Vol. 1,** pages 104–106.

Folklore. See **Vol. 1,** pages 120–126.

Games. See *Play* on this page.

Geography. See *How Different People Live* on this page.

Health Habits. See **Vol. 1,** pages 31, 56, 57; **Vol. 2,** pages 68–72.

History. See **Vol. 2,** pages 159–161, 162–176.

Holidays. See *Parties* on this page.

How Different People Live. See **Vol. 1,** pages 16, 18, 19, 23, 24, 25, 28; **Vol. 2,** pages 55, 77–91.

Making Things. See **Vol. 1,** pages 56, 149–180.

Music and Rhythms. One of the most important elements of music–rhythm–can be learned painlessly. Remember the rhythmic ball-bouncing and rope-skipping rhymes of your own childhood? The best of these have been selected as RHYMES TO SAY AT WORK AND PLAY, in **Vol. 1,** pages 27, 41, 49, 50, 52, 63. See also the songs in **Vol. 1,** pages 137–148 and the rhythm band in **Vol. 1,** page 161.

Number Experiences. See **Vol. 2,** pages 103–112.

Outdoor Education. See **Vol. 1,** pages 10, 15, 34, 35, 36, 37, 38, 39, 79–85, 107–110, 181–196; **Vol. 2,** pages 9–51.

Parties for Children. See **Vol. 1,** pages 9, 69, 72.

People. See *How Different People Live* on this page.

Pets. See **Vol. 1,** pages 44, 45, 65, 93, 94, 95, 96, 97, 99.

Plants. See **Vol. 1,** pages 38, 39, 79.

Play. See **Vol. 1,** pages 41, 43, 49, 50, 52, 56, 57, 63, 104–106, 149–180.

Reading Exercises. See **Vol. 2,** pages 57–67.

Recreational Reading. THE JUNIOR INSTRUCTOR is fun to browse in. Sections especially useful for recreational reading include **Vol. 1,** pages 9–40, 41–48, 49–64, 65–68, 79–85, 86–91, 92–103, 120–126, 199–200; **Vol. 2,** pages 5–8, 9–51, 57–67, 73–76, 77–91, 127–158, 162–176.

Reverence. Prayers and graces suitable for children of all faiths may be found in **Vol. 1,** pages 127–128.

Safety. See **Vol. 1,** pages 50, 53, 107–110.

School. The child often needs help in adjusting to school. You can help him overcome his fear and distrust of this new situation by the use of materials in **Vol. 1,** pages 61 and 111–114.

Science. Simple facts of science are now introduced to children in the primary grades. See **Vol. 1,** pages 33, 34, 35, 38, 39, 40, 116–118, 181–196, 197–200; **Vol. 2,** pages 92–96, 97–102.

Sending Messages (Communication). See **Vol. 2,** pages 92–96. Sign Language, **Vol. 2,** pages 89–91. Writing, **Vol. 2,** pages 52–55.

Skills to be Acquired. Telling Time, **Vol. 1,** page 30; Talking on the Telephone, **Vol. 1,** page 119; Reading, **Vol. 2,** pages 56–67; Writing, **Vol. 2,** pages 52–55.

Social Development of the Child. See **Vol. 1,** pages 48, 111–114.

Space Travel. See **Vol. 1,** pages 197–200.

Story Book Characters. See **Vol. 1,** pages 69–78, 120–126; **Vol. 2,** pages 57–67.

Telling Times. See **Vol. 1,** page 30.

Things That Go (Transportation). See **Vol. 1,** pages 17, 18, 20, 22, 26; **Vol. 2,** pages 97–102.

Travel. See **Vol. 1,** pages 22–25, 26–28.

Weather. See **Vol 1,** pages 115–118.

Writing. See **Vol. 2,** pages 52–55.

The Board of Educators

*This distinguished advisory body enriches The Junior Instructor
with sound educational concepts and techniques.*

Chairman—CAREY CRONEIS, D.Sc., Ph.D., D.Eng.
Provost of Rice Institute
Houston, Texas

SELMER H. BERG, M.A.
Superintendent of Schools
Oakland, California

KARL BERNHARDT, Ph.D.
Professor of Psychology
Assistant Director, Institute for
Child Study, The Laboratory School,
University of Toronto, Canada

WILLIAM VAN TIL, Ph.D.
Chairman, Department of Secondary Education
School of Education,
New York University,
New York City

FRANCIS KEPPEL, B.A.
Dean, Graduate School of Education
Harvard University
Cambridge, Massachusetts

A. J. BRUMBAUGH, Ph.D., LL.D., L.H.D.
Consultant, Programs Branch
Division of Higher Education
United States Office of Education
Washington, D.C.
Consultant, Southern Regional
Education Board

E. T. McSWAIN, Ed. D.
Dean, School of Education
Northwestern University
Evanston, Illinois

Contributors and Editors

Editor in Chief
EVERETTE EDGAR SENTMAN

CATHERINE CORLEY ANDERSON
Recreational Psychologist, Writer of Verse for Children
Specialist in Artcraft and Creative Play

D. R. AUGSBURG
Teacher of Drawing

CAROLYN SHERWIN BAILEY
Author of *For the Children's Hour, For the Story Teller,
Stories Children Need*

VIRGINIA BAKER
Contributor to *Atlantic Monthly*
and Educational Magazines

CAROLINE FRENCH BENTON
Author of *A Little Cook Book for a Little Girl,
Margaret's Saturday Mornings*, and *The Fun of Cooking*

SUSIE M. BEST
Storyteller, Public Schools, Cincinnati, Ohio

HILDEGARD BLUMENSTIEL
Art Director of *Junior Home Magazine*

MIRIAM H. BRUBAKER
Former Director of Junior Kindergarten,
National College, Evanston, Ill.

BERTHA E. BUSH
Writer of Educational Stories
Author of *Great European Cities*

HAZEL CARTER
Playground Director, Public Schools, St. Louis, Mo.

ANN CLARK
Writer of Bilingual Indian Life Readers for
U.S. Indian Service

CARLTON J. CORLISS
Manager, Public Section, The Association of American Railroads
Author of Encyclopedia Articles About Railroads

RHUE COURTNEY
Director, Tangley Oaks Nursery School
Kindergarten Teacher, Lake Bluff (Ill.) Schools

FRED H. DANIELS
Director of Art, Public Schools, Newton, Mass.

HOKE DENETSOSIE
Navaho Indian Artist

MARGARET DIVVER
Director of Award-Winning Series of Paintings on American Life
for the John Hancock Mutual Life Insurance Co.
Selected by *Fortune* Magazine as One of America's
Leading Woman Executives

ANDRE DURENCEAU
Animal-Life Illustrator for *The National Geographic Magazine*,
for *Nature's Ways* by Roy Chapman Andrews, and for Other Books

CARROLL LANE FENTON
Internationally Known Naturalist, Writer, Illustrator
Author of *Basic Biology* and *Riches from the Earth*

DON R. FORSYTHE
Art Director, Tangley Oaks Educational Center, Lake Bluff, Ill.

STAN GALLI
Natural History Illustrator

HARRY ORRIN GILLET
Advisory Editor, THE AMERICAN EDUCATOR ENCYCLOPEDIA and
THE WONDERLAND OF KNOWLEDGE
Supervisor of Education, Museum of Science and Industry
Chicago, Ill.
Formerly Principal, Laboratory Schools, University of Chicago

LAURA HASSENSTEIN
Director of Practice School, Play Material, Games, Handwork
Pestalozzi Froebel Teachers' College, Chicago, Ill.

MABEL G. HEMINGTON
Primary Teacher, Horace Mann School, Chicago, Ill.
Faculty Member, Chicago Teachers' College

HOLLING C. HOLLING
Author and Illustrator of Children's Books

HOTAN-TONKA
Son of the Chief of the Bad River Band
of Lake Superior Ojibway Indians

FAYE MOORE JERNEGAN
Editorial Specialist, The Book House for Children, Lake Bluff, Ill.

VICTORIA S. JOHNSON
Director of Educational Research and Services
Tangley Oaks Educational Center

VERNICE KEENAN
First Grade Teacher, Lake Forest (Ill.) Public Schools

MARTHA BENNETT KING
Author of *Growth of American Family in History*
Folklore and Children's Literature Specialist
Director, Chicago Miracle of Books

MARTHA FELLER KING
Instructor in Art, University of Vermont
Contributor to Manual Arts Magazines

CROSBY J. LISKE
Technical Director, Tangley Oaks Educational Publications

ELISABETH L. MacHATTON
Senior Editor, The United Educators, Inc.

MARIAN MAKOUTZ
Speech Correctionist, Lake Forest (Ill.) Public Schools
BETTY MARTIN
Director of Children's Theater, Lake Forest College
MARCE MAYHEW
Artist and Illustrator
OLIVE BEAUPRÉ MILLER
Editor and Founder, The Book House for Children
RENALD G. MOORCRAFT
Nature Specialist, Tangley Oaks Educational Center
ARNOLD NEWMAN
Photographer for *Holiday* and Other Leading Magazines
EDWARD A. PARKER
Formerly Supervising Agent, Connecticut State Board of Education,
and Superintendent of Schools, Berlin, Conn.
SARA V. PRUESER
Author of *Our Dooryard Friends*
Contributor to Bird Magazines and Manuals
DEBORAH REICHERT
Chief Junior Editor, Primary Department, THE JUNIOR INSTRUCTOR
EDWIN C. REICHERT
Chairman, Dept. of Education, Lake Forest College
Author of Readers; Ph.D. in Education, U. of Minnesota

HAZELLE REICHERT
Kindergarten Teacher, Bell School, Lake Forest, Ill.
AL SCHMIDT
Artist and Illustrator
ALBERITA R. SEMRAD
Author of *The Zoo* and Other Books for Young Children
Winner of Awards in Field of Children's Literature
SUSAN SENTMAN
Chief Junior Editor, Intermediate Department,
THE JUNIOR INSTRUCTOR
MARY SHANK
Editorial Specialist, The United Educators, Inc., and
Publishers Productions, Inc.
MARILYN ROBB TRIER
Writer of Special Articles on Art, Music, and the Theater
ELEANOR USCHAN
Picture Editor, THE AMERICAN EDUCATOR ENCYCLOPEDIA and
THE WONDERLAND OF KNOWLEDGE
ALBERTA WALKER
Teacher of Reading and Dramatization
YLLA
World-Famous Photographer of Animals

JUNIOR EDITORS PRE-TEST STORIES AND PICTURES FOR THE JUNIOR INSTRUCTOR

CONTENTS OF VOLUME ONE

WHAT I LIKE TO SEE AND DO
   (Color Plate).................................... 9
   Animal Homes................................. 10
   Horses Wear Shoes, Too..................... 11
   Ladybug (Color Plate)....................... 12
   Bumblebee (Color Plate).................... 13
   Mother Kangaroo and Her Son Joey..... 14
   It's Dinnertime!............................... 15
   Life on the Farm (Color Plate)............ 16
   The Cow and the Car (Color Plate)...... 17
   Town Life and City Life..................... 18
   Where Do You Live?......................... 19
   Trucks (Color Plate).......................... 20
   Let's Take a Trip in an Airplane......... 22
   We Visit an Indian Chief (Color Plate).. 24
   We Visit Miss Cherry Blossom (Color Plate) 25
   We Visit Jose.................................. 25
   Let's Take a Trip on the Train............ 26
   Aunt Matilda Bakes a Surprise (Color Plate) 28
   Susan Gets a New Dress (Color Plate)... 29
   Learning to Tell Time........................ 30
   Whitey the Bear Says: It's Fun to Take a Bath!................................. 31
   The Rooster and the Hen (Color Plate).. 32
   Mr. Peacock (Color Plate).................. 32
   I See a Chick Hatched....................... 33
   How Living Things Fly...................... 34
   How Living Things Swim................... 35
   The Life Story of a Moth................... 36
   How to Collect Butterflies................. 37
   I Can Grow Plants........................... 38
   I Can Plant a Tree and Watch It Grow... 39
   How an Escalator Works.................... 40

BOYS AND GIRLS AT WORK AND PLAY 41
   Rhymes to Say at Work and Play........ 41
   Helping with Housework................... 42
   Feeding My Doll.............................. 43
   Care and Feeding of a Dog................ 44
   Care and Feeding of a Parakeet.......... 45
   Care and Feeding of a Pony, Horse, or Burro 45
   Fun with Books............................... 46
   Red Squirrel, What Do YOU Do All Day? 47
   Organizations for Boys and Girls......... 48

GROWNUPS AT WORK AND PLAY.... 49
   Postman (Color Plate)...................... 49
   Fireman.. 50
   Gas Station Man............................. 51
   Farmer (Color Plate)........................ 52
   Policeman (Color Plate).................... 53
   Druggist....................................... 54
   Queen Elizabeth II.......................... 55
   Nurse (Color Plate).......................... 56
   Doctor (Color Plate)......................... 57
   Bringing Baby Home........................ 58
   Mother................................... 58-59

   Secretary (Color Plate)..................... 60
   Teacher (Color Plate)....................... 61
   Father Catches a Fish....................... 62
   Milkman....................................... 63
   Machinist (Color Plate)..................... 64

ANIMAL BABIES (Color Plates)........... 65

CREATIVE DRAMATICS (Color Plates).. 69

WONDERS OF NATURE
   How Seeds Travel............................ 79
   What BIG Means............................ 80
   What Lives in the Grass.................... 82
   What Lives in the Water................... 84

COWBOYS (Color Plates).................. 86

LET'S READ ABOUT THESE ANIMALS
   Owl (Color Plate)............................ 92
   Turtle (Color Plate)......................... 93
   Rabbit... 94
   Chick.. 95
   Kitten (Color Plate)......................... 96
   Dog (Color Plate)............................ 97
   Squirrel.. 98
   Chinchilla..................................... 99
   Turkey Gobbler (Color Plate)............. 100
   Goat (Color Plate)........................... 101
   Horses... 102
   Cattle.. 103

FINGER PLAYS............................... 104

BE YOUR FAMILY FIRE CHIEF......... 107

NEW FRIENDS AT SCHOOL............. 111

MY WEATHER BOOK...................... 115

HOW TO TALK ON THE TELEPHONE. 119

FRIENDLY GIANTS FROM MAKE-BELIEVE LAND
   (Color Plates)................................ 120
   John Henry (Color Plate)................... 120
   Gib Morgan (Color Plate).................. 121
   Fire Fightin' Mose........................... 122
   Pecos Bill..................................... 123
   Paul Bunyan (Color Plate)................. 124
   Stormalong (Color Plate)................... 125
   Joe Magarac.................................. 126

MY PRAYERS (Prayers and Graces)..... 127

PLAYS, GAMES AND ACTIVITIES..... 129
   Tap and Run.................................. 130
   Squirrel in the Tree.......................... 130
   Days of the Week............................ 130
   Oats, Peas, Beans, and Barley Grow.... 131

Animals	131
Our Gallant Ship	131
What Is It?	131
Planting Potatoes	132
London Bridge	132
Sun Dial	132
Statues	133
Drop the Handkerchief	133
Buzz	133
Pass Ball	133
Prisoner's Base	133
Still Pond	133
French Blind Man's Buff	134
Fox Trail	134
Three Deep	134
Cross Tag	134
Ball and Bases	134
I Put My Right Hand In	135
The Farmer in the Dell	135
Catch the Salmon	135
The Mulberry Bush	136
Simon Says "Thumbs Up"	136
Siberian Man Hunt	136
Circle Ball	136

THE CHILDREN'S MUSIC

Holy Night! Peaceful Night!	137
Home, Sweet Home	138
Farmyard Song	139
The Birdies' Ball	140
Alphabet Song	141
A Thank-You Song	141
Lullaby	142
The Bird's Nest	142
Soap Bubbles	142
How to Make a Shoe	143
An Indian Cradle Song	144
Falling Leaves	145
Winter Sports	145
The Kitty and the Mouse	146
The Snow Fairies	147
The Star-Spangled Banner	148

CREATIVE OCCUPATIONS ... 149

Clay Modeling	152
Sock Dolls	155
Spool Furniture	158
Spool Dolls	160
Our Neighborhood Band	161
A Peep Show and Moving Pictures	162
Playing Indians	163
Games for Juniors to Make	165
A Croquet Set	166
A Book of Surprises	167
Fun With Valentines	168
May Baskets	170
Party Suggestions	172
Costumes for Plays	173
Plans for Vacation Days	174
Floating Toys	175
Hallowe'en Favors	176
Thanksgiving	177
Christmas Gifts	178
Stick Printing	179
Fresco Painting	180

THE QUESTION BOX ... 181

What *Questions*	181
Why *Questions*	186
How *Questions*	190
Where *Questions*	194

SPACE SHIPS ... 197-200

The very best gifts at my party
Are my books of facts and fun.
They're full of a world of surprises,
I discover them one by one.

I look in my books, and what do I see?
A cow, a bee, a fish in the sea,
An Indian chief, a kangaroo,
All that I like to see and do.
I visit a farm, I ride on the train,
I learn how a pilot flies a plane,
How chicks are hatched, how to plant a tree.
Learning is fun! That's for me!

WHAT I LIKE TO SEE AND DO

ANIMAL HOMES

by Carroll Lane Fenton
Illustrated by the Author

The cottontail rabbit may live in a hollow log on stormy days. Another home for Bunny is a tangle of grass or weeds. Bunny is hard to see in the grass.

This little fish, the stickleback, makes a nest of threads produced inside its body. Mother lays the eggs and swims away. But Father stays close to home, guarding the eggs until they hatch into baby sticklebacks.

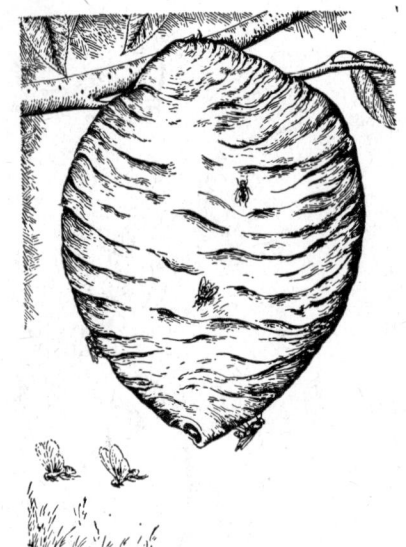

This spider lives in the tentlike shelter above her web. (You may find it by the arrow in the picture.) The web is not her home but is the trap in which she catches her food. Some spiders live in holes in the ground and go out to hunt their food.

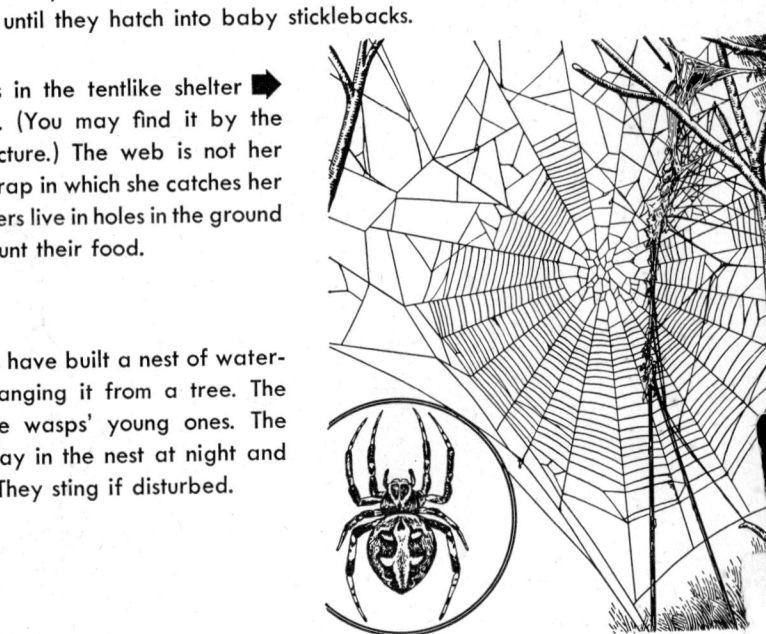

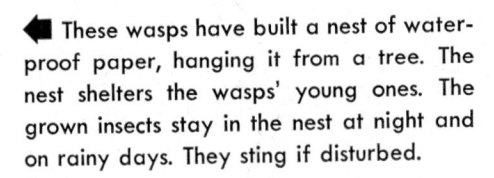

These wasps have built a nest of waterproof paper, hanging it from a tree. The nest shelters the wasps' young ones. The grown insects stay in the nest at night and on rainy days. They sting if disturbed.

In summer the black bear wanders about, but its winter home is a den under logs or a fallen tree. Here it sleeps, or hibernates.

Prairie dogs dig holes in the ground, piling the dirt around their doorways. They like to have neighbors, so they live together in "towns."

Beavers build houses in lakes or ponds. When autumn comes, the beavers mend their houses with sticks and plaster them with mud to keep them warm.

The whitefooted mouse builds a nest of twigs, bark, a grass. He goes out at night for seeds and other food wh he has stored under stones or logs.

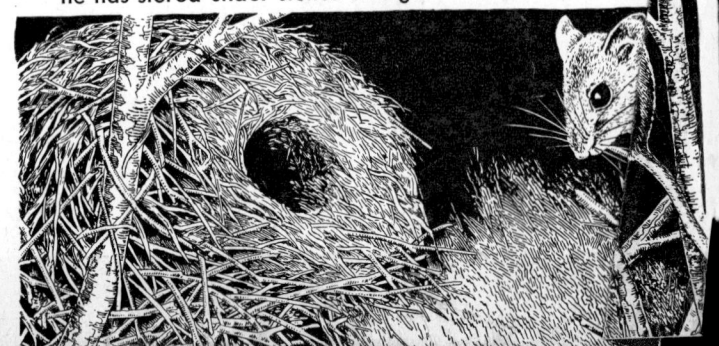

HORSES WEAR SHOES, TOO

You wear shoes. Horses, too, wear shoes. They wear them to keep their feet from breaking and wearing away. A big farm horse wears horseshoes. A pony for you to ride wears horseshoes.

⬅ A big farm horse and a little pony. Both wear shoes.

The blacksmith makes horseshoes. He makes them of iron. He carefully shapes the shoes on his anvil. The blacksmith nails the shoes on the horse. This does not hurt the horse. A horse's hoof is made of horn, somewhat like your fingernails. The horse is not hurt when its shoes are nailed on, any more than you are hurt when your nails are cut.

⬅ Do you like to get new shoes?

The Ladybug

The ladybug is one of our best friends. It helps save oranges and other fruits from insects that would destroy them. Harmful insects suck the nourishing sap from fruit trees and weaken them. They also spoil the fruits. Ladybugs eat harmful insects. In California, men go up to the mountains every year, to the places where the ladybugs sleep during winter. They collect the sleeping ladybugs and carry them down to the valleys. In spring, farmers turn the ladybugs loose in their orchards, and they eat the sap-sucking insects. This ladybug is eating an aphid on a leaf.

This is how big the ladybug really is.

This is the larva, or young of the ladybug.

The Bumblebee

This bumblebee is visiting an apple blossom. The bumblebee has a long hollow tongue like a soda straw. It sucks nectar from flowers through its long tongue. The bumblebee is the only bee with a "soda straw" long enough to reach away down inside the red clover flowers. When it sucks nectar from flowers, it carries pollen from flower to flower. The flowers use the pollen to help make seeds. New red clover plants grow from the seeds. Only the bumblebee can help red clover plants make seeds. Cows like to eat red clover. They make it into milk, from which we get butter, cheese, and ice cream. So the bumblebee helps us to have ice cream!

This is how big a bumblebee is.

MOTHER KANGAROO AND HER SON JOEY

The mother kangaroo carries her baby in a fur-lined pouch. A baby kangaroo is the size of a bee when it is born. It is blind and hairless. But it finds a way to its mother's pouch at once. It stays there until it is three or four months old. Then it comes out to nibble grass beside its mother. When it is scared, it dives headfirst back into the pouch. When a big kangaroo is scared, it can leap high and far. Then the baby kangaroo gets a thrilling ride in its mother's pouch. A baby kangaroo is called a joey. Most of us go to a zoo to see a kangaroo. People in Australia can see kangaroos out in the country.

WHERE DO YOU LIVE?

This picture shows a city, a suburban town, a rural town, and farms. Which kind of place do you live in? How is it different from other places in the picture? What kind of place would you like most to visit?

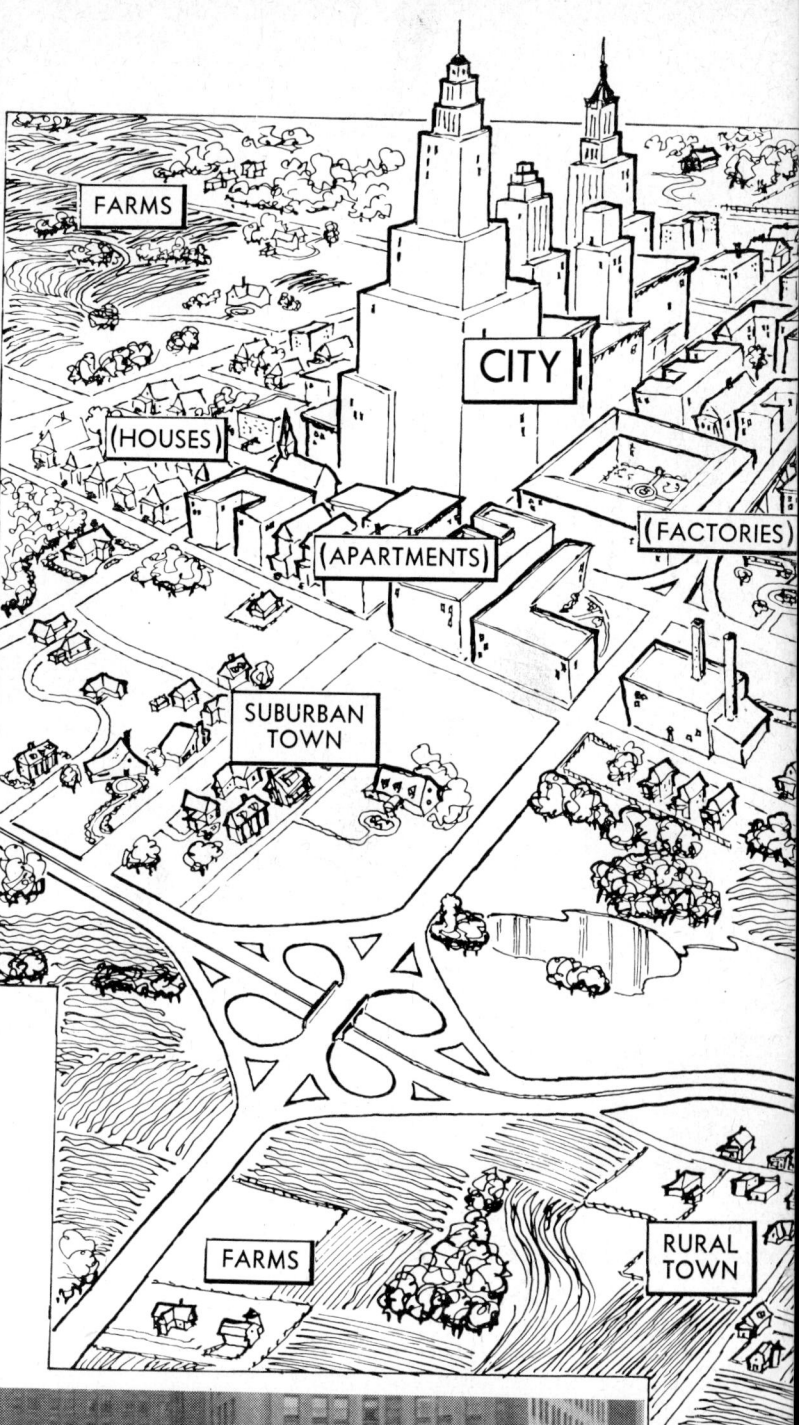

THIS TRUCK DOES NOT NEED A ROAD. IT CAN GO ALMOST ANYWHERE ON ITS BIG SOFT TIRES. ITS BIG TIRES KEEP IT FROM SINKING IN SNOW AND SOFT GROUND. THEY ROLL OVER ROCKS LIKE AIR-FILLED CUSHIONS.

TRUCKS

DUMP TRUCK for hauling rocks

LOGGING TRUCK

↑ HOPPER TYPE TRUCK carries sand or grain and dumps it out the bottom.

↑ MEAT TRUCK has a refrigerator to keep it cool inside. This kind of truck is often called a "reefer." Like some other trucks, it has two parts. The front part is called a tractor. The big part where the load is carried is called a trailer.

↑ BULK MILK TRUCK hauls milk to the city. Its tanks are lined with glass.

↓ BIG FREIGHT TRUCK crosses mountains and deserts.

↑ READY-MIX TRUCK makes concrete out of cement, sand, and water, and delivers it to places where it is needed to make roads, streets, and sidewalks.

↓ PLATFORM TRUCK hauls bales of straw on a ranch.

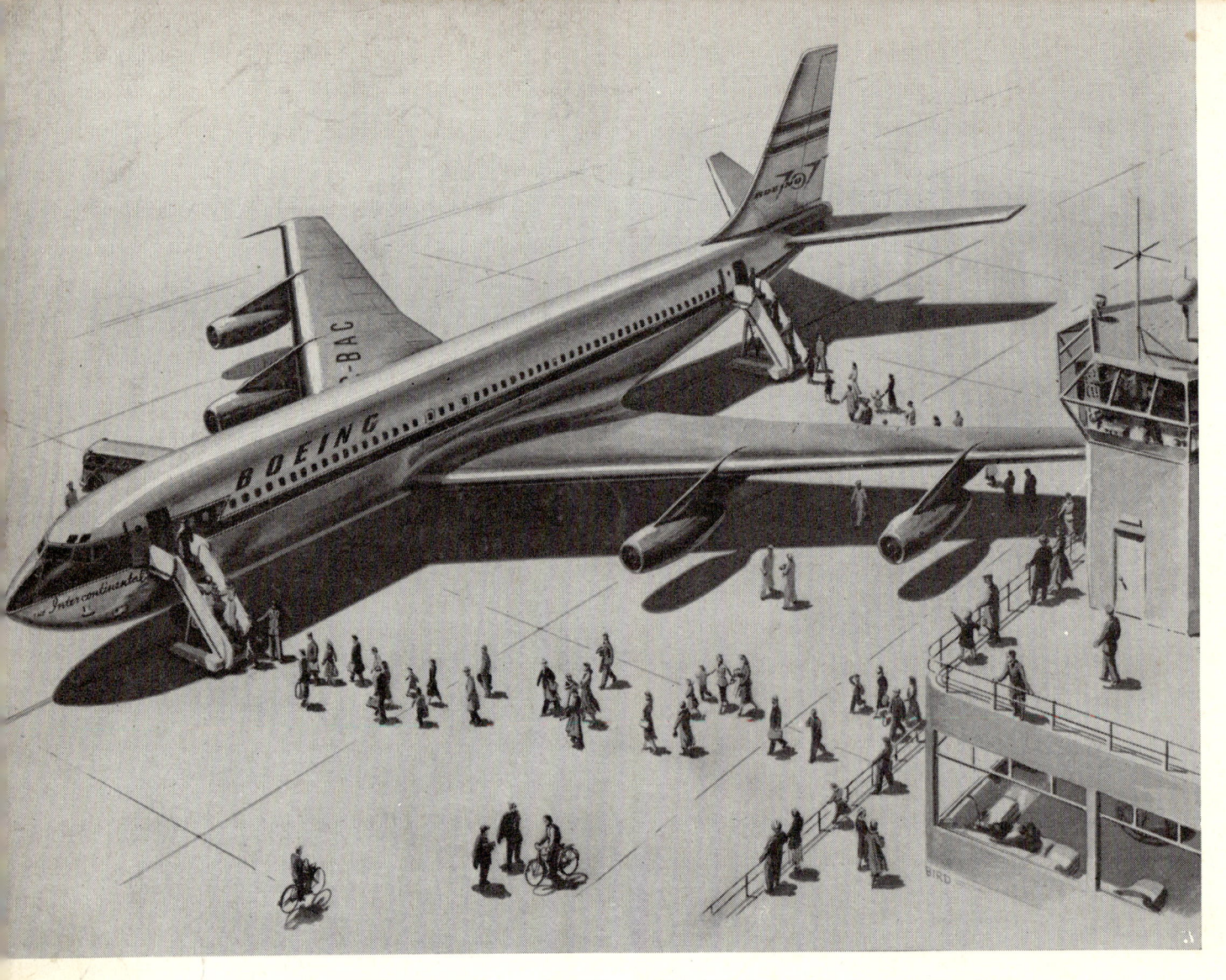

Let's Take a Trip in an Airplane

What a beautiful big plane! It is a jet liner. While we are boarding the plane, the pilot is getting last-minute information about the weather. The man in the airport tower tells him when it is time to take off on our trip. The passengers are in their seats now. We see a message in lights on the wall ahead. It says NO SMOKING— FASTEN SEAT BELTS. Everyone fastens his seat belt. The plane taxis down the runway and waits for the takeoff signal. Then it rushes into the wind. We do not even feel a jolt when it leaves the ground. Up, up we go.

Now we are high in the air, and we can unfasten our seat belts. It is fun to look out the window to see where we are going. The airport from which we started is out of sight. Below us is a great city. It is New York City. See how tiny the cars look, like ants crawling on the streets. The tall buildings of the city look like toys that we could push here and there. Boats skim along like water bugs on the rivers. Our plane seems to be moving very slowly, but it is going six times as fast as a car. It seems slow because we are so far away from the ground. This plane can fly so high that we cannot even see the earth. It can fly over the clouds. On top, clouds look like beautiful pink and white blankets.

Donald is a lucky boy. He got special permission to sit up front with the pilot and watch him fly the plane. The pilot explains some of the dials and instruments to Donald. He shows the boy how he can make the plane turn to right or left, or go higher or lower. After a while the stewardess comes and tells Donald that dinner is ready. He says "Thank you" to the pilot and goes back to his seat. The stewardess brings him a tray of food, with chocolate cake for dessert.

What fine looking soldiers! They seem to be dressed up for a parade. Our plane landed in Quebec, Canada, and we climbed up to an old fort to visit these soldiers and see the cannon. The cannon is three hundred years old.

Isn't it fun to travel in an airplane to places we want to see?

We have some other places to visit, so let's board our plane and zoom-m over to the next page.

WE VISIT AN INDIAN CHIEF

Our jet airliner takes us west toward the setting sun. Suddenly the plane dives through the clouds, circles, and lands. From a nearby hill, we hear loud whoops and yips. Men on horses gallop down to the airfield, waving spears and guns. They are Indians. The leader must be the chief. He leaps off his horse and says "Welcome. We are Sioux Indians. We come in peace. Many years ago we made peace with the white man."

Later, the chief tells us a true story. Hundreds of years ago, he says, the Sioux had no horses. Dogs carried loads, but dogs were not big enough to carry much. One day a Sioux boy named Little Dog went out to hunt. He found a wounded Indian of a strange tribe. Beside the wounded man stood a strange animal. Little Dog was very much afraid, but he put the man on the animal's back and led it to camp. At first the Sioux did not know the animal was a horse. They called it "Mystery Dog." When the wounded man got well he told them that his tribe had many horses. The white man had brought them over the sea from Spain. Because the Sioux medicine men made him well, he brought more horses and showed the Sioux how to ride. They soon became skillful horsemen.

"Today we wear war bonnets only to show you how our people once lived," says the chief. "We now live like the white man."

↑ WE VISIT MISS CHERRY BLOSSOM

We slept on our big plane last night. We tried to stay awake, but there was nothing to see anyway. We were flying over the ocean and it was dark.

This morning we woke up in Japan. See who came to greet us! Her name is Cherry Blossom. Doesn't she have a beautiful costume? She wears a little jeweled crown around the back of her head, with flowers hanging from it. She carries a parasol. Instead of a dress, she wears a bright-colored kimono with a red sash.

"Girls in Japan have lots of fun changing from one kind of clothes to another," says Cherry Blossom. "When I go to school I wear a skirt and blouse just like a girl in Chicago or Toronto. When I ride my bicycle I wear pedal pushers. The costume I am wearing is very old."

WE VISIT JOSE →

On our way home in our giant jet airliner, we decide to stop off in sunny Mexico. We see Jose riding his burro. Jose's name is pronounced hoe-ZAY. Jose lives on a big ranch. He is letting his burro have a drink from the river that runs through his father's ranch. Then he must go home to say goodby to his big sister Angelita. She is going away to school in the city of Chihuahua (chee-WAH-wah). Jose will miss her very much. Jose goes to school in the nearby village. He studies English and Spanish, and can speak and write both these languages. Of all his subjects, he likes arithmetic best. He wants to be an engineer when he grows up. He will go to college in Mexico City, and perhaps in Boston, too.

Jose's big hat keeps the sun out of his eyes. We buy hats just like his. Then we board the plane for the trip home. Isn't it fun seeing the world from an airplane?

Let's Take a Trip on the Train

⬆ Here comes our train. It is a big, shiny, streamlined train. There is the engineer, looking out of his cab window. He blows the loud diesel horn to tell us to stay off the track. He watches for signals that tell him when to make the train go slow and when to make it go fast.

⬇ This man helped us get on the train. He is the conductor. He is in charge of the train, like a manager or a director. He has the right to tell the engineer to stop the train if he thinks there is danger ahead. The conductor likes children. He has children and grandchildren of his own.

This train has big picture windows. We look out at the scenery. Soon we will be passing through mountains. Then we will have lots of fun looking out. Maybe we will see a forest ranger. When the train goes around a curve, we can look back and see the rear cars of the train.

I CAN GO FOR A RAILROAD TRIP
(A rope-skipping rhyme)

How many can hop,
How many can skip,
How many can go
For a railroad trip?

I can hop,
I can skip,
I can go
For a railroad trip.

One jump, two jump,
    three jump, four,
Five jump, six jump,
    how many more?

Catherine C. Anderson

The porter announces that it is time to eat dinner. We follow him through the train. Daddy opens the doors between the cars and helps us through. We come to a long car with dining-room tables in it. This is the dining car. The steward gives us menus, and we select the food we would like to eat. Then the waiter brings our plates. Mmmm! The food smells wonderful. And it tastes just as good as it smells. We eat and eat.

When we return to our own car, we find the seats made up into beds. We go to sleep to the rhythm of the wheels as they rush along the rails. When we get up in the morning, we will dress and eat breakfast. Then we will get off the train. We will visit a very old lady who is a friend of Daddy's. Daddy says she will have a wonderful surprise for us. There is a picture of her on the next page.

AUNT MATILDA BAKES A SURPRISE

No one remembers how old Aunt Matilda is. She can talk about the olden days before Daddy was born.

Aunt Matilda used to grow the biggest pumpkins in the county. Her pumpkins won blue ribbons at the county fair. Once she grew the very biggest pumpkin of all. She watched it ripen on the vine. It grew bigger and bigger. Its color turned from green to yellow. Finally it was almost as big as Aunt Matilda.

"Now I will win the purple ribbon at the state fair," said Aunt Matilda to herself. She brought a wheelbarrow and carefully lifted the huge pumpkin. On the ground under the pumpkin stood a trembling little mouse. The mouse stood on her hind legs and tucked her front paws under her chin. She looked up as if to say "Please don't hurt us, Aunt Matilda." Then Aunt Matilda looked at the pumpkin. There was a big hole in it and inside the hole were six baby mice.

"I won't hurt you, Mrs. Mouse," said Aunt Matilda. "And I won't hurt your children. But you have put me in a pretty fix. Now I will never win the purple ribbon at the state fair. They don't give prizes for pumpkins with holes in them."

She put the pumpkin back on the ground and left it there.

"That was the last time I ever tried to grow the biggest pumpkins," says Aunt Matilda. "I learned a good lesson. I learned that the biggest things aren't always the best."

Now Aunt Matilda grows the *best* pumpkins in the world, not just the biggest. She grows them for a very special purpose. She cuts open the ripe pumpkins. She takes out the seeds. She peels off the rind. She chops the pumpkin into small pieces. Then she adds sugar and salt and secret things. While the pumpkin cooks on the stove, she mixes the dough for the crust. Then she rolls out the crust, pours in the pumpkin, and pops it into the oven. Soon you can smell a wonderful smell that means only one thing: PUMPKIN PIE!

Aunt Matilda makes the best pumpkin pies in the world. She cuts extra big slices for boys and girls. Her pies are good because she puts good things in them. She puts in pumpkin, she puts in spice, she puts in sugar and everything nice. But best of all, she puts in an invisible "spice" called LOVING CARE.

SUSAN GETS A NEW DRESS

This is a happy picture. Susan is happy because the postman brought her a new blue dress. It came in the green box. Mother is happy because Susan is happy. The cat is happy, too.

Daddy is not in the picture because he is at work. There is someone else in this family besides Mother, Daddy, and Susan. Can you tell who it is?

HOW MANY THINGS CAN YOU FIND IN THIS PICTURE?

HOW MANY COLORS CAN YOU FIND IN THIS PICTURE?

LEARNING TO TELL TIME

The clock tells us what time it is. Donald drew these pictures of the clock. They show what Donald does at different times in a day. They help Donald remember how to tell time. Can you draw clocks, too?

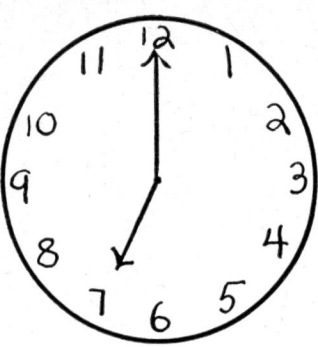

SEVEN O'CLOCK Time to wake up.

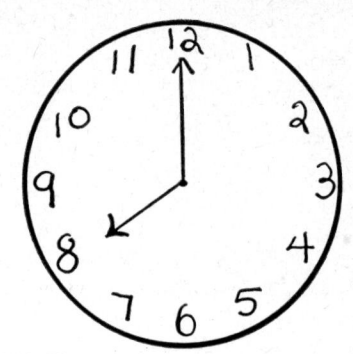

EIGHT O'CLOCK Time to eat breakfast.

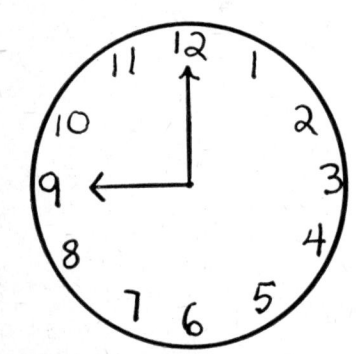

NINE O'CLOCK Time to be in school.

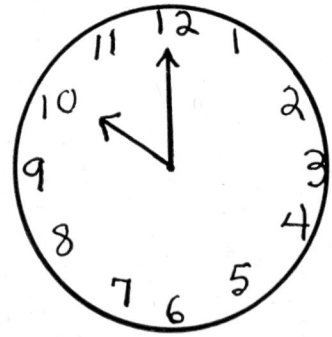

TEN O'CLOCK Time for milk at school.

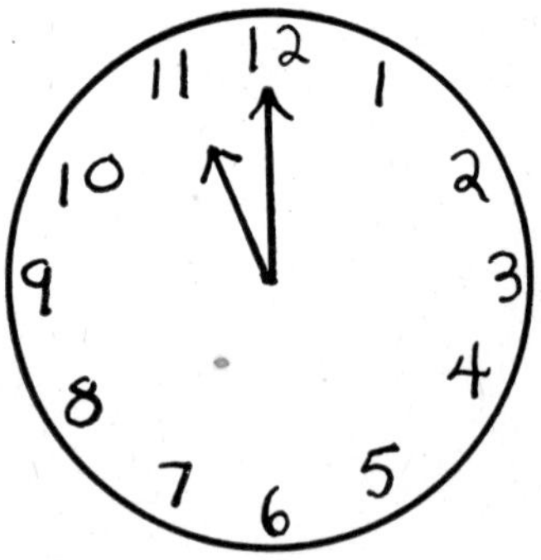

ELEVEN O'CLOCK Time to read a story.

TWELVE O'CLOCK Time for lunch.

ONE O'CLOCK Time to draw a picture.

TWO O'CLOCK Time for afternoon recess.

THREE O'CLOCK Time to go home from school.

FOUR O'CLOCK Time to play outdoors.

FIVE O'CLOCK Time to help Mother.

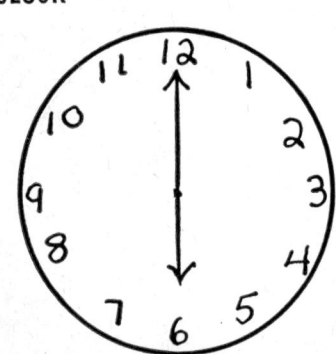

SIX O'CLOCK Time for dinner.

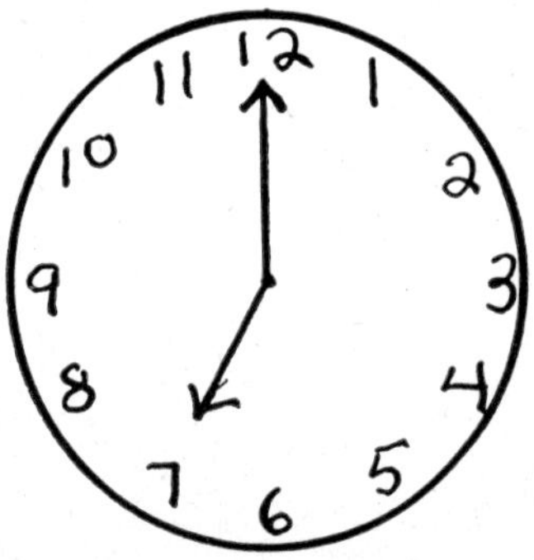

SEVEN O'CLOCK Time to read with Father.

EIGHT O'CLOCK Time to say a prayer and go to bed.

Photo by Ylla

Whitey the Bear says: IT'S FUN TO TAKE A BATH
He can bathe in ice cold water. His long fur protects him.

Boys and girls take their baths in warm water. They use plenty of soap.

Trix the dog wants to take a bath with Julie. Julie says no. Daddy will give Trix a bath.

THE ROOSTER AND THE HEN

Daddy Rooster crows and crows,
He stretches proudly on his toes.
Says Mother Hen, "You're boasting! Why?
Who laid these eggs—was it you or I?
And if we have chicks, a fine little batch,
WHO will sit on our eggs till they hatch?"

Written Expressly for The Junior Instructor by Olive Beaupré Miller

MR. PEACOCK

My word! What a bird!
 Mr. Peacock, hail!
Who ever saw such a
 beautiful tail?
Spread out your fan
 and lo and behold,
It has eyes like jewels
 all set in gold.

Written Expressly for The Junior Instructor by Olive Beaupré Miller

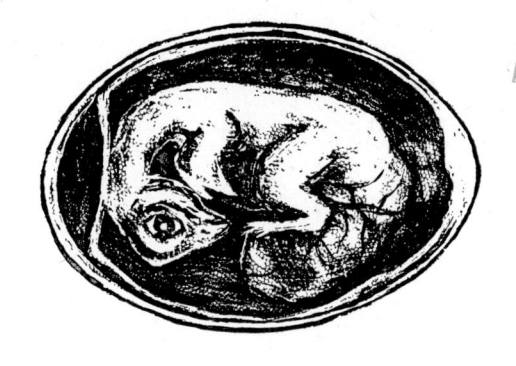

I SEE A CHICK HATCHED

Here the chick is growing, snug and safe inside the shell of the egg. It takes about three weeks to be hatched.

The chick knows just what to do when the time comes for it to hatch. First it pecks a breathing hole in the shell.

Then it pecks a ring all around the egg. When that is done, it struggles to get out.

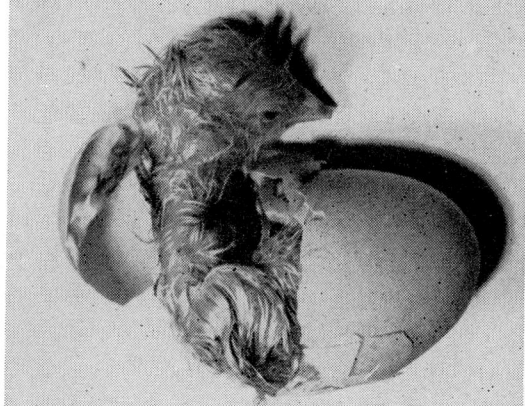

← This is hard work for the baby chick. It must rest a while. It is wet from being inside the egg.

The chick soon dries out and becomes soft and fluffy. Then ↓ it begins to look for food.

HOW LIVING THINGS FLY

Written and Illustrated by Carroll Lane Fenton

Birds fly by means of wings that are covered with feathers. Most birds, like this nighthawk, beat their wings up and down. In this way they travel through the air as easily as you and I are able to walk on the ground.

Flying fish do not really fly. They glide through the air like sailplanes. They leap into the air while swimming at high speed. Then they spread their big fins like airplane wings. Some can glide three hundred feet or more.

Bats fly with skin-covered wings, which they beat up and down just as most birds do. Here we see a bat with its wings stretched widely. It is flying at night, catching insects for its supper. When day comes, the bat will fold its wings and hang head downward in a dark place.

Long ago there were flying reptiles whose wings were covered with skin. Some people think they soared like vultures. Others say they flapped their wings and were able to fly like bats. Here is the biggest of these strange old reptiles. Its wings were more than twenty feet wide from tip to tip.

Insects fly with thin wings made of hard material like their body covering. Grasshoppers and beetles fold their flying wings and tuck them under hard covers, where they cannot be damaged. But the wings of the butterfly are broad and flat, and they cannot be folded away.

Vultures are birds with feathered wings, which they beat up and down when they start to fly. After that, the big birds soar by tilting their wings this way and that way to catch currents of the air that rise from the ground. In this way vultures can fly hour after hour without becoming tired. When they see something to eat, they tilt their wings in a new direction and swoop down to the ground.

Balloon spiders cannot fly, but many are able to sail. They sit on tall weeds or fence posts and spin tufts of silk. When wind catches the silk and blows it away, each spider hangs onto its own special tuft. A spider may travel hundreds of miles on its silken parachute.

Flying squirrels do not really fly. They jump from trees and spread out their legs, which are connected by skin. The skin forms a broad sail on which the squirrels glide to other trees. After alighting they climb to high branches and are ready to glide again.

HOW LIVING THINGS SWIM

Written and Illustrated by Carroll Lane Fenton

Different kinds of creatures swim in a variety of ways. Penguins, for example, swim with their wings, which move to and fro like oars. Though these wings work well under water, they are too narrow to be used in flying.

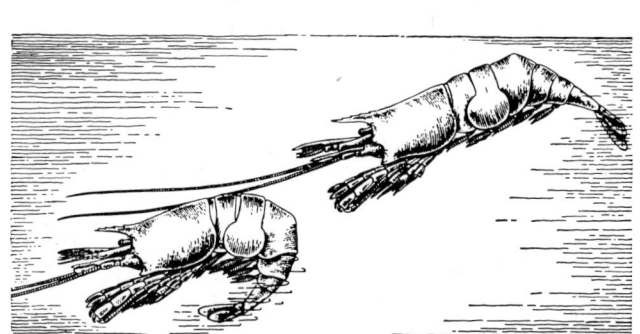

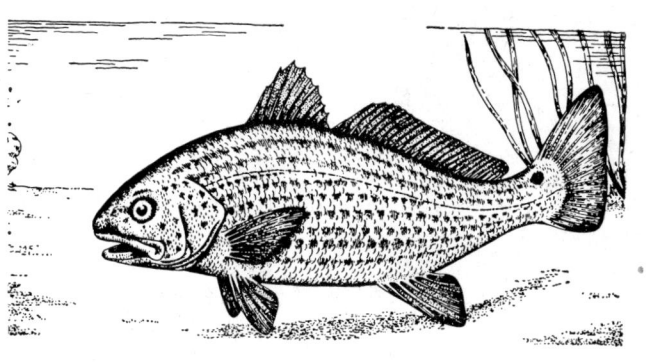

We often say that fish swim with their fins, but that is not true. A fish swims by moving its body from side to side, thus pushing itself through the water. Fins help to keep it upright, and help it to turn.

Shrimps, lobsters, and their relatives swim backwards. They swim by flicking their tails. Their tails are like little fans. When the fan is jerked forward, it pushes against the water and drives the creature backward. Shrimps also have little paddles with which they can swim forward.

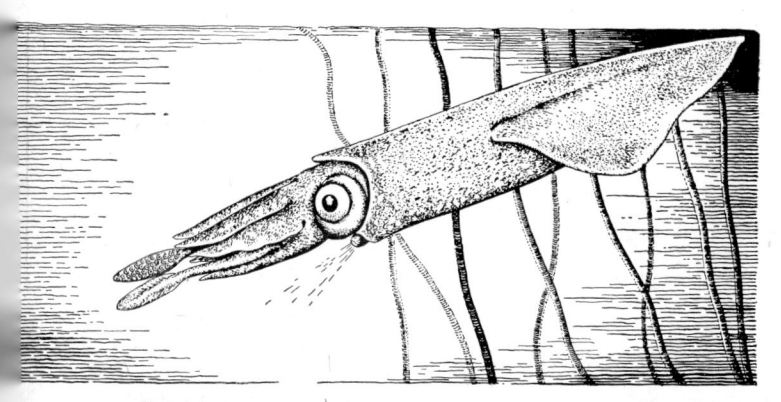

The otter is slow and clumsy on land but is swift and graceful in water. It swims with its legs and its four webbed feet, while its tail helps it steer and balance itself. An otter can twist and turn as easily as any fish.

Squids also swim backward but in another way. They draw in water and then squirt it out through a tube under their big goggle eyes. Squids are actually jet-propelled. They can swim much faster than fish of their size. They are called "sea arrows" because of their shape and speed.

Seals hobble or wriggle clumsily on land, for their real home is sea water. Their smooth bodies are torpedo-shaped, just right for speedy swimming. Their forelegs are broad paddles. Their hind legs extend backward in a way that resembles the tail fins of fish.

A jellyfish is not a true fish, for it does not have a backbone. The creature swims near the surface of the sea by spreading its soft umbrella-shaped body and then partly closing it. Slender tentacles and lacy streamers trail behind.

Ducks, gulls, and many other birds swim with broadly webbed feet, instead of with wings like penguins. Here are two famous swimmers, called grebes, skimming over a lake. Their feet can be seen through the water. When these birds are alarmed, they dive and swim below surface like submarines.

THE LIFE STORY OF A MOTH

Written and Illustrated By Carroll Lane Fenton

One spring evening a mother cecropia moth alighted on a willow tree. There she began to lay her eggs. She laid them in rows, or chains, and fastened them to leaves with glue made in her body.

The cecropia eggs were oval in shape and were flattened. Their shells really were white, but they were stained a dull, brownish red by the glue that held them to the leaves. The surface of each egg was covered with tiny pits.

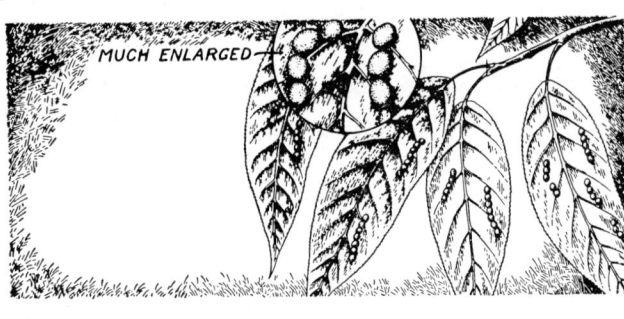

MUCH ENLARGED

After two weeks the eggs began to hatch. Out came little black caterpillars. They had greenish knobs on their backs and long spines upon the knobs. Each caterpillar crawled to the edge of a leaf and began to eat. It ate and ate all day long as if it never could get enough food.

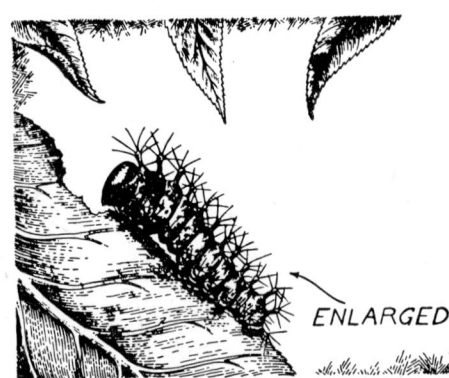

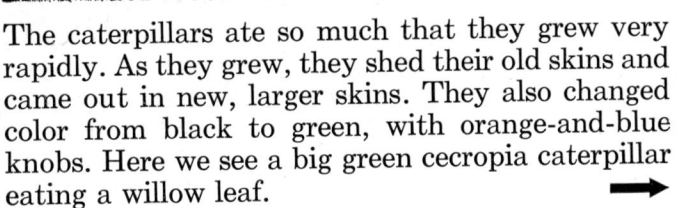

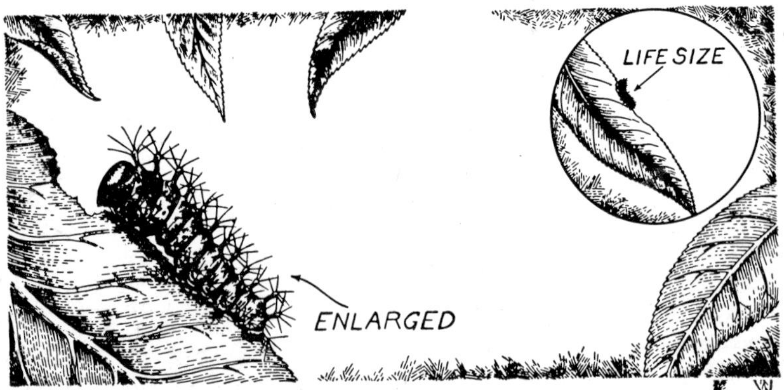

LIFE SIZE

ENLARGED

The caterpillars ate so much that they grew very rapidly. As they grew, they shed their old skins and came out in new, larger skins. They also changed color from black to green, with orange-and-blue knobs. Here we see a big green cecropia caterpillar eating a willow leaf.

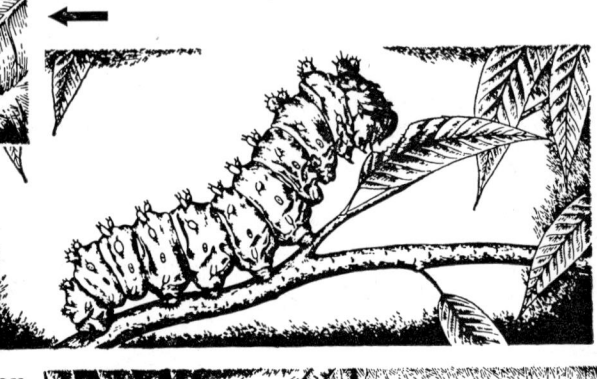

At last the big caterpillar covered itself with a cocoon made of silk. Inside the cocoon the caterpillar shed its skin once more and became a pupa. But the pupa soon began to change, too. Under its hard, dark-brown case it turned into a cecropia moth with wings and jointed legs.

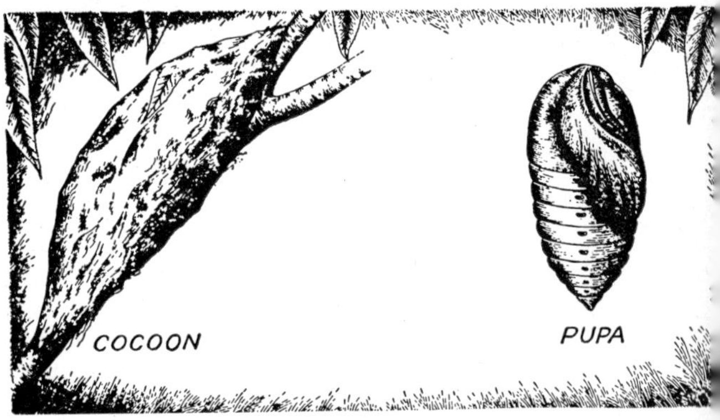

All winter long the moth lay in its pupa case, covered by the silken cocoon. At last spring came again, and new leaves began to grow on the willow tree. One warm night the pupa case split, one end of the cocoon opened, and out came the moth. At first it was wet and weak, and its wings were crumpled against its back. The moth could not fly. It crept out upon the twig and hung there.

COCOON

PUPA

Hour after hour went by, while the moth's four wings spread wider and became stronger. At last it was able to move them so fast that it fluttered to another tree. There it sat until evening, for it did not like to fly in the daytime.

As the new moth clung to the twig, its body became dry and fluffy. Its wings became larger, too. But they did not grow, for they were fully grown inside the pupa. They spread out almost like four fans. As soon as they began to harden, the moth moved them to and fro. This spread the wings still more and helped make them strong.

When evening came, it would fly away to meet other cecropia moths that had just come out of their cocoons.

This is a
Tiger Swallow-tail
Butterfly

HOW TO COLLECT BUTTERFLIES

You can easily collect butterflies. First catch the butterfly in a light net. Before you take it out of the net, pinch its chest, or thorax, until it stops moving. Pin it on a piece of cardboard. Spread its wings out and keep them in position by pinning strips of paper over them. After a few days take off the paper strips. Pin the butterfly in a shallow box with a glass cover. Keep some moth flakes in the box to stop insects from coming in to eat the butterflies.

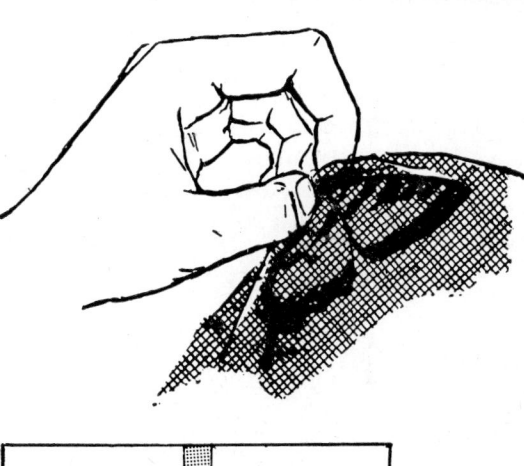

I CAN GROW PLANTS

A great miracle takes place every year. It is the miracle of plants growing from seeds. This miracle gives us all our food, for plants are the world's food makers.

Plants make food from water, air, and sunlight. Cows turn this food into milk and beef. Chickens make it into eggs. All our food comes from plants. We cannot make food. We can only help plants perform this miracle.

Most plants make seeds. Every seed has a tiny new plant inside it. A bean is a seed. Here is something interesting to do. Put a bean in a glass of water today. Wait until tomorrow. Then pour off the water. Take the white or brown coat off the bean. Open it up and look inside. You will see the baby plant inside the bean. After you have looked at this bean, throw it away. It will not grow because you opened it.

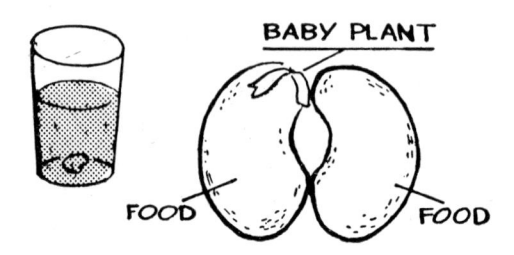

Some seeds are much smaller than a bean. They are so little that you can hardly see them. Other seeds are bigger than your head. Some coconuts are that big.

LET'S GROW A BEAN PLANT

A bean plant is easy to grow. You can grow one from a bean. A bean will grow best if you put it in soil to grow. But you cannot see it grow inside the soil.

A bean will grow in water, too. Here is a way to watch it grow.

First, soak two or three beans overnight in a glass or cup of water. Next morning, line the inside of a drinking glass with a blotter. With a pencil or a little stick, push the soaked beans between the glass and the blotter.

Pour just enough water in the glass to reach the bottom of the blotter. The water will soak into the blotter and make it moist. Place the glass in a warm place, not too dark and not too sunny. Cover the glass with a saucer or jar cover.

Keep the blotter moist. Put in a few teaspoons of water every day. It will take several days for the beans to sprout.

The food inside the bean will turn to liquid, a little at a time. This liquid is like soup for the little plant to drink. The plant feeds on it much as a baby feeds on milk.

Tiny leaves will grow up. Little roots will grow down. No matter which way the bean is placed, leaves go up toward the light, roots go down toward the water. Turn the glass on its side. Leave it this way for a few days. You will see the leaves grow out from the rim of the glass and turn upward again. (Be sure to keep the blotter moist.)

Plant a bean in soil. Put it about as deep as your thumb and cover it. It will grow big and make more beans.

LET'S GROW A CARROT

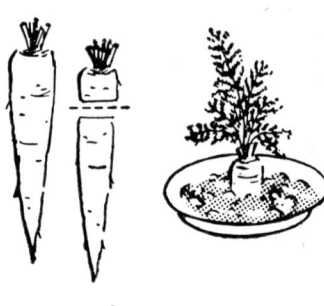

Carrots grow from seeds and from roots. Cut off a two-inch piece from the carrot Mother buys at the store. Set it in a shallow dish of water. Put pebbles around it to hold it upright. It will grow pretty, feathery leaves. It uses the food stored in the root.

LET'S GROW A SWEET POTATO

Put the sweet potato in a jar of water, narrow end down. Keep it dark until the leaves start to grow, then move it into the light.

LET'S GROW AN AFRICAN VIOLET

Put an African violet leaf in damp sand with the stem buried. A new plant will grow.

I CAN PLANT A TREE AND WATCH IT GROW

It is best to plant trees in the spring. Small trees are easiest to plant.
First pick your tree. Pick a good straight one.
Then dig a new hole for the tree to go into. Make the hole deeper and wider than you need for the tree. Then you will have plenty of room for the roots and for good soil for them to grow in. Put the topsoil to one side. Take the other soil away and get more topsoil in its place. Trees grow best in topsoil.
Next dig up the tree. Dig far back from the trunk so as not to cut the roots.
Put the tree in the hole. Put topsoil under its roots to bring the tree to the level at which it grew. It will die if planted too deep. Then put the rest of the topsoil around it. Pour plenty of water on the soil as you do this. The water will wash the soil about the roots. Pack the soil down with your foot. Keep the tree well watered until it begins to grow.

HOW A TREE GETS FOOD

An animal must move around to look for food to eat. A tree does not have to move to find food. A tree stands in one place and makes its own food. It makes its food from water, air, and sunlight.

The tree takes water from the soil through its roots. The water enters tiny tubes in the roots. The tubes go all the way up the tree to the leaves. In the leaves, these tubes branch into veins. You can easily see veins in a leaf. The water passes into the veins of the leaves. Air, too, enters the leaves, through tiny pores.

Chemicals called enzymes in the leaves take air and water apart, add sunlight to them, and make them into food for the tree. You have enzymes in your body. Have you ever wondered why you are not made of milk and vegetables and candy and other things you eat? It is because enzymes take your food apart and make it into flesh and blood and bones and hair.

A very important enzyme in leaves is called chlorophyll. If we had this enzyme in our bodies we would not have to eat. We would be able to make food. Chlorophyll is green. Chlorophyll makes leaves green.

Chlorophyll works with sunlight. Sunlight is energy. That means it can do work. If you have ever been sunburned, you know one way it can work—it can partly cook you. Chlorophyll uses energy from sunlight to split water apart, and adds some of the sunlight to the water. Then other enzymes go to work and finish the job of making food from sunlight, air, and water.

You cannot see the sunlight in food, but it is there. It does not shine because it is changed into food. All the energy we get from food comes from sunlight. Did you know that you eat sunlight when you eat an apple from an apple tree? Sunlight in your food gives you energy to run and jump and breathe and do other things.

My name is Wally. I planted this tree when I was four years old. The tree was one year old. Daddy took this picture.

When I was seven years old, the tree was four years old. See how I grew. The tree grew even faster.

Now I am ten years old. The tree is seven years old. The tree seems to say "Wally, you will never catch up with me." Isn't it fun to watch your own tree grow?

How an Escalator Works

The escalator is a moving stairway. It takes us up to higher floors. Another escalator takes us down to lower floors. We like to ride the escalator in the big department store, because we can see so many things as we ride.

Here are the traffic rules for riding the escalator:

STAND QUIETLY. FACE FORWARD. KEEP ONE HAND ON THE HANDRAIL.

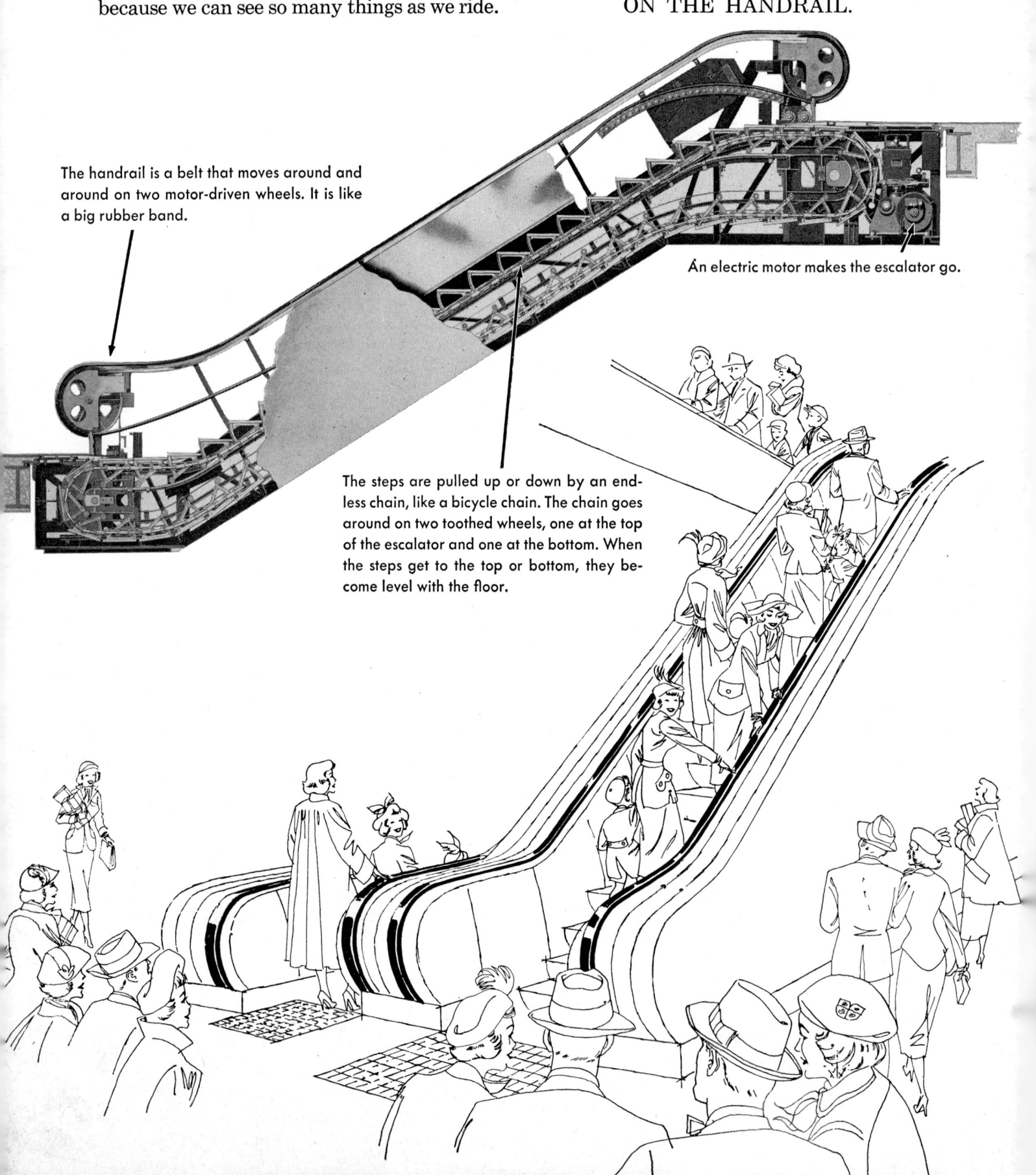

The handrail is a belt that moves around and around on two motor-driven wheels. It is like a big rubber band.

An electric motor makes the escalator go.

The steps are pulled up or down by an endless chain, like a bicycle chain. The chain goes around on two toothed wheels, one at the top of the escalator and one at the bottom. When the steps get to the top or bottom, they become level with the floor.

RHYMES TO SAY AT WORK AND PLAY

These are fun for rope skipping, ball bouncing, dusting, setting the table, and other activities.

Skipping is fun, skipping is fun,
Skipping is fun for everyone—
The more you skip, the better you skip—
So skip, skip, skip, skip—

Television, radio,
Father's shoe,
How many bounces
Of the ball can I do?
One, two, three, four
(Keep counting until you miss).

Cadillac, Chevrolet, Chrysler, Ford,
Now I jump my shining cord.

Jean, Jean, dressed in green,
Went downtown to eat ice cream—
How many dishes did she eat?
1, 2, 3, 4, 5, 6, 7, 8
(Keep counting until you miss).

Down in the valley
Where the green grass grows,
There sat _____,
As sweet as a rose.
She sang so sweet,
And she looked so neat,
Along came Daddy
And kissed her on the cheek.
How many kisses did she get that week?
1, 2, 3, 4, 5, 6, 7, 8, etc.

All in together,
How do you like the weather?
January, February, March, April,
May, June, July, August,
September, October,
November, December.
(Start over again).

Off I go to music land,
Training ear and eye and hand—
C-d-e-f-g-a-b-c.

Here is the beehive,
Where are the bees?
Hiding away where nobody sees.
They are coming out now,
They are all alive,
One, two, three, four, five.

One potato, two potatoes,
Three potatoes, four,
Five potatoes, six potatoes,
Seven potatoes more.

Boys and Girls at Work and Play

'Way down south where the bananas grow,
An ant stepped on an elephant's toe—
The elephant cried with tears in his eyes,
"Why don't you step on someone your size?"

Helping With Housework

← The best game of all is helping Mother with the housework. It isn't work, it's fun! With a soft cloth and furniture polish, I make the table-tops shine like mirrors. Mother is very proud of me. She calls me her little helper.

We like to help Mother prepare breakfast. We know how to set the table and get little Sister's orange juice ready for her to drink. Our toaster goes POP! when the toast is done. Up fly the warm golden slices, all ready for butter and jam. After breakfast, little Sister will have a nap. We will go outdoors to play.

↓

My Doll

My baby sister's name is Mary Ann. My baby's name is Anne Marie. They look alike. When Mother gives Mary Ann her orange juice, I feed my doll some, too. It's fun to be a Little Mother.

The Care and Feeding of a Dog

The dog must have his own place to sleep. This should be in a warm (not hot) part of the house, especially if he is a puppy, or if he is short-haired. A large, strong dog likes a certain amount of cold and can sometimes sleep outdoors. But he must be given a dog house large enough for his comfort. It should have small open windows. But your dog must not sleep in a draft, either indoors or out. Straw or strips of newspaper make a good bed. The bed must be changed often. Toy breeds of dogs must be kept warm at night. During cold weather they should sleep under a light covering.

All dogs require regular outings and exercise. A small dog needs a sweater or coat in very cold weather.

Dogs should be bathed often enough to keep them clean. There are some good "dry" dog shampoos which may sometimes take the place of a scrubbing with soap and water. When water is used, rub the fur with a towel and keep the dog indoors until he is thoroughly dry. Some dogs take cold very easily. Regular brushings of the fur will help to keep it clean.

Teach your dog to be obedient. But be patient with him. Dogs are smart and enjoy learning to follow simple commands. You can teach your dog to come when he is called. He can learn to pick up and bring a newspaper or Daddy's bedroom slippers. He should be taught not to run in the street and not to chase cars or bicycles.

Give your dog wholesome, fresh food. All dogs need meat to eat. Some table scraps may be added to the meat. But do not give your dog starchy, sweet, or greasy foods. Be sure that your dog's food is free from bits of bone, or anything that could get caught in his throat. Prepared dog foods of good quality will provide a healthful diet. Dogs like variety and should sometimes be given dog biscuits and other changes from their regular food. These changes should not include candy or other sweets. But large beef bones, of a kind that will not splinter, will be fine for your dog. He must NOT be given bones from lamb, pork, chicken, or fish. Do not overfeed your dog. And remember—ALWAYS keep a bowl, filled with fresh, cool water where he can reach it easily.

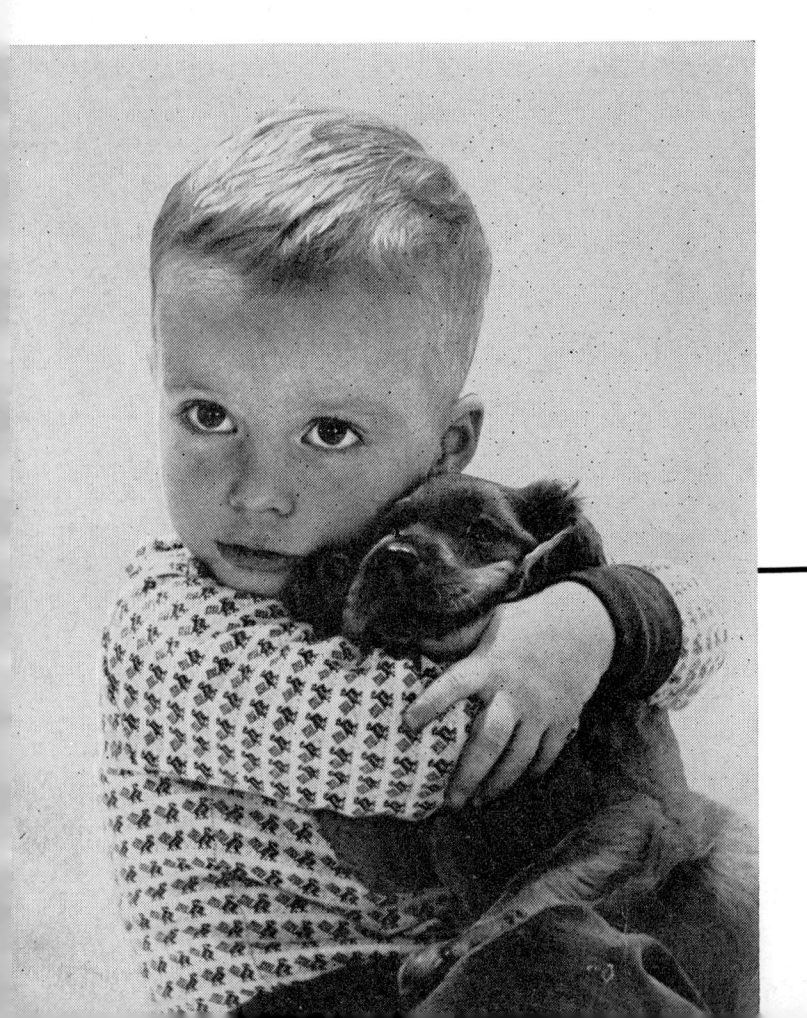

My dog's nose is damp and cold,
His eyes are warm and brown.
His tail points up; his ears point down,
He is the finest dog in town.

I call my puppy Buff,
He's the BEST dog I know.
His ears are shaggy, his tail is waggy,
And oh, I love him so!

The Care and Feeding of a Parakeet

Parakeets make fine pets. Many of them learn to speak whole sentences, such as "I'm a pretty bird."

The parakeet's cage should be large enough for the bird to hop around in freely. A pair of parakeets will sometimes raise babies in captivity. They need a birdhouse for this purpose.

Your parakeet's food will be mostly seeds which you buy at a pet store. You must also give it bits of apple, and green foods such as lettuce. Fresh water must be provided for both drinking and bathing.

Parakeets enjoy flying around a room and perching on the hand, shoulder, or head of a member of the family. Close unscreened windows and doors while the parakeet is outside its cage. A pet bird can easily be lost through a window or door carelessly left open.

My parakeet's feathers
   are green and blue,
He comes from a faraway land.
He can talk and sing and whistle too,
And he eats right out of my hand.

The Care of a Pony, Horse, or Burro

Taking care of a pet is part of the fun of owning it. This is especially true of a pony, horse, or burro.

Your pony, horse, or burro must have his own stall in a stable or barn. The floor of his stall must be well covered with clean straw or wood shavings. This covering must be changed often. When he feels like lying down, he must have a roomy, clean, dry bed to lie on.

Feed him at about the same time every day. Oats and hay are his main foods. Small amounts of wheat and corn should be mixed with the oats. And he should have more than one kind of hay. All his foods should be clean and fresh looking. Be very careful not to overfeed him. The amount of feed given him will depend upon his weight and the amount of exercise he gets. His best food is green grass, so give him pasture if possible. Always keep a salt block in his stall and let him lick it as much as he wants. For a special treat, let him nibble a carrot or a lump of sugar from your hand.

Plenty of fresh water must be provided. In this, as with feeding, a regular schedule is followed. In warm weather your pet needs three waterings a day. Do not let him drink freely when he is hot from exercise. Let him have just a swallow or two with short rests between swallows. You can control this by gently guiding his head away from the pail or trough between sips.

Once a year he will shed his hair and grow a new coat. The coat and the mane and tail must be brushed and currycombed regularly the year around. Get new shoes for your pony, horse, or burro as often as needed. If the insides of his hoofs get packed with dirt they should be scraped out very carefully.

My pony's coat is gray and white,
His whinny is soft and his step is light.
He sleeps in his stable every night
And dreams of the meadow and me.

Fun With Books

Daddy sometimes takes me to visit the ➡ big library. I like to go with him to the shelves where the grownup books are kept. After Daddy selects the book he wants, we will go to the Children's Room. There the librarian knows just the stories that little boys like best. We will take a book home for Daddy to read to me. Maybe the story will be about Peter Rabbit.

⬅ After playtime we like to sit down quietly and journey to Story Book Land. The heroes and the children of all the countries of the world come alive between the covers of our books. We take turns reading to each other. We read some stories over and over.

"Red Squirrel, What Do You Do All Day?"

This is a story about a little girl and a little boy who didn't want to do anything the livelong day but play. Their mother knew that children have to play a lot if they are to be healthy and happy. So she let them play to their hearts' content. Sometimes, though, she would ask them to do some small task to help her or Daddy. Like setting the table, or helping to weed the garden. But the children would say, "Oh, Mother, can't we play instead?" And off they would go to the nearby woods, as fast as their feet would carry them.

One day a small Red Squirrel jumped across their path. The little girl said to him: "Red Squirrel, you don't do any work, do you? You just play and eat nuts from morning till night."

"Not do any work!" chattered Red Squirrel. "Why, I am working now! My parents and I live in an old oak tree and I am helping them store the nuts we will need for the winter."

Just then a Bee came buzzing by and the little boy said: "Bee, do you ever have to work? Can't you just buzz among the flowers all day?"

"Work!" buzzed Bee. "Right now I am gathering sweets to make honey for you to eat."

The children walked along very slowly, for they were thinking. Along came an Ant down the path, carrying a large crumb of bread. "Ant," the little girl said, "that crumb looks too heavy for so small an Ant to carry. Drop it and come play with us."

"Oh," said Ant, "I'm carrying it to our Ant House to help feed our large family. Later, when the work is done, I will come back and play with you."

After a while, the little boy said to his sister: "The creatures all have tasks to do, but I don't believe the flowers work, do you?"

"Let's ask them," the little girl said.

"Do you work, Pink Clover?" she asked the flower growing at their feet. "Yes, I'm often quite busy," answered Pink Clover. "I gather sunbeams each morning, and soak up rain when it falls. Even flowers must work."

The children then decided to go home to their mother. "Please, Mother," they said, "give us some work to do. The Squirrels and the Bees and the Ants all work. Even the flowers have tasks to do. We are the only idle ones."

The mother was pleased that her children had made this important discovery. She gave her little girl a pretty apron to put on. And she gave her little boy some nice garden tools. And they both began to help their mother and father.

Girl Scouts saluting their country's flag

Boy Scouts camping out

ORGANIZATIONS FOR BOYS AND GIRLS TO JOIN

	AGES	FOR INFORMATION WRITE TO:

BOY SCOUTS
- Cubs — 8 - 10
- Scouts — 11 - 13
- Explorer Scouts — 14 - 18

Boy Scouts of America, New Brunswick, New Jersey
or Boy Scouts of Canada, 306 Metcalfe Street,
Ottawa, Ontario, Canada

GIRL SCOUTS or GIRL GUIDES
- Brownies — 7 - 10
- Intermediates — 10 - 13
- Seniors — 14 - 17

Girl Scouts of America, 155 East 44th St., New York 17, N.Y.
or Girl Guides Canadian Council,
125 Yorkville Street, Toronto, Ontario, Canada

CAMP FIRE GIRLS
- Blue Birds — 7 - 10
- Camp Fire Girls — 10 - 13
- Horizon Club — 14 - 17

Camp Fire Girls of America,
16 East 48th Street
New York 17, New York

4-H CLUBS
- Boys and Girls — 10 - 21

4-H Clubs of America, Federal Extension Service
U. S. Dept. of Agriculture, Washington 25, D. C. or

4-H Clubs of Canada, 536 Confederation Building
Ottawa, Ontario, Canada

AUDUBON JUNIOR CLUBS

Audubon Society, 1130 5th Avenue, New York 28, N.Y.
or Audubon Society of Canada,
181 Jarvis Street, Toronto, Ontario, Canada

(See also BE YOUR FAMILY FIRE CHIEF
on pages 109-112.)

A Camp Fire Girl serves the dessert she baked

THE POSTMAN BRINGS US LETTERS

POSTMAN, POSTMAN
(A ball-bouncing rhyme)

Postman, postman, bring some mail
Cowboy Pete has hit the trail.
Susie gets postcards without fail
But I never, never, never get any mail.

Write a letter, you shall see
Postman's pouch upon his knee.
Come from the land and come from the sea,
How many letters are for me?
One, two, three, four
    (keep counting until you miss).

GROWNUPS AT WORK AND PLAY

THE FIREMAN PUTS OUT FIRES

He also tells us how to prevent fires. If you would like to be your FAMILY FIRE CHIEF, see pages 109-112. Read about Fire Fightin' Mose on page 124.

FIREMAN, FIREMAN
(A good lawn-watering or rope-skipping rhyme)
Fireman, fireman, I smell fire!
I give my address on the telephone wire.
Turn the nozzle round about,
Thank you, fireman, fire is out.

THE GAS STATION MAN
FILLS THE GASOLINE TANK

Gasoline makes the car go.

The gas station man puts oil in Daddy's car.
Oil makes the car run smoothly.

He repairs truck tires,
car tires, and bicycle tires.
He cleans the windshield, too.

THE FARMER GROWS FOOD

FARMER, FARMER
(A rhyme for work or play)

Farmer, farmer, make some hay,
Make it on a sunny day.
Horse neigh, donkey bray,
Cow moo — all eat hay.
Eggs and carrots, milk and meat,
Farmer makes food for us to eat.

The farmer's son likes watermelon. ➡

THE POLICEMAN PROTECTS US

He helps us find Mother if we are lost. Sometimes he helps children across the street on their way to school. The policeman is our friend.

The policeman has his own telephone. He uses it to call the police station. He wears a badge and a special cap, so we will know he is a policeman.

THE DRUGGIST SELLS MEDICINE TO HELP US GET WELL

When you are ill, the doctor gives Mother a prescription. The prescription tells what medicine you need. But Mother cannot make the medicine. She takes the prescription to the druggist. He reads it. He may telephone the doctor and ask "Is this right?" He wants to make sure the medicine is the kind you need. Then he shakes out a pinch of this and a pinch of that and a pinch of something else. He puts them together to make your medicine. When you get well, you may go to the drugstore and say "Thank you" to the druggist. You may buy a strawberry sundae.

ROYAL PARENTS LOVE THEIR CHILDREN

Great Britain's Queen Elizabeth and her husband, Prince Philip, spend a sunny afternoon with their children, Prince Charles and Princess Anne. This picture was taken in the park at Buckingham Palace. Mama is not wearing her diamond crown and beautiful court dress, nor is Daddy dressed in his fancy uniform with his sword at his side. They look like our own parents. And they seem to be very interested in the children's book. Charles and Anne have a little brother, Andrew, who was born February 19, 1960.

THE NURSE TAKES CARE OF PEOPLE WHO ARE ILL

Nurse Murphy works at the hospital. She brings you a glass of water. She brings you a dish of ice cream. Nurse Murphy takes your temperature to see if your body is too hot inside. She puts her cool fingers on your wrist to see how fast your heart is beating. As your heart beats, the pulse in your wrist goes one-and-two-and-three-and-four. Nurse Murphy looks at the fast-moving second hand of her watch to see how many times a minute your heart beats.

Nurses help doctors make you well. They are often called "Angels of Mercy." You can make a nurse's cap. Fold a sheet of paper three times the long way. Punch a hole in each end and tie on a string. Tie the other ends of the two strings around the back of your head. You can draw a stripe on the cap with colored crayon to make it pretty.

56

GROWNUPS AT WORK AND PLAY

THE DOCTOR HELPS US STAY HEALTHY

The doctor works in his office. He works at the hospital, too. Mother calls for an appointment with the doctor at his office. The doctor's secretary looks at her appointment book and says "Joan may see the doctor at 5 o'clock on Thursday." Joan goes to the doctor's office for her physical examination. She is getting ready to go to school, and Mother wants to make sure she is healthy. The doctor listens to Joan's heartbeat with his stethoscope. He also hears other sounds inside Joan. He hears her lungs go in and out as she breathes. The doctor says "You are a very healthy girl, Joan. You can go to school. You can run and play." Joan likes to play nurse. Her brother Jim likes to play doctor.

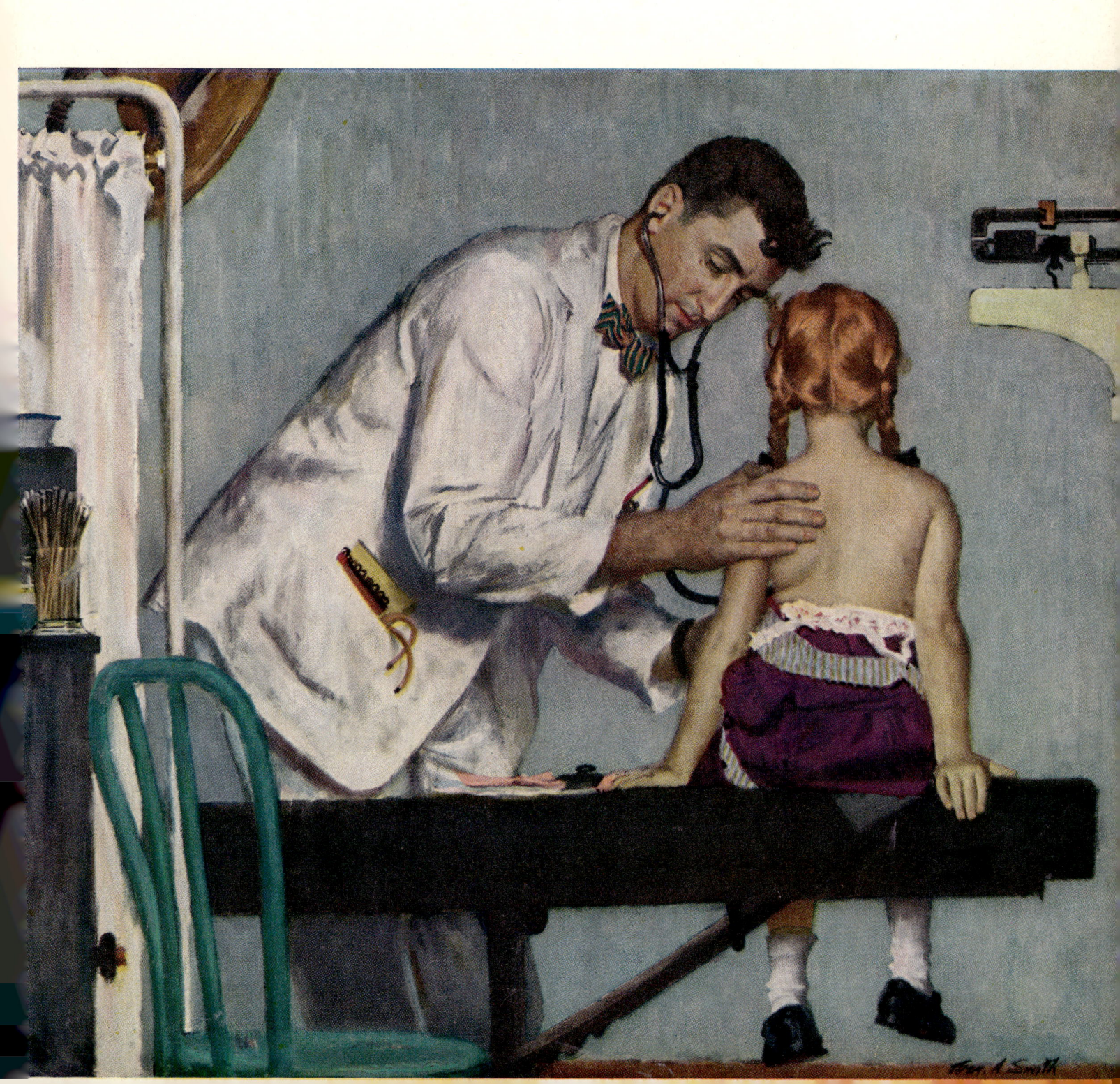

THE JUNIOR INSTRUCTOR

↑ COMING HOME FROM THE HOSPITAL WITH THE NEW BABY

Aunt Helen and Uncle Bob are proud and happy. They are bringing their new baby home from the hospital. Before the baby came, Aunt Helen and Uncle Bob went to school to learn how to take care of him. They learned how to feed him, how to hold him, how to diaper him, and how to dress him. They learned that he must sleep quietly most of the time, so that he can grow.

MOTHER'S WORK IS VERY IMPORTANT WORK

Did you ever think that everyone starts out as a baby? You were once a baby. Your mother was a baby long before that. So was your father. When they were little, their mothers loved them and took care of them. Your mother loves you and takes care of you. The mother in this picture loves her baby very much. Someday her baby will grow up to be as big as you. He will grow to be a man. Perhaps he will be a doctor or a grocer or a lawyer. →

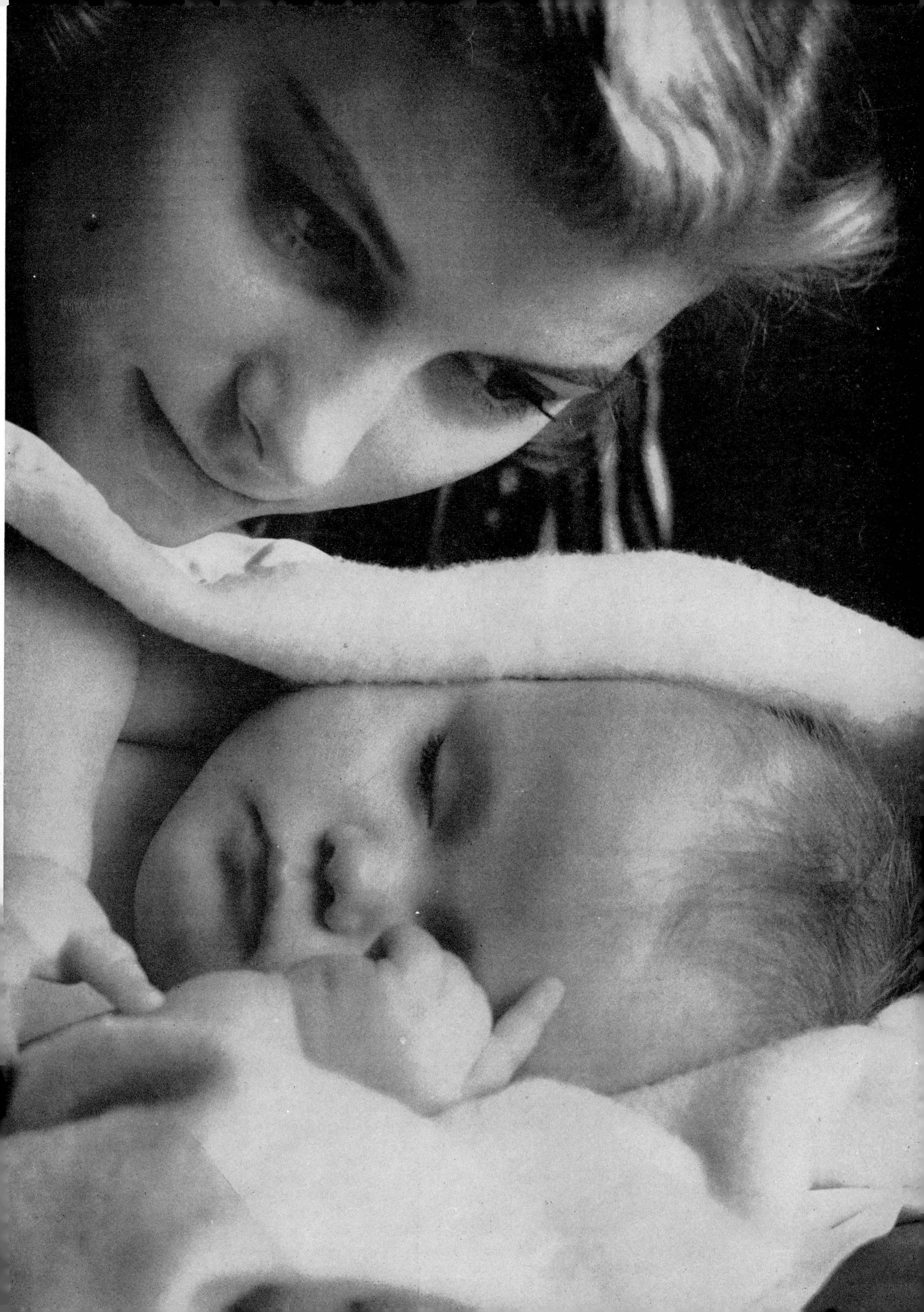

THE SECRETARY WORKS IN AN OFFICE IN THE CITY

Miss Moore can type fast. She can type a hundred words a minute. She puts a blank sheet of paper in her typewriter, and then she makes her fingers fly over the typewriter keys. Out of the typewriter comes a beautiful letter. Miss Moore takes this letter and other letters to the man she works for. He is the president of a bank. His name is Mr. Clark. He says "These are beautiful letters, Miss Moore." Then he signs his name at the bottom of each letter.

Sometimes Miss Moore uses a dictating machine. This is like a little record player. Mr. Clark talks into the machine and it makes a record. Then Miss Moore plays the record and listens to it. The record tells her what Mr. Clark wants to say in his letter. She types the letter as she listens.

Miss Moore reminds Mr. Clark about people he has to see and things he has to do. She makes suggestions for doing the work better. She is an important person.

After work, Miss Moore rides the bus to her home in another part of the city.

THE TEACHER HELPS US LEARN

Miss Anthony teaches a fourth grade class at the Blossom Hill School. She loves boys and girls, and she likes to help them learn. She knows that it's fun to learn. The more you learn, the more fun you can have. Miss Anthony is a good friend to children.

Every day, Miss Anthony drives to school in her car. She waves hello to the grocer as he sweeps the walk in front of his store. One morning she stopped and asked his permission to bring her class to visit his store. He said, "Fine!" Miss Anthony also took her class to visit the fire station, a dairy, and the post office. The boys and girls learned that the people of the community help one another. All the grownups are community helpers: the postman, the fireman, the gas station man, the farmer, the policeman, the nurse, the doctor, the banker, the grocer, the baker, the musician, the artist, and the hardware man. What do these community helpers do for us? What other community helpers can you think of?

The teacher helps us to learn many other things, too. It is fun to play school with your friends. You may take turns playing teacher.

FATHER CATCHES A FISH

Fathers who work hard need to play once in a while. Going fishing is one of the best ways for grownups to play.

This father has just caught a trout in a mountain stream in the Canadian Rockies. He thinks how good it will taste when it is broiled over his campfire. He wears hip boots so that he can wade into the stream and cast the lure in the pools where trout like to hide. The lure looks like a fly, and trout like to eat flies. But inside it is a hook to catch the fish.

MILK BOTTLES' SONG
(A rope-skipping rhyme)

Milk bottles bump along
In the milkman's tray.
As they bump they sing a song,
Here is what they say:
"Tinkle tink,
Tinkle tink,
Good for boys
And girls to drink."

Catherine C. Anderson

THE MILKMAN IS HERE

The milkman drives the milk truck. He stops at the store on the corner. He stops at my house and your house. He brings us lots of milk to drink, and cream and butter, too. We may buy the milk from the milkman, or we may buy it from the store.

Where does the milk come from? It comes from the dairy farm. The farmer milks the cows. Then the milk is cooled and brought to the city in big trucks. It is heated to destroy germs, then cooled again to keep it fresh. It is poured into bottles and loaded onto the milkman's truck. Then he brings it to your house, my house, and the store.

THE MACHINIST MAKES THINGS WORK

We have lots of machines that do work for us. Mother has a clothes washer and drier, an electric iron, a mixer, an automatic stove, a refrigerator, and a vacuum cleaner. Father has a lawn mower, a power saw, and a car. And don't forget the family bicycles and tricycles and wagons — they are machines, too. So is the television set.

All these machines were made to work easily and well. Lots of workers helped to make them. One of the most important of these workers is the machinist. The machinist has great skill. He must make parts that fit just right when the machine is put together. An inch looks as big as a mile to the machinist. A hundredth of an inch looks almost as big. He makes parts that are just right in size. The machinist is like an artist or a surgeon in the skillful way he uses his hands.

The place where the machinist works is called a machine shop. In the machine shop, there are many wonderful tools. There are tools for sawing metal and for drilling holes in metal. There are tools for cutting and shaving and polishing. The machinist knows how to use all these wonderful tools. He is proud of his work. He likes to know that his work makes your machines run better.

ANIMAL BABIES

A CAT AND HER KITTENS

The mother cat is one of the most gentle mothers in the animal kingdom. She usually has from four to six babies at a time. She cares for them tenderly. She licks their fur to keep them clean. If she feels the kittens are in danger, she takes them to a hiding place. She carries each kitten in her teeth. She holds it by the loose skin on the back of its neck.

What is the biggest baby in the world? It is the whale baby. It lives in the ocean. At birth, a baby whale often weighs more than seven tons, or as much as four automobiles. Its mother may weigh more than forty tons, or about as much as 23 automobiles.

Mouse babies are very small. Four to ten brothers and sisters are born at one time. One mouse baby is so small that it could sleep in a teaspoon.

A COW AND HER CALF

This mother cow is gentle most of the time. But when she has a young calf, the cow is fierce. She drives animals and people away to protect her calf. She butts them with her head. When the calf is only about half an hour old, it can stand up and walk a little. Then it nuzzles its mother. She gently pushes the calf toward her udder, which is filled with warm milk to drink. The calf in the picture is several weeks old. It will soon learn to eat grass and corn. It makes a "Baa-a-a!" sound. Soon its voice will deepen and it will say "Moo-oo!" as its mother does.

A DOE AND HER TWIN FAWNS

A mother deer, or doe, often has twin fawns. The deer in the picture belong to the Virginia, or white-tailed, deer family. Fawns can stand and walk when they are a few minutes old. Soon they can run fast. When the mother deer smells an enemy, she lifts her white tail like a flag. The fawns understand that this means danger. Then they all bound away very fast. The fawns are weaned when they are four months old. Then they eat grass and other plants. Soon after they are weaned, the white spots disappear from their coats.

All animal babies, even tiny insects, have fathers as well as mothers. But usually it is the mother who has to do most for the baby.

An exception is the South American bird called a tinamau. This mother lays a single egg and then flies away. The father tinamau must keep the egg warm and care for the baby when it is hatched. He gets no help from Mother!

A MARE AND HER COLT

A mother horse is called a mare. Her baby is a foal. When the baby gets a little older it is called a colt, if it is a boy. If it is a girl, it is called a filly. By the time the foal is about an hour old, it is able to stand. At first, its legs tremble and shake. But soon it can walk. Before many days it can run around playfully. It has a fine time teasing its mother.

A SOW AND HER PIGS

◀ A mother hog, or sow, may have as many as twenty-two babies at one time. And she can usually nurse them all at once. This is a good thing, because young pigs have big appetites. The sow is fond of her family, and seems contented when the babies crowd close to her for their dinner. As the pigs drink her warm milk, they make little squeaky grunts. These grunts are like music to Mother Hog's ears.

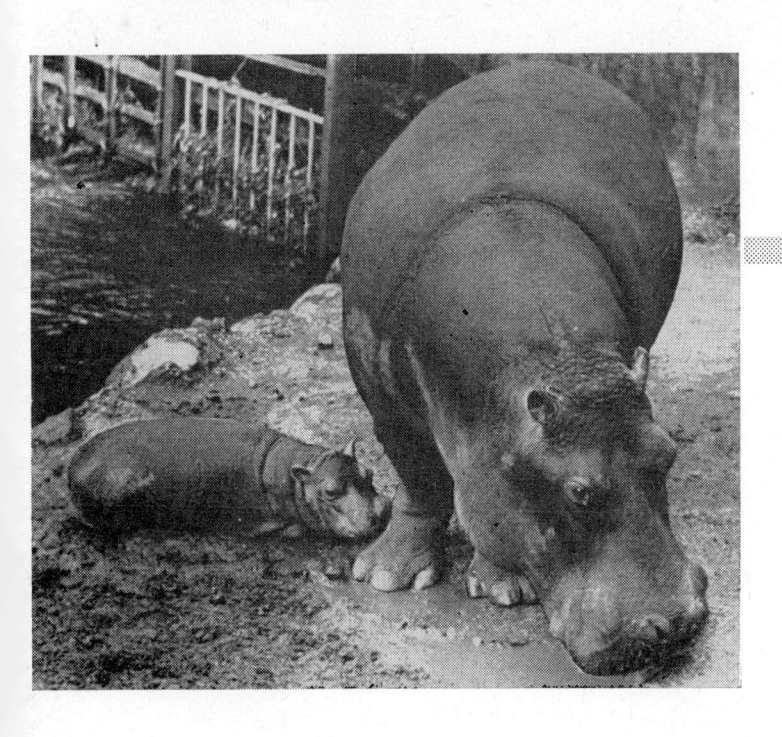

A HIPPOPOTAMUS AND HER CALF

▲ Mrs. Hippopotamus' new baby looks small beside its mother. But it weighs sixty pounds, about as much as an eight-year-old boy. Hippopotami spend time both on land and in water. Mother Hippo began to give her baby swimming lessons soon after it was born. Between swimming lessons, the baby likes to ride on its mother's back. Mrs. Hippopotamus and her baby live in a zoo. The mother came from Africa.

A GIRAFFE AND HER CALF

Next to trees, giraffes are the tallest living things. Even ▶ the baby is five feet tall when it is born! The baby can stand when it is twenty-minutes old. But to its mother it seems a helpless infant, and she guards it carefully. It is said that giraffes have no voices. But if the baby strays too far away from its mother, she can make a low sound that will bring her baby back to her side.

THE MALLARD DUCK FAMILY

Here we have the whole duck family—Mr. and Mrs. Mallard Duck and their seven little ducklings. Daddy Duck is called a drake. He is proud of his family. Mother Duck laid the eggs. Then she kept them warm for twenty-eight days to hatch them, while Daddy Duck went on a vacation. Daddy came back soon. Here he watches Mother Duck give the children their first swimming lesson. Their oily feathers keep them dry in the rain.

"SOMEBODY HAS BEEN TASTING MY PORRIDGE!"

Creative Dramatics

The Value of Dramatization

The dramatic instinct is paramount in the little child. He lives in a make-believe world, in which he is at one and the same time the hero, the villain and the victim of the piece. He becomes a bear, a locomotive, a robber, an Indian or a hunter in rapid succession, with no feeling of incongruity and no sense of the ridiculous. In the same manner, the little girl plays house, or dolls, or school; imitating her mother or her teacher in a manner that is purely dramatic, purely "acting." The purpose of this chapter is to apply this instinct for imitation

Reading stimulates the child's imagination, and provides new subjects for play-acting.

and for impersonation to its proper use in the scheme of the child's education.

The sufficient guarantee of this method of instruction is that the child learns quickly by it.

First, because the sensory and motor responses to object stimuli are added to the formal book or oral recall. By that is meant that things are remembered by being associated in the mind with things previously learned, and with the memory of sights, sounds and actions which originally accompanied those things when learned. It is clear that the more associations a fact has, the more threads there will be by which to draw it back to the mind when wanted. The dramatic method supplies those added stimuli.

Second, because the imagination is quickened. Imagination makes the play seem real, and consequently the desired facts are remembered as happenings, not as abstract ideas. In this way, the reading lesson becomes connected with the activities which to the child are of vital worth and interest, and the two in close conjunction are graven deep on the brain, where the record will be permanent; that is, they are permanently learned.

The fundamental prerequisite of child dramatization, as far as the adult is concerned, is to *let the child give his own interpretation.* The adult may mistakenly look for polished action, for smooth diction and flowing rhetoric, for logical sequence. If the adult attempts to make the child learn his role by rote, the result is likely to be wooden and certainly uninteresting to the child. Children want to pretend in their own way, and not be regimented by adult requirements. Play-acting is just pretending. The child's imagination covers all defects.

Again, the adult must have accessories; he wishes costumes, scenery, and stage properties; he must visualize the scene to make it real. On the contrary, the child works better when the entire scene is projected into the realm of the unreal. The child has the gift of second sight which is forbidden to adults. He can see a throne in a high-backed chair, and a sword of lath becomes a Ferrara blade; the cast-off clothing of the attic serves to make a suit of velvet and ermine, and the bare rafters become the oaken arches of a royal hall. Whoever, then, attempts to direct the dramatics of young children, must approach with insight and sympathy, lest ridicule and insensibility not only wound but affront those whom we would help.

We have already touched upon the value of early dramatization in learning to read. In addition we may suggest other values:

Dramatization supplies the first steps toward original conversation and an improved vocabulary; it makes speech both spontaneous and free. It helps the children to acquire natural manners, with a lack of self-consciousness and awkwardness. It teaches them to attack difficulties with zest, and not to worry over hard problems. It results in a freedom from nervousness and self-distrust.

First in order are the child's everyday experiences, and those of the adults he knows. Playing doctor, playing nurse, playing postman, playing mother to dolls—all these are creative dramatizations of the child's daily experiences. With a little encouragement and unobtrusive direction, the child can make rather elaborate dramatizations from daily life. Along with these, the child loves to dramatize simple fairy tales, Mother Goose rhymes, and Aesop's Fables. It must be emphasized that children should not be required to stick to a script; they should be encouraged to make up their own dialogue. They also like to act out an idea or story in pantomime. Fairy tales make excellent subjects for pantomime.

The educational value of dramatization later in

Robin Hood

the life of the child is of a different quality from that of earlier years, but is none the less real and vital. Formerly, it was the harnessing of an instinct to the load of learning, an act of which the child remained unconscious. Now it is the deliberate choice of a method, realized by the boy or girl as such, for the understanding and appreciation of the great men and great events in history and literature. This change in view-point necessitates a change in method of presentation.

To children from ten to fifteen, dramatization serves the following very important ends:

It develops an interest in literature and history, by making the events and characters real. It teaches research and original compilation of material, and also the writing of good English, in the composing of "original plays." It develops mechanical skill and resourcefulness in making costumes, scenery, and stage properties.

It develops character. Constant association, in mind, with the great and the good of the world, and an attempt to look, act and talk like those characters must have its effect upon the child.

The materials available for dramatization by older children embrace the entire field of history and literature. A suggestive list might be this:

Great Heroes:
Beowulf   Arthur

Bible Stories:
Joseph   Daniel
David   Good Samaritan

Historical Novels:
Lorna Doone   Harold
Last of the Barons   Talisman
Ivanhoe   Kenilworth

Great Leaders:
Alfred   Caesar
Charlemagne   William and Harold
Henry VIII and Wolsey Cromwell
Washington   Lincoln

Heroes of Fiction:
Leatherstocking   Harvey Birch
Oliver Twist   Nicholas Nickleby
Scrooge   Pickwick

The question of scenery never troubles the young child. A robber's cave, or the giant's castle, or the dwelling of a fairy, are produced at any time or place, regardless of accessories, by the power of imagination. For the simple stories for dramatization by younger children, this will be sufficient; the older children enjoy and appreciate some tangible prop on which to base their dissimulation. Although perfectly able to manufacture a gallant out of a broomstick or two and a ragged coat, as Mother Rigby did Feathertop, they no longer have the infant faculty of creating him "out of whole cloth," from the imagination.

For the history and literature plays, therefore, we shall need scenery. It need not be elaborate, and it must not be costly. If it is appropriate in form and color, and suggestive of the real, it will be amply sufficient. In so far as possible, the natural out-of-doors will be superior to any indoor scene. That will depend on the play itself,

Noble Lady

LOOK WHAT A CROP JACK IS HARVESTING FROM HIS BEANSTALK. AN EVIL GIANT, AND BUSHELS OF BEANS BESIDES. SEE PAGE 75.

Dear Mother,

May I tell you a secret? This is a secret way to get the television set turned off. Make me a Costume Treasure Chest. A Costume Treasure Chest may be a drawer or a box or a corner of a closet. It may be an old blanket chest that rolls under the bed. Please put into my Treasure Chest the old clothes and other things you no longer want. I can use almost anything for my costumes. But I especially want old shoes (yours and Daddy's), hats, bracelets, necklaces, ties, dresses and skirts, gloves, and eyeglass frames (no glass, please). You'd be surprised what fun I can have with such treasures. Thank you, Mother.

                Love,
                      Your Child

Pilgrim

and the season when it is proposed to give it.

Children's outdoor plays may call for a forest, a cave, a mountain, or a castle. A forest may be made in this way: Nail wide boards together to form a U-shaped frame about 6' x 6'. Hammer nails in the top edges of the boards, three pairs on either side, each pair about 6" apart. Stretch wires across from nail to nail and let the children fill the spaces between the wires with upright branches and saplings. Pack turf in front of the first row of "trees."

To make mountains and caves, take ten yards or more of cheesecloth, cut in strips and sew into a large square. Fasten the four corners securely to the ground with spiked sticks. Dissolve a pound of glue in enough water to make a good paste, and apply freely to the cloth with a large brush. As fast as the paste is applied, sprinkle sand and gravel liberally over the cloth, being sure to cover it fully. When the cloth is dry, remove the securing pegs. Mica, artificial snow, scraps of colored plastic, and glass marbles, scattered over the sand and gravel, will make the surface glitter as with precious stones. This may serve as an interior for the cave of Aladdin or Ali Baba. For a different effect the sand cloth may be left plain.

Next, prepare a small platform of planks. Bore from eighteen to twenty holes in this, at irregular intervals, and insert in these holes wooden pins of lengths varying from six inches to four or five feet, according to the irregularity desired. Drape the sand-cloth over these pegs and your mountain is complete. The base of the mountain should be built up with turf, moss, ferns, rocks, and small trees, so as to give a foreground with which the mountain will blend.

To make the cave, throw the cloth over a large box, placing moss, rocks and other objects as before, to complete the picture.

To build a palace, construct a light framework of lath or other light material. Instead of sand, coat the cloth with a plaster composed of three parts table salt and one part white wheat flour, with water added to make a workable paste. It may be colored dark, and represented as moss covered and weather beaten, or left white and sprinkled with artificial snow. Cover the framework, and build the surroundings to conform.

As far as possible let the children make their own costumes. Resourcefulness, ingenuity and perseverance are qualities more to be desired even than dramatic excellence, and the elaboration of costumes and stage-settings from the chance materials of the home will develop these desirable traits.

For fairy tales cheesecloth is a satisfactory material for costumes, as it drapes prettily. For a fairy queen nothing can be prettier than white cheesecloth, effectively draped in flowing outlines, and sprinkled with "diamond dust." (Put dabs of mucilage thickly all over the draperies and sprinkle with the dust.) A cardboard crown, covered with gold paper, set upon flowing hair, completes the costume. A wand may be made of a slender stick covered with gold paper. For the other fairies, use cheesecloth of green, yellow, pink and blue, trimmed with gummed paper stars or hearts of gold or silver. Wings are made of light cardboard, covered with gold or silver

Fairy Queen

paper, and attached to the dress by means of small-sized safety pins. Butterflies are gowned in the same way, but have the wings gorgeously colored, and cut to resemble butterfly wings.

Gnomes and brownies may be costumed in full blouses, knee-breeches, high-pointed caps, long stockings and sandals, all made of gunny-sacks. If the sacks are not available, use brown or tan colored cambric.

For the literary and historical plays, there will be certain classes of costumes and properties which may be used again and again, and which therefore should be kept on hand. They may be classified in four groups. The fairy costumes described above may be considered group five.

The first group is the Royal. The robes may be made of white, scarlet or purple cambric. Cotton batting, with little black spots marked on in ink, will represent ermine. The crown can be made of cardboard, as described above, or of brass if the materials and skill be available. The sword, scepter, and shield with coat of arms can be made of wood and cardboard respectively, covered with gilt or silver paper. The coat of arms should be cut out of gilt paper or a contrasting color, and pasted to the shield.

The second group is the Ecclesiastical. In plays of European history, the Church figures very largely. A bishop's robes, mitre and crosier should be kept for use in different plays.

The third group is the People. This includes noblemen, countrymen, peasants, Robin Hood and his archers in Lincoln green, and Puritans. The flowing wig for the Cavaliers may be made as follows: Crochet a skull cap of wool for a foundation. To this sew strands of frayed rope, which look like fine, glossy hair. Try on, and trim so that the ends are even. Do it up in curl papers and iron it, and you have a Cavalier's wig.

The bows and arrows, spears and halberds, and swords and daggers of the various characters, can be easily evolved.

The best guide to accuracy in this regard will be the illustrations of histories and historical novels, and the cheap copies of great historical paintings.

The fourth group is the Classical. Plays of Greek and Roman history, especially scenes from Shakespeare, will need togas, sandals, and Roman armor. The toga can be made of white cambric. The border, which was so important a feature of the toga, can be applied in the following manner: Cut the desired border pattern from gold or purple paper. Mix a tablespoonful of starch with boiling water. When cool apply to the back of the strips and patterns of paper. Then lay them carefully in position on the cloth and iron them flat with a hot flatiron. They will look as though they had been painted or embroidered on the cloth.

Corslet, helmet, greaves, armpieces and shield can be made of cardboard, steamed into the curved shape, and covered with gold, silver or bronze paper. Elaborate "embossed" designs may be pasted on the corslet and shield.

With these suggestions the ingenuity of children should be adequate to costume and produce any plays their fancy leads them to take up.

Mother Goose Rhymes Dramatized

PUSSY CAT

Characters: Pussy Cat; Little Girl.

Pussy Cat is somewhere out of sight, but is within hearing. Little Girl looks under the desk, table and chairs, calling: "Pussy Cat, Pussy Cat!"

Pussy Cat comes stealing along with a soft "Mew, mew, mew." Imitate as closely as possible. Then follows the rhyme dramatized.

Little Girl—

    Pussy Cat, Pussy Cat,
      Where have you been?

Pussy Cat—

    I've been to London
      To visit the queen.

Little Girl—

    Pussy Cat, Pussy Cat,
      What did you there?

Pussy Cat—

    I frightened a little mouse
      Under her chair.

LITTLE BO-PEEP

Characters: Little Girl; Little Boy.

Little Girl (in tones of anxiety to Little Boy)—

  Little Bo-Peep has lost her sheep,
    And can't tell where to find them.

Little Boy (in spirit of recklessness)—

  Leave them alone, and they'll come home,
    Bringing their tails behind them.

LITTLE BOY BLUE

Characters: Farmer Day; His wife; Boy Blue; Cows; Sheep.

The cows are in the corn. (Corner of the room.) The sheep graze in the meadow. (Another corner of the room.) Boy Blue is asleep under the haycock. (Chair inverted.) Near Boy Blue lies a roll of paper for a horn.

Farmer Day—

Little Boy Blue, come, blow your horn,
The sheep's in the meadow, the cow's in the corn.
(*To his wife.*)
Where's the little boy that looks after the sheep?

Farmer and Wife (in surprise)—

He's under the haycock, fast asleep!

Farmer (to wife)—

Will you wake him?

Wife—
No, not I;
For if I do, he'll be sure to cry.

(*Farmer picks up horn and toots it. The boy wakes, is given the horn and runs, tooting, after the cattle.*)

BAA, BAA, BLACK SHEEP

Characters: Master; Dame; Sheep; Little Boy.

Master—
    Baa, baa, black sheep,
      Have you any wool?

Black Sheep—
    Yes, sir, yes, sir,
      Three bags full.

(*Points at master.*)
    One for my master,

(*Points at dame.*)
    One for my dame,

(*Points at boy.*)
    And one for the little boy
      Who lives in the lane.

Jack and the Beanstalk

CHARACTERS

Widow	Jack
Butcher	Cow
Fairy	Giant
Giant's Wife	

PROPERTIES

Rope with which to lead the cow.
Beans to pay for cow.
Branch from tree for beanstalk.
Fairy's wand, made of pine stick covered with tinfoil.
Reading table, or desk, for dining table.
Clay hen.
Toy money bags.
Toy harp, or one made of soft wood.
Small hatchet.

ACT I

Widow (*crying*)—Jack, you are a lazy boy. I have worked hard to earn food and shelter for us, and now all we have left is a cow.

Jack—Mother, let me take the cow and sell her. I will make a great bargain.

Widow—Well, Jack, you may sell the cow. I have no food and no money. I am not strong enough to work any longer.

(*Jack runs and gets the cow and starts to market.*)

Jack—Come on, Bossy, I am going to sell you for a great deal of money.

Butcher—Good morning, Jack, where are you taking your cow?

Jack—I am going to sell Bossy. How much will you give for her?

Butcher—See this bag of wonderful beans. Plant them in your garden and they will make you rich. I will trade them for the cow.

Jack—I believe I like the beans and I will trade.

(*Jack runs home to his mother.*)

Jack—Oh, Mother! Mother! See what a bargain I have made. This large bag of beans for our cow!

Widow (*angrily*)—Give me those beans. There they go out of the window. Now, you go to bed without any supper.

(*Jack goes into the garden the next morning and finds a huge beanstalk has grown up in the night.*)

Jack—Oh, Mother! Mother! Come and see the huge beanstalk. I am going to climb to the top.

Widow—You must not do so. You will fall.

Jack—Oh, I am not afraid.

(*Jack passes around the beanstalk and finds himself in a strange country.*)

ACT II

Jack—I am tired and hungry, and wish I had obeyed my mother.

(*Fairy suddenly appears before him, waving her wand.*)

Fairy—Good morning, little boy; your name is Jack, is it not?

Jack—Yes.

Fairy—I know all about you. I am going to tell you a strange but true story. Never tell anyone, not even your mother. Your father was a rich man. A cruel giant robbed him of all his riches, and afterwards killed him. You must now help your mother by getting this money from the giant. It belongs to you.

(*Fairy disappears. Jack sees a large house in the distance and runs toward it.*)

ACT III

Jack—Good morning, dear lady; will you give me something to eat, and let me rest in your house a while?

Giant's Wife—Oh, little boy, no one ever comes to this house. My husband is a cruel giant and eats little boys.

Jack—Couldn't you hide me for just one night?

Giant's Wife—Come into the kitchen and I will give you food and drink.

(*Loud knocks are heard at the door.*)

Giant's Wife—Oh, boy, jump into the oven!

Giant (*stalking in*)—Wife! Wife! I smell fresh meat!

Giant's Wife—Oh, no, my dear, it is only the prisoners in the dungeon.

Giant (*gruffly*)—Bring me my supper. Bring me my pet hen. Lay, hen, lay! Lay! Lay!

(*Giant tires of the hen and falls asleep. Jack seizes the hen and runs home.*)

Jack (*excitedly*)—Oh, Mother! Mother! here is a hen that lays golden eggs.

Widow—I am so glad to see you. With the golden eggs we can have everything.

(*Jack goes to the giant's house again.*)

Jack—Dear, kind lady, won't you give me my supper?

Giant's Wife—Come into the kitchen. You may eat the scraps.

(*A loud knocking and stamping of feet are heard.*)

(*Giant's Wife*—Run, little boy, and jump into the closet.

(*Giant enters and eats his supper.*)

Giant—Wife! Wife! bring me my money bags.

(*Giant falls asleep counting his money. Jack seizes the money bags and runs home.*)

Widow—Jack, where have you been? And where do you find all these treasures?

Jack—Dear mother, some day I can tell you all.

(*A third time Jack goes to the giant's house. When he hears the giant coming he hides in a boiler.*)

Giant—Wife! Wife! I smell fresh meat. I am going to search this house.

Giant's Wife—Oh, husband, come and eat your nice warm supper and play on your harp.

(*Giant plays on the harp until he falls asleep. Jack seizes the harp and runs for home. Giant wakes and runs after Jack. Jack outruns the giant and cuts the beanstalk. The giant is killed by the fall.*)
—Roberta Howell.

The Three Bears

A Pantomime

CHARACTERS AND COSTUMES

Goldilocks: Child of six to ten years with long fair hair or curls. Wears a black velvet bodice, laced across front; white chemisette with short sleeves and Dutch neck; scarlet or pale-blue skirt, white stockings and buckled shoes. Carries quaint little black velvet bonnet in hand. (This costume is a mere suggestion. A Red Riding Hood cape would do perfectly well with a white dress, or a Kate Greenaway dress and wide hat with flowers. The costume must be picturesque, however.)

Large Bear: Costume of dark brown canton flannel, cut like a child's sleeping suit, with a hood attached to be pulled down over forehead. Stiff pointed ears, wired or lined to stand erect, are sewed to sides of hood. Brown gloves or mittens cover the hands. A bear's face may be procured from a mask or toy-shop, or if this is impracticable, a mask with holes for eyes, nose and mouth may be cut from the flannel and fastened to the hood. Large bear may carry cane and wear hat and also coat and gay waistcoat, if desired.

Middle-Sized Bear: Same costume as above. May wear large white apron, a shoulder shawl, a cap and spectacles, and carry work-bag and knitting.

Little Bear: Same costume as above. May wear gay gingham rompers and carry a Teddy-bear, a return-ball, or other plaything.

(The large bear must be very tall, the middle-sized bear shorter and plump, and the part of the little bear taken by a boy about Goldilock's size and age.)

SCENE I—GOLDILOCKS IN THE WOOD

The frame of a small house is required for this scene, its size fitted to whatever stage is to be used. The front only, with a bit of roof and sidewall need be shown, but a practicable door is essential and a window or two are attractions. Four uprights, four cross-beams and a ridge-pole with a few supports are needed if whole house is shown, and the sides and roof may be covered in with brown paper, imitating red bricks. If stage is small and house must be removed before next scene, frame should be bolted together, or fastened with steel hooks and eyes so that it can be taken down quickly. If possible, however, house should be set in corner of stage and screened or curtained when not in use, so that it may be shown again in Scene VI. It need occupy but a few feet of room if front is set across a corner; and the necessary measuring and planning for it and the actual erection and decoration give the boys and girls joyful occupation for several days. A few trees, set here and there about the stage in stands, represent the wood; and bunches of paper flowers set in concealed tins of earth or in moss, are growing in suitable places.

Goldilocks is first seen at extreme rear of stage, coming slowly along, swinging bonnet, bending down boughs of trees as if to look for nests, and picking flowers now and then. If some of the boys who are expert whistlers can imitate bird trills and calls during this scene it will be an attraction. The by-play of Goldilocks here will depend on her accomplishments. She may pick a lapful of flowers and, sitting down on front of stage, arrange them in a wreath for her hair; when this is done dancing a little rustic dance under the trees. She may find a nest and pretend to feed birdlings; she may discover a rabbit beneath the fir-boughs, and fondle and caress it. At length, however, she lifts her head as if listening to a distant voice, catches up her bonnet and skips off stage.

SCENE II—THE BEARS' HOUSE

The screen or curtain which has concealed this building is now removed and the children gaze on it with delight, for there is nothing they love better than a house large enough to be real, yet small enough to suit their own Lilliputian size. If there are windows these should be open and white curtains shown. The door is ajar and a canary in cage hangs beside it. A border of paper flowers is growing in front of the cottage. Goldilocks appears from rear, is astonished at sight of cottage, looks it all over, stoops down to smell flowers, picks some, fingers curtains admiringly, then notices that door is not shut. (A brass knocker on door makes an enchanting detail for children.) Goldilocks taps softly, then louder, then peeps in, and withdraws suddenly as if frightened, dropping her flowers on steps as she runs away. She appears a second time, finally makes up her mind to enter, and after she has gone inside peeps out again. Leaves door wide open.

SCENE III—THE BEARS' KITCHEN

An interior is here shown so furnished as to be transformed by slight changes from kitchen to sitting-room and that again to bedroom. Old-fashioned fire-frame may easily be made of wood or cardboard and lined with red brick Dennison paper. For kitchen scene, it may have a crane, pot-hooks and hanging kettle, these being removed for two following scenes. There should be a door opening into another room, and a window is an essential for Scene V. A broom made of twigs or fir-branches stands in corner. A warming-pan and other old-fashioned articles may hang on the walls, if desired. If there is room on stage for a couch or lounge it should be placed there in the beginning, so as to be quickly made up in bedroom scene. An essential is a large table in center with three bowls and spoons,—one a wash-bowl, one a yellow mixing bowl, and one of ordinary size accompanied by suitable spoons or ladles. Stool in front of table. Goldilocks makes a timid entrance, peeping in first and withdrawing, finally closing door behind her. She investigates kitchen as long as time allows, then spies bowls and approaches table, indicating hunger. Moves stool in front of biggest bowl, climbs up, takes hold of spoon and drops it, as if too heavy. Moves stool to middle-sized bowl, grasps spoon and tastes porridge. Drops it on table and makes wry face as if disliking flavor. Sees small bowl, tastes contents with pleasure, takes it from table, sits on stool and eats porridge all up, returning bowl and spoon to place. Then after looking around room and out of window, goes out by door.

SCENE IV—THE BEARS' SITTING-ROOM

Remove crane, pot-hooks and kettle for this scene, substituting andirons and laying a fire, if there is time. Remove broom and kitchen furniture, bowls, spoons and stool. Change window-curtain, cover table with bright cloth and set vase of flowers on it, with candle-stick and work basket. No other furniture needed save three chairs, one very large and high with arms and a cushion, one middle-sized, with cushion, and one a child's chair in corner.

Goldilocks enters, investigates room as before, and finally, showing signs of fatigue, attempts to climb up in big chair, but finds it too high. Pulls cushion half-way out in attempt. Next tries middle-sized chair; bounces about on cushion and finds it too wide and soft, jumps down, pulling cushion to floor, and spies child's chair. Claps hands, runs to it and sits down so hard that it breaks and she falls to floor. Goldilocks gives signs of fright, and after trying to straighten up chair and failing, runs from room in tears.

SCENE V—THE BEARS' BEDROOM

Chairs and table are removed for this scene, all other furniture remaining same. Stool under window. Three beds are shown, one an army cot perhaps, one made up on a lounge or sofa, and the third a crib, or child's bed of any sort. (One may be made up on a lounge, one on floor, and the third be improvised with three chairs.) It does not matter what the beds are if fresh and white and differing considerably in size. Goldilocks enters in tears and stands in doorway, wiping eyes. Recovers herself and looks about room. Sighs wearily, rubs eyes and looks at largest bed. Shakes her head, as if too high, and tries to climb up. Fails, but disarranges bedding in effort. Next tries middle-sized bed and succeeds in getting up, but finds it uncomfortable and pillows too hard. Shakes head in impatience and suddenly catches sight of little bed. Tumbles out of middle-sized bed, dragging counterpane and pillows to floor and runs to small bed. Claps hands in joy and dances around it. Lays bonnet, which she has carried by knotted strings over arm, on foot of bed, jumps in, pulls counterpane up and goes to sleep.

INTERLUDE

Three voices behind the scenes now repeat the classic words of the three bears when they returned from their morning walk, accompanying them with suitable growls and nicely-proportioned thunders from the piano:—

"SOMEBODY HAS BEEN TASTING MY PORRIDGE!!!"

The mother may help the development of the expressive instinct even in early childhood. Even a baby ought to be treated as a playmate, not as a plaything. There is an old-fashioned game known as "Come to Me." The little damsel with her doll, and perhaps "dressed up" in some of her mother's wardrobe, came to call on mother. Her efforts to behave exactly as a lady should were aided and guided by the mother's careful behavior as hostess. It was training in manners. When the children played visit each other they used all the manners they had. They were practicing useful lessons without knowing it.
—*William Byron Forbush.*

"SOMEBODY HAS BEEN TASTING MY PORRIDGE!!"

"Somebody (*high squeaky voice*) has been tasting my porridge and has eaten it all up!"

SCENE VI—THE THREE BEARS RETURN

(This may be omitted if not practicable to show the Bears' House again.)

The Bears' House is shown as in Scene II, and presently the three bears come waddling in. Father comes first, with hat and cane, fanning himself with red bandanna. Mother may carry parasol, if desired, and leads little Bear dangling a toy from his paw. When all are well in sight, Father notices door is open and calls Mother's attention to fact. Mother nods head, shows excitement and points to window where curtain is disarranged. Little Bear waddles forward and picks up Goldilocks' bunch of flowers, showing it to parents. Pantomime of consternation. Mother Bear wrings hands. Father shakes fist threateningly. Little Bear shivers in fright and clings to Mother, then all hurriedly waddle into house.

SCENE VII— THE BEARS' KITCHEN
(as in Scene III)

Father Bear enters first, cautiously, beckons his family and begins to look about for supposed intruder. Mother Bear enters more timidly and goes through same pantomime, but with starts and signs of fear. Little Bear not appearing, Mother goes out and brings him in, crying. She is consoling him when Father suddenly goes to table and discovers, with every sign of surprise and horror, that somebody has been tasting his porridge. Mother rushes to table, makes similar discovery and waves spoon in air, threateningly. Little Bear follows, looks into his bowl and finding it empty, holds it out to parents with simulated howls of rage. They rush to him and dry his tears, and then leave room in determined way as if to bring culprit to justice.

INTERLUDE

Voices behind the scene, accompanied by appropriate growls, repeat following words:—

"SOMEBODY HAS BEEN SITTING IN MY CHAIR!!!"

"SOMEBODY HAS BEEN SITTING IN MY CHAIR!!"

"Somebody has been sitting in my chair and has broken it all up!"

SCENE VIII—THE BEARS' SITTING ROOM
(as in Scene IV)—

Same by-play as in Scene VII on part of parent Bears. Little Bear stands on threshold, timidly, paw in mouth, and takes no share in investigation until parents discover damage to chairs. Then, dropping toy, he waddles to corner and discovers his own broken chair. Great grief, hardly to be consoled by parents. Bears take one another's paws and leave room like conspirators, glancing fearfully about as they go.

INTERLUDE

As before:—

"SOMEBODY HAS BEEN SLEEPING IN MY BED!!!"

"SOMEBODY HAS BEEN SLEEPING IN MY BED!!"

"Somebody has been sleeping in my bed and here she is!"

SCENE IX—THE BEARS' BEDROOM
(as in Scene V)

Father Bear opens door slowly and carefully, looking around room several times before he enters. Finding all quiet, turns and beckons Mother who comes as far as threshold, but is evidently afraid to venture farther. Little Bear peeps in under her arm. Face of Goldilocks must be turned from door so that she will not be noticed at first. Father goes to his bed and shows by excited gestures that someone has been in it. Drops to floor and looks underneath, but finding no one begins to re-arrange bedding. Mother gathers courage and seeks her bed. Same pantomime of astonishment and fear. Little Bear, left alone in doorway, suddenly drops on all fours and scrambles to his bed, where he stands erect. Sees Goldilocks, throws up paws in astonishment and crosses room to tell parents. Goldilocks still sleeps quietly. Bears hurry to bedside, being careful to stand at foot of bed and on side away from window, to give Goldilocks opportunity to escape. Mother catches sight of Goldilocks' bonnet, takes it up and inspects it with surprise and pleasure. When the three stand beside Goldilocks, looking down on her, she awakes. She appears to scream and hides face in bedclothes, peeping out again at once to see if Bears are still there. Repeats action while Bears remain transfixed with astonishment. Little Bear, head on one side, regards Goldilocks with admiration, nods head and rubs paws together.

Goldilocks, without removing her eyes from Bears, slips slowly out of bed and stands up. Surprise of Bears and pleasure at her appearance. Show by gesture that they notice her long hair, gay dress and buckled shoes. Little Bear holds out arms to her. Father begins to move towards her when she runs across room at full speed, climbs on stool and out of window. (If this is impossible, escape by door.)

Bears run to window as quickly as possible, little one falling down on the way, in his hurry, but Goldilocks has escaped them. Little Bear tries awkwardly to climb out of window, but gets caught and hangs there struggling violently. Parents facing audience, stand looking at each other in astonishment, Mother still holding Goldilocks' bonnet and shaking head as if to say, "Wonders will never cease!" —*Nora Archibald Smith.*

HOW SEEDS TRAVEL

Written and Illustrated by Carroll Lane Fenton

Seeds have various ways of going to places where they are able to grow. Milkweed seeds have tufts of silk that act almost like balloons. Wind lifts the silken balloons and carries the seeds long distances before they settle upon the ground.

The Russian thistle is a tumbleweed. In the autumn, when their seeds have ripened, tumbleweeds break loose from their roots and go rolling across fields and along roads. As each tumbleweed rolls and bounces along, it scatters thousands upon thousands of its tiny seeds.

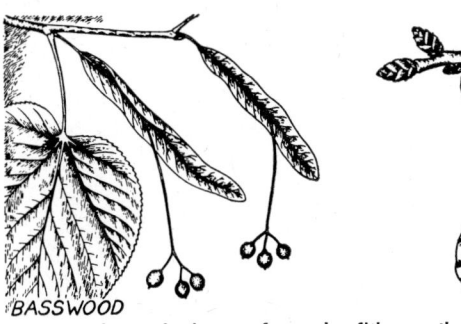

BASSWOOD   *ELM*

Basswood seeds hang from leaflike sails, just as paratroopers hang from their drifting parachutes. Elm seeds have broad, flat sails that float or drift on the wind. They take the ripe seeds far from their parent elm tree.

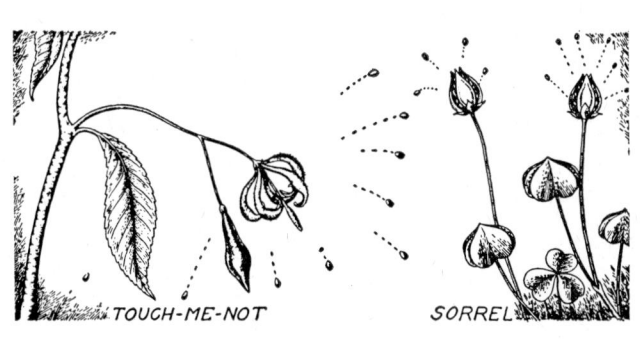

TOUCH-ME-NOT   *SORREL*

Touch-me-nots and sorrel, or sour grass, have pods that shoot their seeds in all directions. Violets also shoot their seeds from pods.

Squirrels give nuts and acorns free rides and then hide them in the ground. This squirrel has carried an acorn out of the woods to bury it. He may dig up the acorn next winter and eat it. But if he forgets to eat the acorn, it may become a seedling oak tree.

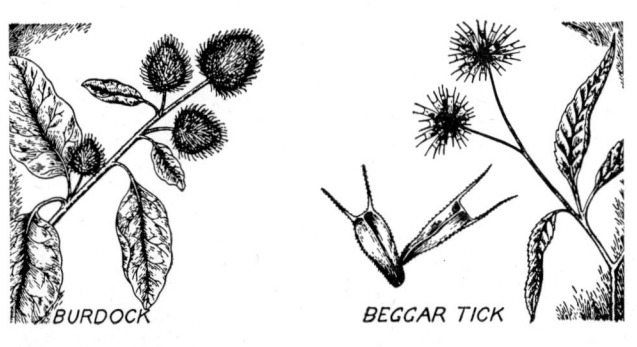

BURDOCK   *BEGGAR TICK*

Burdock and beggar tick are two of the many plants whose seeds are enclosed in cases provided with prickly hooks. These hooks catch upon the hair of animals or the clothing of people, who often give the seeds long rides.

Cherry seeds are the stones, or pits, at the center of the bright-colored fruits. Birds often pick the ripe cherries and carry them away. After eating the juicy pulp, the birds let the cherry seeds fall to the ground. The seeds then grow into trees.

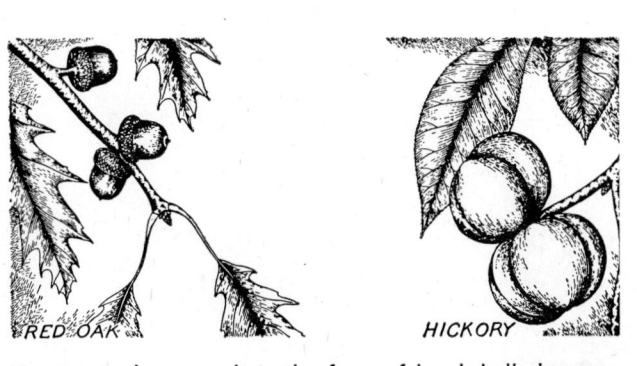

RED OAK   *HICKORY*

Many trees have seeds in the form of hard-shelled acorns or nuts that fall to the ground when ripe. They sometimes tumble into streams, which carry the seeds along and leave them in fertile places to grow.

What BIG Means

A boy is bigger than a dog.

A dog is bigger than a flea. This flea looks tiny even through a magnifying glass.

A flea is bigger than a mite. Some mites live on fleas.

An elephant is lots bigger than a boy, a dog, a flea, or a mite.

A whale is bigger than an elephant.

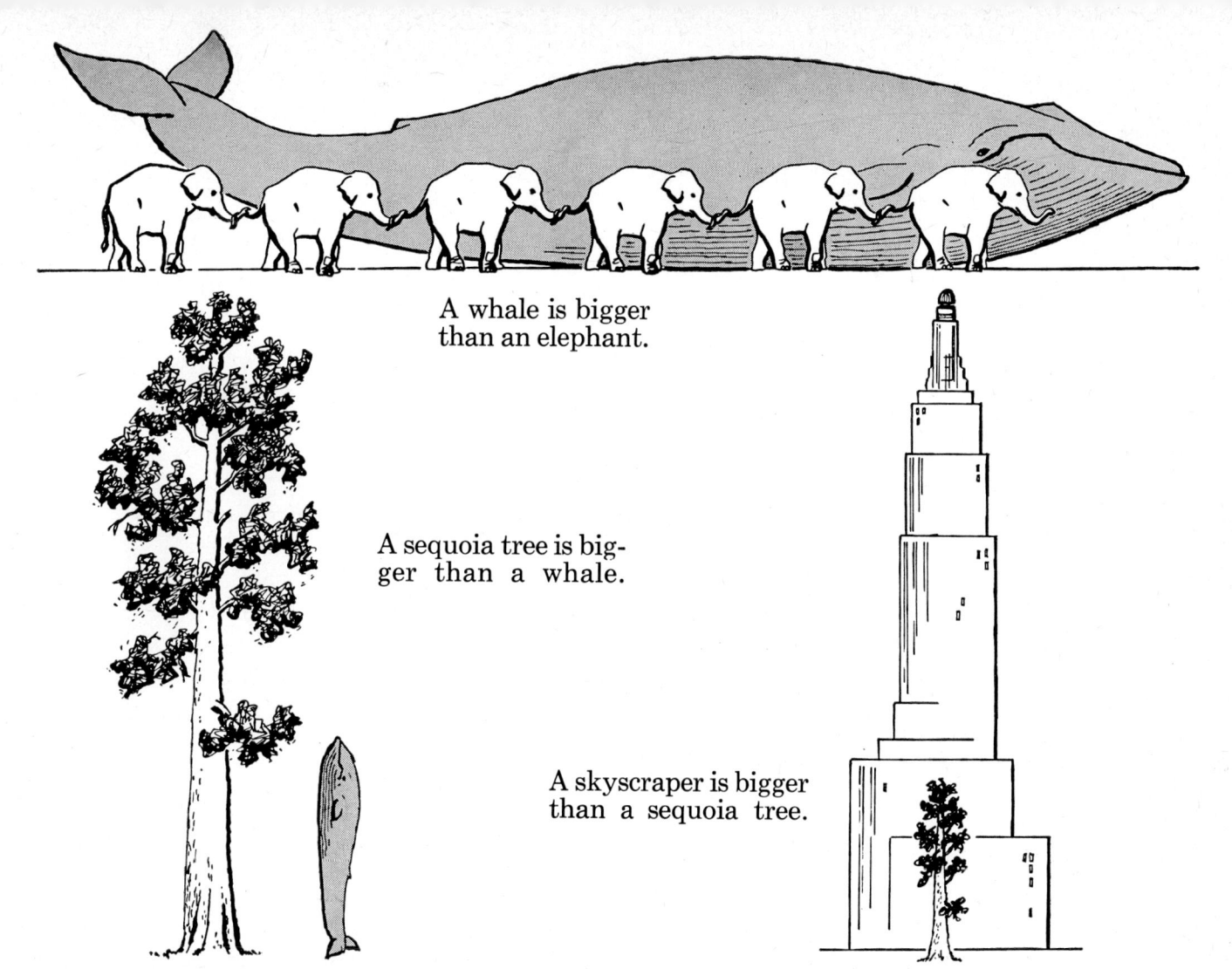

A sequoia tree is bigger than a whale.

A skyscraper is bigger than a sequoia tree.

A mountain is much, much bigger than a skyscraper. What is bigger than a mountain? The earth, the sun, the stars.

EDGAR OWL TELLS ME...
WHAT LIVES IN THE GRASS

The grass is a home for many creatures. Some are so tiny that stalks of grass are like trees to them and a backyard is a mighty forest. Most of them have strange ways of living, and they can do surprising things.

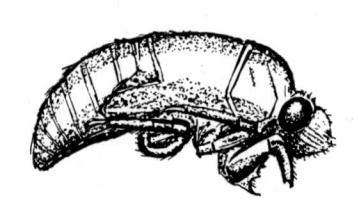

The froghopper is a tiny insect you can hardly see. Many people have never seen it, though they have often seen its house. Have you ever found a little piece of froth on the grass? This bit of froth is the froghopper's house. The froghopper makes it by pouring out a sticky juice and then beating the juice with its tail. Your mother can show you how to beat egg whites to a froth. The froghopper knows how to make froth as soon as it comes from its tiny egg. It is the only creature in the world that knows how to make a froth house. The froth hides it from its enemies and protects it from the hot sun. Snug in its house, the froghopper lives on juice it sucks from the grass until it grows up and grows wings. Then it does not need its froth house. It can hop around and fly away from its enemies.

Another kind of hopper lives in the grass—the grasshopper. With its long, strong hind legs it can jump many times its own length. If you were able to jump as well, you could easily jump across a large room. Grasshoppers eat grass and other plants. A grasshopper can eat its own weight in food every day. A huge swarm of grasshoppers can quickly eat all the grass or grain in a field. Some kinds of grasshoppers have wings. They are called locusts. At times they appear in such great numbers that they make the sky dark. They fly across the land, eating the leaves of every plant in their path. A great swarm of grasshoppers once started to eat all the crops of early settlers in Utah. Then a large flock of seagulls came and ate the grasshoppers. That is why Utah, so far from the sea, has the seagull as its state bird.

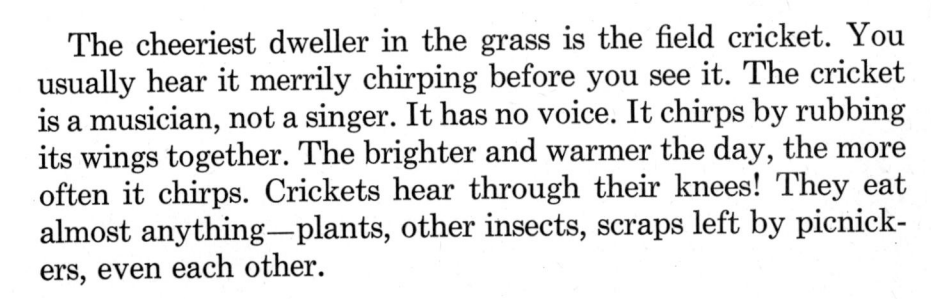

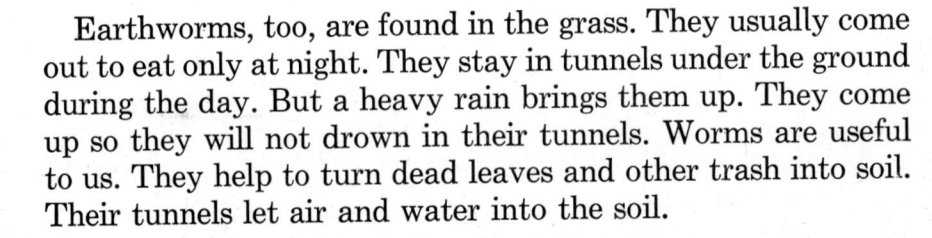

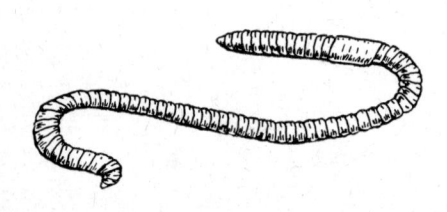

The cheeriest dweller in the grass is the field cricket. You usually hear it merrily chirping before you see it. The cricket is a musician, not a singer. It has no voice. It chirps by rubbing its wings together. The brighter and warmer the day, the more often it chirps. Crickets hear through their knees! They eat almost anything—plants, other insects, scraps left by picnickers, even each other.

Earthworms, too, are found in the grass. They usually come out to eat only at night. They stay in tunnels under the ground during the day. But a heavy rain brings them up. They come up so they will not drown in their tunnels. Worms are useful to us. They help to turn dead leaves and other trash into soil. Their tunnels let air and water into the soil.

Ants are the most interesting of all the creatures that live in the grass. They build cities under the ground. In an ant city there are special places where the eggs are laid, nurseries where the young ants are raised, storehouses for food, and garbage dumps.

Each ant community has a queen that does nothing but lay eggs. Workers look after the queen, take care of the eggs, gather food, feed the young, and keep the community clean. The community even has an army, made up of soldier ants that do nothing but fight the enemies of the community. Some ants keep "cows." The cows are really aphids, insects that suck sap from plants and turn it into honeydew. The ants stroke the aphids until the aphids give them some of the honeydew.

You may find a bumblebee's nest in a hole in the ground in the grass. In spring, a queen bumblebee brings pollen and honey to the nest. She makes bread of the pollen and honey. Then she lays eggs. When the young hatch from the eggs, they live on the stored bread. When they grow into bees, they look after the young and find food for them. Bees drink nectar from flowers. Only bumblebees visit red clover plants, for they are the only bees with sucking tubes long enough to reach the nectar in red clover flowers. When the people of Australia first grew red clover, the flowers produced no seeds. There were no bumblebees to carry pollen from flower to flower to make seeds. After they brought in some bumblebees, the red clover plants grew seeds.

The grass spider builds a funnel-shaped web in the grass. It hides near the small end of the funnel, waiting for an insect to stumble into its web. Then it rushes out and binds its victim with spider web and kills it with a poisoned bite. The golden garden spider, beautifully marked in black and gold, is sometimes seen in the grass. It builds a round web. Every kind of spider weaves a special kind of web. It does not learn to do this. It knows how the minute it is born.

Meadow frogs often live in the grass during the summer. They, too, help us, for they eat many harmful insects. They catch flies and other insects with their long sticky tongues. A frog can flick its tongue out and in as quick as a flash.

EDGAR OWL TELLS ME...
WHAT LIVES IN THE WATER

Many things besides fish live in water. If you watch a pond closely you will see many queer creatures in it. The odd things they do make every pond a wonderland.

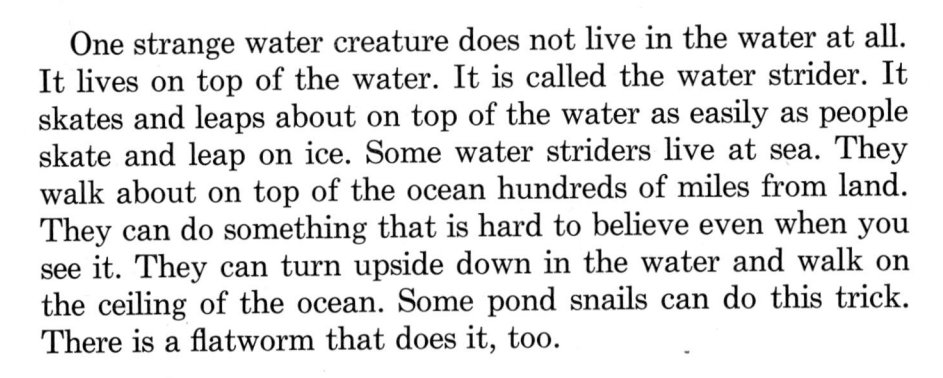

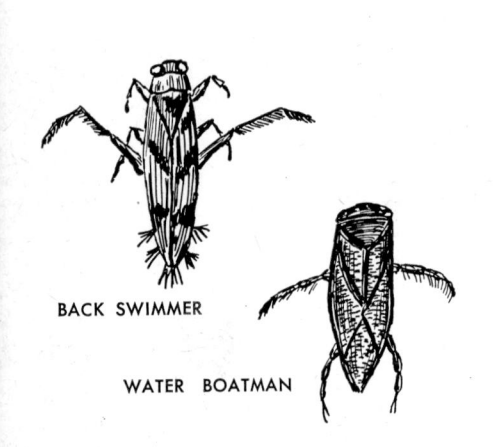

One strange water creature does not live in the water at all. It lives on top of the water. It is called the water strider. It skates and leaps about on top of the water as easily as people skate and leap on ice. Some water striders live at sea. They walk about on top of the ocean hundreds of miles from land. They can do something that is hard to believe even when you see it. They can turn upside down in the water and walk on the ceiling of the ocean. Some pond snails can do this trick. There is a flatworm that does it, too.

Another queer upside-down creature is a bug called the back swimmer. With its long oarlike hind legs, it rows about under the water like a little round-bottomed boat. It goes on its back because it carries its air supply in a hair-covered groove on its belly. The water boatman looks like the back swimmer, but it rows about right-side up. It is right-side up because it carries its air on its back, under its hard wing covers. It flies about at night. It is both a submarine and an airplane!

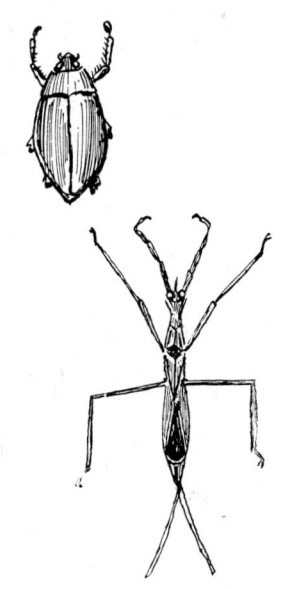

BACK SWIMMER

WATER BOATMAN

The whirligig beetle lives at the top of the water, with part of its body under the water. The top half of each of its eyes is made to see in the air. The bottom half is made to see in the water. It can see food and enemies in the water and in the air at the same time. Some people call the whirligig beetle write-my-name, because it seems to be writing as it whirls and spins about in the water. Sometimes a hundred or more beetles may be seen dizzily streaking about in a small space. Although they whirl all over the place, they never crash into one another.

Water scorpions look like tiny twigs in the water. Their front legs are made like pocket knives. The lower part of each leg fits into a groove in the upper part. When an insect or other tiny water dweller mistakes the water scorpion for a twig and gets too close, the water scorpion seizes it in its strong front legs and sucks the juice from its body.

The caddis worm (top of next page) is the young of a moth-like insect called the caddis fly. Caddis worms look like little white caterpillars. The amazing thing about them is that they make little silk-lined houses for their soft bodies. Some make their houses of little pieces of stick. Others use tiny stones, pieces of leaf, scraps of bark, or grains of sand. They drag their houses with them wherever they go. Some caddis worms actually fish with nets! They make little nets between stones or on top of stones. Then they wait for the flowing water to carry tiny creatures into their nets.

Water spiders can scurry about on top of the water, but they raise their young under the water. The mother spider first attaches a thimble-shaped web to an underwater plant. She rises to the top of the water and catches air bubbles on her hairy body. Then she returns to the web and brushes the bubbles into it. She keeps doing this until the web fills with air. Then she lays her eggs in the web. She feeds her young in the web until they can take care of themselves.

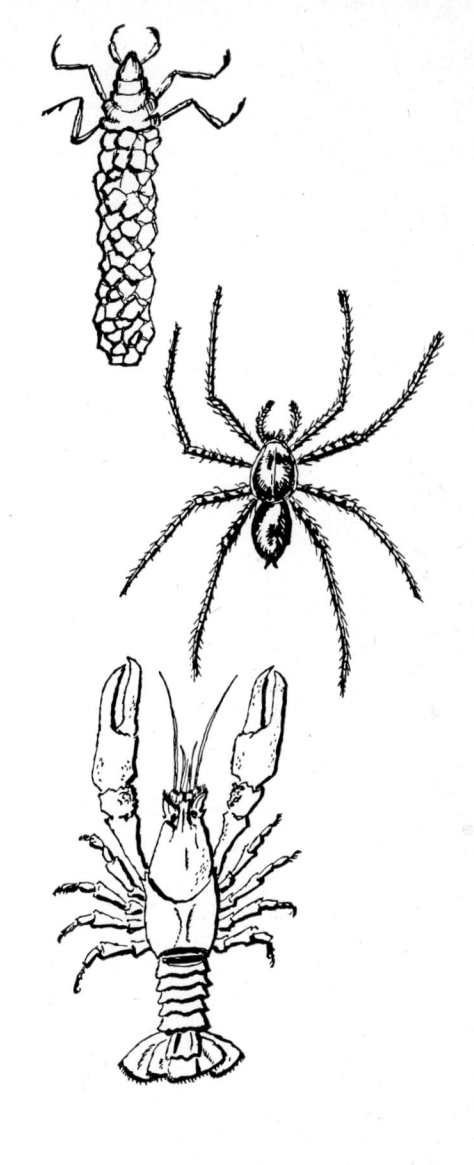

The crayfish is protected by a hard shell and armed with strong pinching claws. The crayfish's shell does not grow. When its shell gets too small, the crayfish sheds it and grows a new one. The crayfish crawls about on the bottom, looking for food. When alarmed, it holds out its claws like a boxer and swims backward. It swims by flicking its fan-shaped tail to and fro. Crayfish fight fiercely among themselves. When a crayfish loses a claw or a leg, it simply grows a new one.

The turtle is another armored water dweller, but its shell grows. Turtles come from eggs that look like little table tennis balls. The mother buries the eggs in the ground. The little turtles have to find their own way to the water. Turtles eat fish, frogs, worms, snails—almost anything. The alligator snapping turtle is a fisherman. It stands on the bottom with its mouth open. Its waving white fishing "tongue" looks like a grub in the water. When a fish swims over to take the bait, the turtle's strong sharp jaws snap on it. In winter, turtles sleep in the mud.

ALLIGATOR SNAPPING TURTLE

In spring, you may see little tadpoles in a pond. They seem to be "all heads and tails." As they grow larger, they slowly grow legs. At last, their tails disappear, and they become frogs. Some frogs sleep in the water in winter, some in the mud. The frog's skin does not grow. When the skin gets too tight, it splits up the back. The frog then pulls it off over its head, like someone taking off a sweater.

TADPOLE

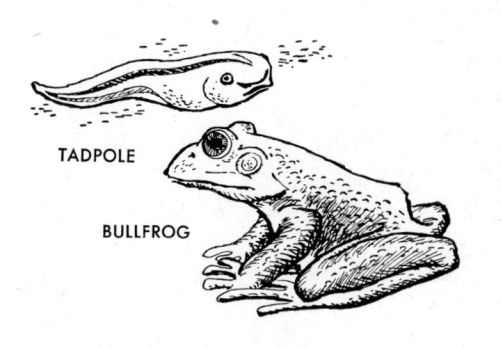

BULLFROG

The brightly-colored sunfish is one of the bravest of all fish. The mother sunfish scoops out a nest on the bottom and lays her eggs in it. The father sunfish guards the eggs until they hatch. He does not leave, even to eat. He attacks anything that approaches the nest, even fish several times larger than he is.

COWBOYS

Cowboys are the workers on cattle ranches. They live outdoors most of the time. There are large cattle ranches in the western United States, western Canada, Florida, and parts of South America.

These cowboys are herding wild horses into a corral. Sometimes cowboys capture wild horses and "break" them. This means that they train them to be ridden. A cowboy's horse must learn how to help herd cattle.

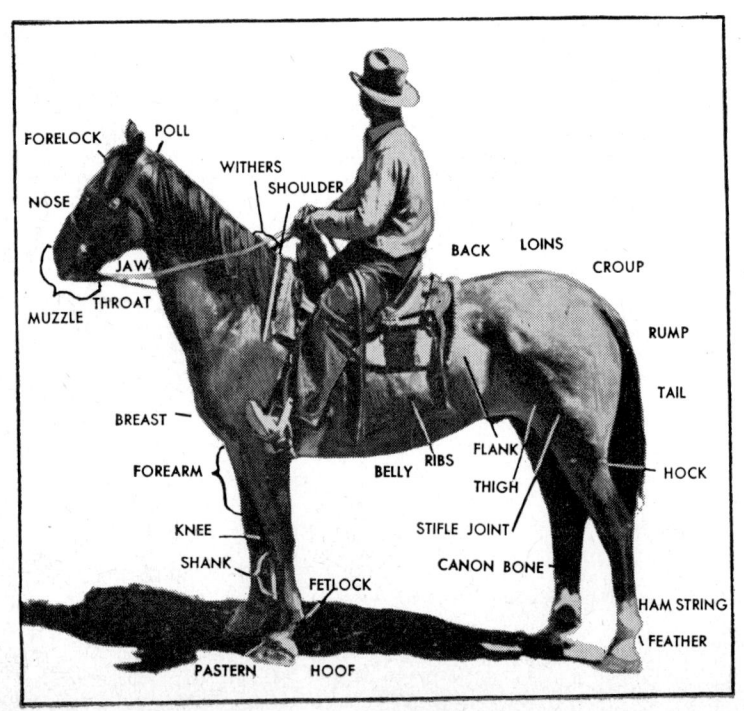

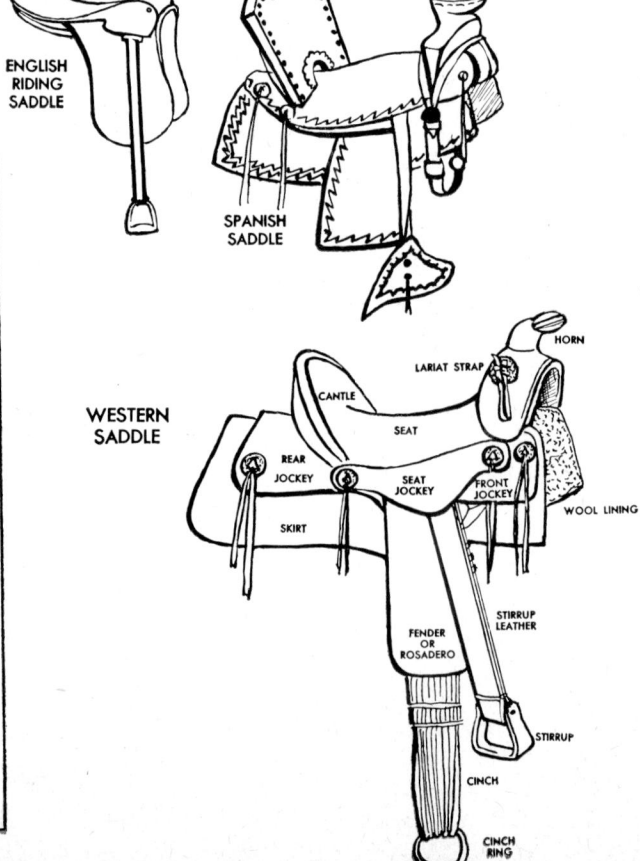

ENGLISH RIDING SADDLE

SPANISH SADDLE

WESTERN SADDLE — HORN, LARIAT STRAP, CANTLE, SEAT, REAR JOCKEY, SEAT JOCKEY, FRONT JOCKEY, WOOL LINING, SKIRT, STIRRUP LEATHER, FENDER OR ROSADERO, STIRRUP, CINCH, CINCH RING

Horse parts: FORELOCK, POLL, WITHERS, SHOULDER, BACK, LOINS, CROUP, RUMP, TAIL, HOCK, FLANK, THIGH, STIFLE JOINT, CANON BONE, HAM STRING, FEATHER, PASTERN, HOOF, FETLOCK, SHANK, KNEE, FOREARM, BREAST, RIBS, BELLY, MUZZLE, THROAT, JAW, NOSE

COWBOYS
AT THE RODEO

Cowboys go to the rodeo to show their skill at riding, roping, branding, and other kinds of ranch work. They enter contests to see how long they can stay on a bucking horse or a wild bull. The rodeo is a cowboy circus.

THE ROPE TWIRLING ACT. This twelve-year-old cowboy has become a star performer at the rodeo. He twirls three ropes at once. You can practise this act with short lengths of clothesline. Make a slip knot in one end, and pass the other end through the knot to make a loop. Note that this horse is ground-tied. He stands as though tied when the reins are dropped to the ground. Any horse can learn to do this.

GOING UP! At the famous Calgary Stampede in Alberta, Canada, a cowboy struggles to stay on the back of an untamed horse. When the snorting horse comes down, he will hit the ground with a jolt that will jar the cowboy's teeth.

HITTING THE DIRT. A cowboy takes a spill from the back of a wild bull fresh from the range. In this rodeo contest, the cowboy holds on to the rope tied around the animal's middle. But he never holds on very long.

"The Old and the New" (detail) by Bennie, Julian Ball, J. B. Ranch, Cresson, Texas. THE CATTLEMAN.
Cowboys drive a herd of longhorns along a Texas trail under sunny Western skies.

A Cowboy Story

BY ALBERITA R. SEMRAD

What keeps the herd from running,
Stampeding, far and wide?
The cowboy's long, low whistle,
And singing by their side.

"Did you sing that song when you were a cowboy, grandpa?"

"Three of us cowboys sang that very song, years ago, while we punched along the drags behind a

Indian warriors encircle a band of pioneers, who fire back from their covered wagons.
"The Wagon Box Fight" by Gollings. Wyoming Commerce and Industry Commission. THE CATTLEMAN.

"The Wagon" by Bassett. Michaux Nash, Empire State Bank, Dallas, Texas. THE CATTLEMAN.
"Soup's on" at the chuck wagon, and the cow punchers ride in from the herd for their grub.

At Vera Cruz, in 1521, a Spanish ship unloads the first cattle to be brought to North America.
"Vera Cruz, 1521" by Lea. Museum of Fine Arts, Dallas, Texas. THE CATTLEMAN.

GUN IN HOLSTER

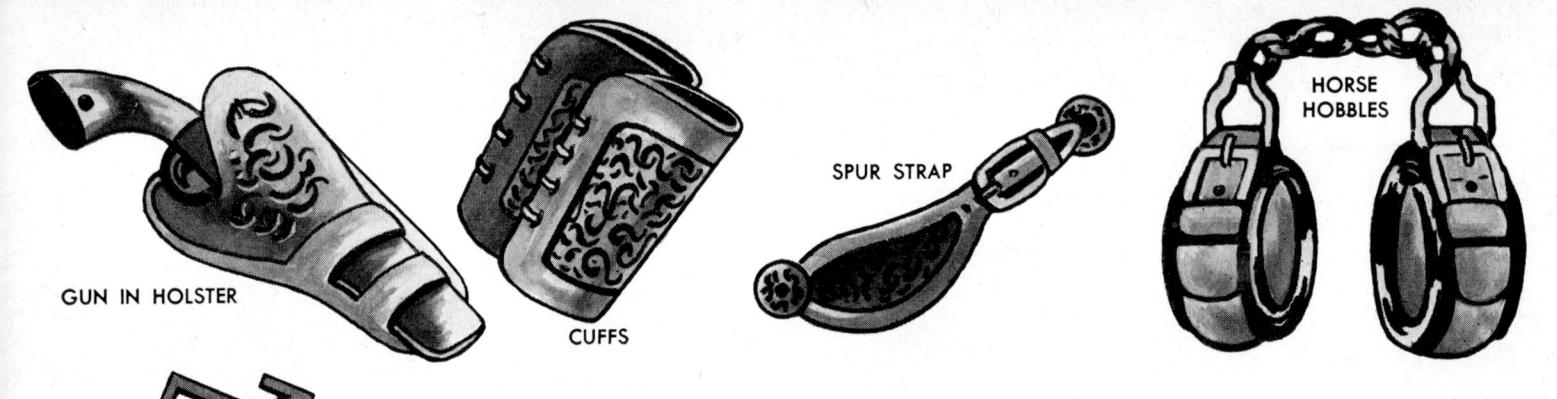

CUFFS

SPUR STRAP

HORSE HOBBLES

BRAND

COWBOY BOOTS

COWBOY HAT

SPUR

BELT

STIRRUPS

LASSO

EAR BRIDLE

trail herd of 5,000 longhorn cattle coming up from Texas on the Chisholm Trail to get to the railroad in Kansas where the cattle could be shipped East.

"What does 'punching along the drags' mean, grandpa?"

"Well, Timmie, 'drags' were baby calves. Their mothers couldn't stop to feed them, so these drags ate grass as they trailed along at the tail end of the herd. They were too young to digest it easily, and what a sight those baby drags were!—spindly legs and bellies too fat with undigested grass and weeds. The cowboys said, 'Calves look like they are stuffed with dough!' They called the calves little doughies, or dogies, a word that rhymes with old fogies."

"Were cowboys good men, grandpa?"

"Yes siree, Timmie. Our talk got pretty strong at times, and once in a while we had to shoot to protect ourselves, but on the whole a braver, finer band of young men than cowboys never lived. We were young—in our teens and twenties — and most of us came from fine homes in the South and East. After a cowboy had been riding the hot, dusty trail for weeks and months, had slept on the ground with his hard saddle for a pillow, and maybe had lost his favorite pony that had stepped in a prairie-dog hole and broken his leg—naturally most every cowboy spent a good portion of his pay on fun when he got to where a town was.

"Riding the trail was hard work, and dangerous; cowboys served their country well, as they broke the trails that opened up the country for settlers who came later on. If you had a cowboy for a friend, Timmie, then you had a *real* friend."

"Were you ever in a stampede, grandpa?"

"Stampede? That's what I was starting to tell you about. I remember one April night when the sky was black as new ink, with the thunder rumbling like Indian war drums calling the braves to battle. Suddenly the sky poured rain.

"A coyote's dismal, shrill cry came close to the herd, and one cow, crazed by fear of wild, hungry wolves and mountain lions, and by long days of heat and no rest, lowered her head, bellowed her terror, and charged at the cows around her. I sang out firm, loud, and slowlike the song that begins

On the lone pra—ir—ie

and every cowboy in the outfit joined me. We dug our knees in our ponies' sides as we sang against the pounding noise of the rain and thunder.

"The terrified cattle in that herd were moving like an avalanche of rock. If one of our ponies should trip, we would be trampled dead underfoot, and we knew it.

"Water poured down our bodies and off the flanks of our ponies. We sang as we'd never sung before—plenty loud so that every cow could hear

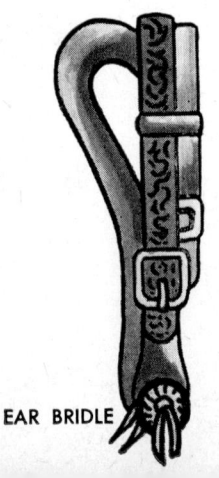

ROPING GLOVES

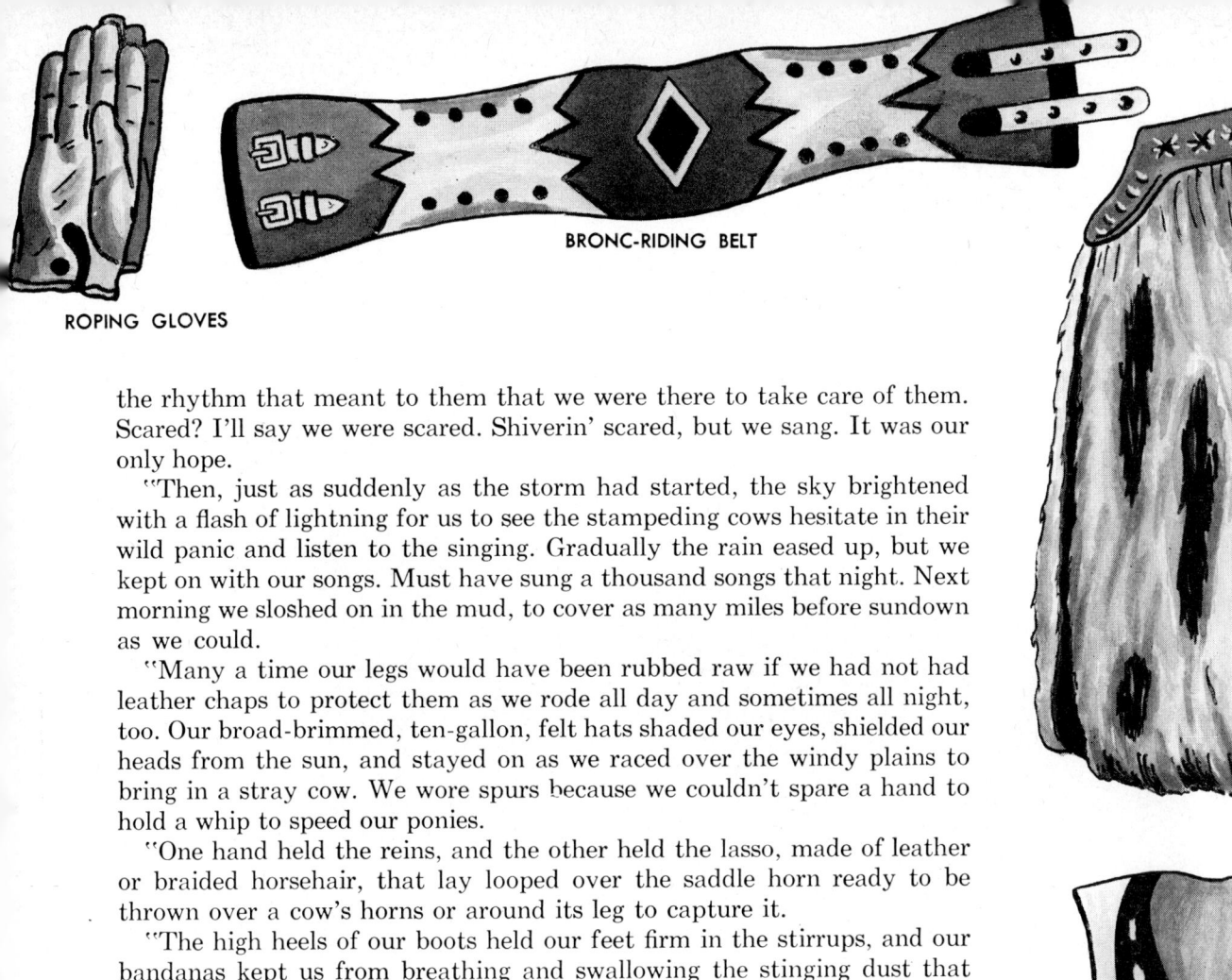

BRONC-RIDING BELT

CHAPS

the rhythm that meant to them that we were there to take care of them. Scared? I'll say we were scared. Shiverin' scared, but we sang. It was our only hope.

"Then, just as suddenly as the storm had started, the sky brightened with a flash of lightning for us to see the stampeding cows hesitate in their wild panic and listen to the singing. Gradually the rain eased up, but we kept on with our songs. Must have sung a thousand songs that night. Next morning we sloshed on in the mud, to cover as many miles before sundown as we could.

"Many a time our legs would have been rubbed raw if we had not had leather chaps to protect them as we rode all day and sometimes all night, too. Our broad-brimmed, ten-gallon, felt hats shaded our eyes, shielded our heads from the sun, and stayed on as we raced over the windy plains to bring in a stray cow. We wore spurs because we couldn't spare a hand to hold a whip to speed our ponies.

"One hand held the reins, and the other held the lasso, made of leather or braided horsehair, that lay looped over the saddle horn ready to be thrown over a cow's horns or around its leg to capture it.

"The high heels of our boots held our feet firm in the stirrups, and our bandanas kept us from breathing and swallowing the stinging dust that rose thick enough to choke a man.

"One day in Texas, I got up onto a bucking bronco. That bronco whirled, leaped toward the sky, plunged to earth with a thud, reared on its hind legs, swung its body in what seemed to be two directions at once, and with a mighty lunge, threw me off in a heap. All I could see was a cloud of dust!

"It is thought that broncos buck because long ago, when wild horses roamed the West, they threw panthers off their backs by bucking—sometimes even before the quick panther could sink its teeth through the horse's mane and into its neck. The broncos probably thought that men on their backs would be as cruel as the panthers had been, so they did what the wild horses before them had done—they bucked.

"Cowboys know how to touch a hot branding iron to the outer skin of a calf so that the letter, or number, or figure of the ranch that the calf belongs to will be there forever. In days gone by, a cowboy knew how to ride and rope, shoot and sing. He had courage and strength and worked hard day after day, month after month.

"The cowboy of many years ago quieted his cattle and lightened his work by song. He

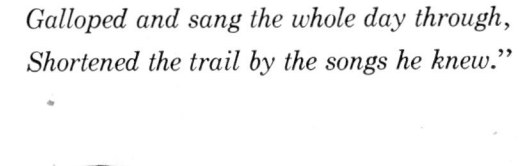

*Galloped and sang the whole day through,
Shortened the trail by the songs he knew."*

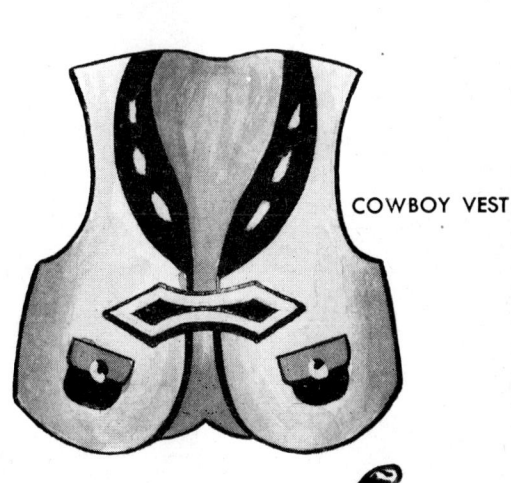

COWBOY VEST

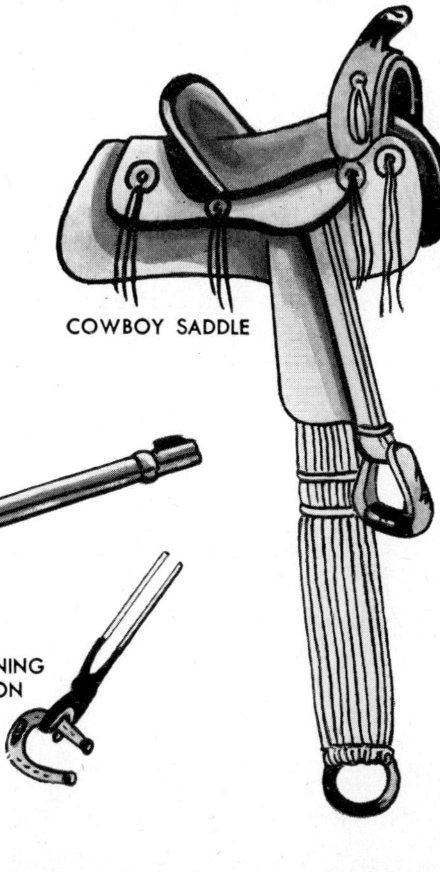

COWBOY SADDLE

BRAND

HORSE-SHOE

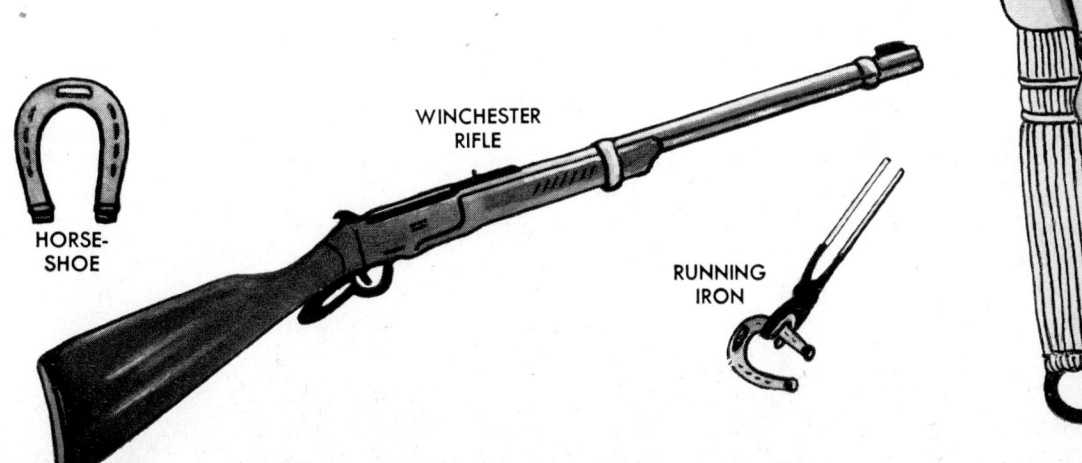

WINCHESTER RIFLE

RUNNING IRON

Let's Read About These Animals

By Mabel G. Hemington
Primary Teacher, Horace Mann School, Chicago, Ill., Faculty Member, Chicago Teachers' College

Bundy Tubing Company

CHILDREN who live in the city do not often see or hear an owl. That is why Pat was surprised one night after he got into bed. Through the open window came a very strange call. It did not sound like a cat. It did not sound like a dog. It did not sound like any bird Pat had ever heard.

"I wonder what that can be," thought Pat, but he was too tired to find out.

The next morning Pat looked everywhere outdoors. He did not know what to look for, but he thought he would find something. And, sure enough, he did. Up on a telephone wire, almost under the roof of the house, sat a fat, feathery bird, asleep.

"Hey, Bob," he called to his friend, "what in the world is it? I've never seen a bird like that."

"Oh, that's an owl," said Bob. "My uncle has owls on his farm. They sleep in the daytime and fly around at night. They live in the trunks of his apple trees as woodpeckers do. My uncle is glad the owls live there because they eat the mice and rats and some insects that spoil his crops."

"I wonder why this owl came here to our house," said Pat.

"I suppose he lost his way when he was flying around out in the country. I wish he would stay, but he'll go back to some farm," said Bob.

That night Pat did not hear the owl. The next morning it was gone.

Bundy Tubing Company

BILLY had a turtle. It was not so big as the turtle in this picture, but Billy liked it because he could hold it in his hand. When he lifted the turtle out of the box he carefully took hold of the hard shell. The turtle pushed its head out as far as it would go and winked its eyes. On each side of its thin, green neck Billy could see pretty yellow and red marks on the soft skin. The turtle started to walk right out of Billy's hand by pushing hard with the claws on its green, webbed feet. The sharp little claws tickled Billy. He liked that.

Once, when the turtle was walking on the floor, Billy hurried to get it. Billy's sudden footsteps frightened the turtle. Very quickly it pulled in its head, feet, and tail. It looked almost like a flat, green stone.

One day Billy took his turtle to school to show his friends. The turtle would not stay on Billy's desk. It kept trying to walk off. What could be done with it? The children thought and thought.

Judy asked, "Will it be all right to put it in the terrarium?" The terrarium was a tall, square, glass bowl which had dirt in the bottom. Plants grew in it. It looked very much like a little green garden.

"Yes, that is a good place," said the teacher. "We shall put a little pan of water in the terrarium. Sometimes turtles like to be in water. Sometimes they like to be out of water."

The children went back to their work. After a while someone said, "I don't see the turtle. Where is it?"

"It couldn't get out of the terrarium," said Billy. "It must be here."

The children looked and looked. Then Judy saw something. It was not the whole turtle. It was only part of the turtle. The other part of it was under the dirt.

"There it is!" she called. "How did it get there? Let's take it out!"

"Put it back in the water," said Jack.

"No," said Billy. "Maybe the turtle knows that winter is coming. Maybe he knows that it is time to go to sleep."

By that afternoon not even a little part of the turtle could be seen. It had crawled down into the dirt for its long, winter sleep.

ONE DAY when the children came into the schoolroom they saw something new. It was a big cage. Nothing was in it. On the cage there was a sign. The sign said:

What is this cage for?
Is it for a bird?
Is it for a rabbit?
Is it for a dog?

The children read the sign. They thought and thought. What was the cage for?

"Please tell us," said the children.

"No," said the teacher. "It is a surprise. Tomorrow you will find out."

The next day the children went to school in a hurry. There was the surprise—a pretty white rabbit. It had pink eyes and the insides of its ears were pink, too. It wiggled its nose and whiskers.

"His back legs are bigger than his front legs," said Joany.

"Yes," said the teacher. "A rabbit can jump far because it has strong back legs."

"Look," laughed Don, "he can wash his face like a kitten."

"What does a rabbit eat?" asked Mike.

"A rabbit eats these little round balls of food. It is something like dog food. I got it at the pet store," said the teacher. "It also eats green vegetables. The vegetables must not be cooked. The rabbit must have fresh water every day."

"I will bring some green vegetables tomorrow," said Sue.

"So will I," said Betty.

"May I give him fresh water every day?" asked Joany.

"I will help you keep the cage clean," said Don to the teacher.

The children were happy. They had a new pet and they wanted to take good care of it.

American Cyanamid Company

CAROL'S Grandpa did not live on a farm, but he did live in a big house which had a big yard. In the back of this yard he had a chicken house and a chicken yard.

Carol and Grandpa were good friends. He would take Carol's little hand in his big one, and together they would go out to feed the chickens, who would come running for their dinner.

One morning when they went to the chicken house something was wrong. A hen that had been sitting on her eggs just got up and walked away. All but one of the baby chicks had hatched out of the eggs.

"Peep, peep, peep," they called.

"This is queer," said Grandpa. "Most hens take care of their chicks. A good hen waits until all of her chicks have hatched and then she lets them stay under her wings to keep warm. We must keep that one egg warm until the chick hatches." Grandpa took the egg into the house.

"What shall we do to keep this egg warm?" he asked.

"Why not use the electric pad?" asked Carol.

Grandpa put the egg on the warm electric pad and held the corners of the pad around the egg.

Soon Carol heard a funny sound. Then she saw a tiny hole in the eggshell. The hole got bigger and bigger and bigger.

"Oh, what is happening?" she asked. Carol really knew, but it was the first time she had ever seen it happen. Soon "crack," and the shell broke; then the baby chick walked out.

"There it is," said Grandpa. "You may have that chick for your own, Carol. It can live here with all of my chickens, but I will put a band around its leg so we will always know it is yours."

SALLY and Jill were looking in a toystore window. Jill felt something rub against her leg. She looked down and saw a pretty little kitten. The girls patted the kitten and talked to it. Then they walked on. They did not know that the kitten was walking behind them. Soon they came to Sally's house.

"Good-by," said Jill. "I will come to play with you after awhile."

"Mew, mew," said the kitten.

Sally and Jill were surprised.

"I guess the kitten wants to play too," said Sally. "I wonder whose kitten it is."

"Do you think we could keep it?" asked Jill.

"I know I can't keep it because I have a bird," said Sally. "Birds do not like kittens."

"Maybe my mother will let me keep it. Let's go and see," said Jill, and she picked up the kitten.

"Mew, mew," said the kitten.

"Mother," called Jill, "Sally and I found this kitten. May I keep it?"

"I don't know," said Mother. "We must find out whose it is. It looks like one of the butcher's kittens."

Mother called the butcher and told him what the kitten looked like. The butcher said it was his, but he would let Jill keep it because he had three more.

"It really is a pretty little kitten," said Mother, "but we do not have much room."

"Please let me keep it," said Jill.

"All right," said Mother, "but remember, it is your kitten. You must take good care of it."

"I will," said Jill. "I will feed it milk and meat and fish. I will call it Butch because the butcher let me keep it."

"Purr, purr," said Butch.

Bundy Tubing Company

Mike and Jim sat on the steps talking.

"If I had three wishes," said Jim, "first, I'd wish for hundreds of dollars. Next, I'd wish for an airplane. Next, I'd wish for all the candy in the world."

"Those are foolish wishes," said Mike. "If you had hundreds of dollars you might lose them. If you had an airplane you couldn't fly it because you are not old enough. If you had all the candy in the world you would get sick."

"Well, then, what would your three wishes be?" asked Jim.

"If I had three wishes," said Mike, "my first wish would be for a dog, my second wish would be for a dog, and my third wish would be for a dog."

"You must like dogs," laughed Jim.

"Yes, sir, I really do," said Mike.

"Do you want a dog like Tony's?"

"No," answered Mike, "I want a hound dog."

"A hound dog is to take with you when you go hunting. Are you going hunting?" asked Jim.

"No, I'm not going hunting," said Mike, "but still I want a hound dog."

"Why?" asked Jim.

"I like a hound dog's face. His skin is loose. His eyes are sad. His ears are long. Once I saw one. When he looked at me he looked as if he loved me more than anyone else in the world."

"I saw a greyhound once when I went to a dog show, but he was big and thin. He had a long, sharp nose and little ears," said Jim.

"Oh, well, there are different kinds of hound dogs," said Mike. "The kind I saw was not very big, but he had a thick body, thick legs, big feet, and such a wonderful face. I wish I had him now."

"Do you suppose our wishes will come true?" asked Jim.

"I don't know about yours," said Mike, "but I am going to make mine come true. Maybe it will not come true until I am a big man, but someday I am going to have a hound dog with loose skin, sad eyes, and long ears."

Ewing Galloway

"MOTHER," called Joan from outdoors one cold autumn day, "may I please have some nuts? A squirrel is out here."

Mother gave Joan some nuts. Joan put them on the sidewalk and watched.

First the squirrel took a nut in his two front paws. He sat on his back legs while he bit the shell with his sharp teeth. He put the nut inside his cheek. Then he took another nut, bit it just a little, and put it inside his other cheek. He looked as if he had the mumps. Next, the squirrel took another nut, bit it and put it into his mouth. But he did not eat the nuts.

Away he ran to a tree. He climbed up high in the tree to where there was a hole in the trunk. Into the hole he went. Soon he came out and quickly ran headfirst down the tree. His sharp claws kept him from falling.

The squirrel came back to Joan for more nuts, but this time he made a hole in the ground and put the nuts in it.

The squirrel was getting ready for winter because it was cold. He had moved from his summer home, which looked like a big bird's nest, to his winter home high in the trunk of the tree. He was putting food away so that he would be sure to have something to eat.

Squirrels sleep much of the time in winter. When they wake up they go out to find the food they hid. They eat some of it and then go back to sleep again.

The squirrel came back to Joan. He looked at her. He ran this way and that way. He shook his tail. But Joan had no more nuts.

"Good-by, Mr. Squirrel," she called as she ran into the house. "Don't forget where you put those nuts when winter comes."

Genesee Mountain Fox & Mink Farms, Inc.

FRED went to Dan's house after school one day to see the new pets.

"My mother and father bought a pair of chinchillas," Dan told Fred. "These chinchillas will have baby chinchillas, and when we have a lot of them we will sell them and make money. We keep them in the cellar."

When Fred saw the chinchillas he wanted to hold one, but they were asleep.

"They like to sleep in the daytime and stay awake at night, but it will be all right if we wake them up," said Dan.

At first when Fred took hold of the chinchilla it tried to get away. Fred was careful. He started to pet the chinchilla. Then it was more quiet.

"Its fur is softer than kitten's fur," said Fred, "and it wiggles its nose and whiskers like a rabbit."

"When I first saw them I thought they were squirrels," laughed Dan. "They do look somewhat like squirrels but they are not so wild. A chinchilla makes a good pet because it makes friends fast."

"What do they eat?" asked Fred.

"We buy these little, tiny balls of food for them," said Dan. He showed some to Fred. "They eat hay, too, and sometimes a little apple."

"Hay?" said Fred. "You will have to make a barn to keep hay in."

"Oh, no," answered Dan, "they do not eat much. We feed them only once a day."

All at once Fred remembered that he had to be home by five o'clock. He put the chinchilla into the big box.

"Good-by," he said to the chinchilla, "I'll come to see you tomorrow."

The chinchilla didn't seem to care. It went right back to sleep again.

Bundy Tubing Company

It was Thanksgiving Day. Grandmother and Grandfather had come from the farm to stay a few days. All morning the good smells from the kitchen had been floating through the air. The children were very hungry. At last Mother called everyone to the table. As Father cut the turkey, he talked to it, just for fun.

"Well, Old Tom," he laughed, "you won't eat any more of Grandfather's corn."

"He won't flap his wings and peck at my legs the way he did one time," said Grandmother.

"You should have run fast, the way Carl and I did when he ran after us," said Jean. "Do you remember that, Carl?"

"How could I forget?" asked Carl.

"He was a cross old bird," said Grandfather. "He made too much trouble, so we thought we would eat him for Thanksgiving."

"When I was a boy like Carl," Grandfather went on, "there were many wild turkeys in the fields near our farm. They didn't belong to anyone. They just lived in the fields. A wild turkey makes its nest on the ground. Turkey eggs are twice as big as hens' eggs. They are cream color with tiny dark spots."

"Are there any wild turkeys living now?" asked Jean.

"Oh, yes," said Grandfather.

"If they do not belong to anyone, who feeds them?" asked Carl.

"No one feeds them," answered Grandfather. "They find their own food. They eat nuts, berries, and grasshoppers."

"I know this turkey was not wild, but I wonder if he ever ate any grasshoppers," said Jean.

"I wouldn't be a bit surprised if he did," said Grandfather. "But why he would want any after all the corn I gave him is more than I know."

By that time Father had cut all the turkey.

"May I please have a drumstick?" asked Carl.

"Yes, and here it is," said Father.

After that, Carl was too busy eating to talk any more about turkeys.

DURENCEAU

Bundy Tubing Company

Down came the rain. Mary and Kate sat in the house looking out the window. It was too wet to go out to play.

"What shall we do?" asked Kate.

"I don't know," answered Mary.

Mother asked, "Why don't you play 'Guess'?"

"How do you play 'Guess'?" asked the girls.

"Well, one of you will tell something about an animal. Don't tell much. Tell just a little. Then the other one will try to guess what the animal is," said Mother.

"All right," said Kate. "I am thinking of an animal that has four legs."

"Tell more," said Mary. "Many animals have four legs."

"It is bigger than a dog, but not as big as a horse," Kate went on.

"Does it live on a farm?" asked Mary.

"Yes," answered Kate. "Some people like to drink its milk."

"A cow?" asked Mary.

"No, I said it was not as big as a horse," said Kate. "Some farmers keep these animals for their milk and some farmers keep them for their hair, which they cut off and sell."

"Is it a sheep?" asked Mary.

"No. People don't drink sheep's milk," said Kate. "This animal eats grass, corn, oats, and apples, but sometimes it eats paper and other funny things."

"Oh, now I can guess. It is a goat," said Mary. "But I didn't know that anyone ever drank goat's milk."

"Yes," said Mother. "Goat's milk is good. Sometimes people make cheese from goat's milk."

"Well, I guessed what it was, so now it is my turn," said Mary. "This is fun."

U.S.D.A. Photograph by Knell

PETE was very happy when Uncle Jim asked him to come to the farm this summer. He had been to the farm before but he was always too little to help. This time Uncle Jim told him he was big enough to do some work.

The first morning Pete went out to the barn with Uncle Jim.

"Well, my boy," said Uncle Jim, "can you climb up the ladder and throw down some hay for the horses?"

Up went Pete and down came the hay.

"That is enough," called Uncle Jim. By the time Pete got down, Uncle Jim was giving the horses oats and corn, too.

"Put out some fresh water," he said to Pete. "The horses will want a drink after they eat."

Pete was happy because Uncle Jim told him what to do. Helping Uncle Jim made him feel good.

Then Uncle Jim took the horses out of the barn. He lifted one of the horse's feet to look at it.

"Do you see where the horse's shoe is nailed on?" he asked Pete.

"Yes, but doesn't it hurt the horse when the shoe is nailed on?" Pete asked.

"No," answered Uncle Jim. "The part where the nails go in is something like a very thick fingernail. Does it hurt when your mother cuts your fingernails?"

"No," answered Pete.

"Well, it doesn't hurt the horse when his shoes are nailed on. Sometimes he doesn't like to have it done, but if he didn't have shoes his feet would hurt."

"Where are his toes?" asked Pete.

"He has only one toe on each foot. That is the one the shoe is nailed to. That is the one he walks on," answered Uncle Jim. "How would you like to sit up on this horse?"

"That would be fun," said Pete.

"One, two, three, up you go," said Uncle Jim.

"Oh, boy," said Pete. "I did not know a horse was so high up. I did not know a horse's back was so wide. This is fun."

"You will have to come down now because I have to get the horses ready to pull the wagon. You play around and I will see you at lunch time. Maybe by then I will have more work for you to do," said Uncle Jim.

LET'S READ ABOUT THESE ANIMALS

The American Guernsey Cattle Club

Jack and Peggy were visiting a farm. It was the first time they had ever been on a farm, so they wanted to see everything at once.

"Now, see here," said the farmer, "don't you two young ones move around so fast. You'll frighten the animals and then they'll run away. Just walk up to them quietly and wait. The cattle are over in the next field. We'll go there."

Jack and Peggy started toward the field with the slow-moving, easy-going farmer. The children had to slow down so they could talk to him as they came closer and closer to the animals.

Peggy looked ahead and said, "What are cattle? Those animals look like cows."

"Cattle are not cows; they are bulls," said Jack, who was ready to argue.

"You are both right," laughed the farmer. "When I say 'cattle' I mean cows and bulls and calves."

By that time they had reached the fence. Soon a bull and a cow came slowly to the fence.

"Why does the bull have a ring in his nose?" asked Peggy.

"Sometimes a bull won't go where I want him to go," said the farmer. "I can lead him by the strap in the ring in his nose, and he will keep with me."

"Does it hurt the bull?" asked Jack.

"No, it doesn't hurt unless he pulls the wrong way," answered the farmer.

"What are they chewing?" asked Peggy.

The farmer told the children that cattle swallow grass almost without chewing it when they eat it. After a while they can make it come back up into their mouths a little at a time, and then they slowly chew and chew. This time when they swallow the food it goes down to a different place and stays down. Cattle chew from side to side instead of up and down the way people do, because their teeth are different. They have no top front teeth. They do have eight bottom front teeth which help them pull up the grass. They chew with their top and bottom side teeth.

Jack and Peggy tried to chew from side to side but it felt funny.

"Are you hungry?" asked the farmer. "I think my wife has something good to fill your breadbaskets. Let me see which one of you will get to the house first."

The children raced back to the house.

Finger Plays •

Fingers, fingers! Oh the fun of finding your fingers . . . when you are tiny and the world is new! Laugh with delight at YOUR own baby's expression on discovering these ten fascinating toys, for fingers are truly a child's first toys. They're a means of expression, preceding speech . . . a happy means of personality development, entertainment and joy.

Hands and fingers are of great value all through life, and so it's a fortunate baby who is taught very early the facile control of his hands. The happiness and satisfaction a baby gets from finger plays is enough to recommend them . . . but over and above this is the amazing dexterity and grace which comes to the child in using his hands. Research studies indicate that there is an orderly sequence in natural development of muscular control and skill. FINGER PLAYS delight the child, giving him a dramatic reason for using his hands. Each finger play is a complete dramatic action, ending in a delightful climax! Each finger play uses all ten little digits.

Here's the Church

Here is the church,   And here's the steeple;   Open the doors,   And here are the people.

Pat-a-Cake

Pat-a-cake, pat-a-cake, baker's man,   Bake me a cake as fast as you can;   Pat it and prick it, and mark it with B,   Put it in the oven for baby and me.

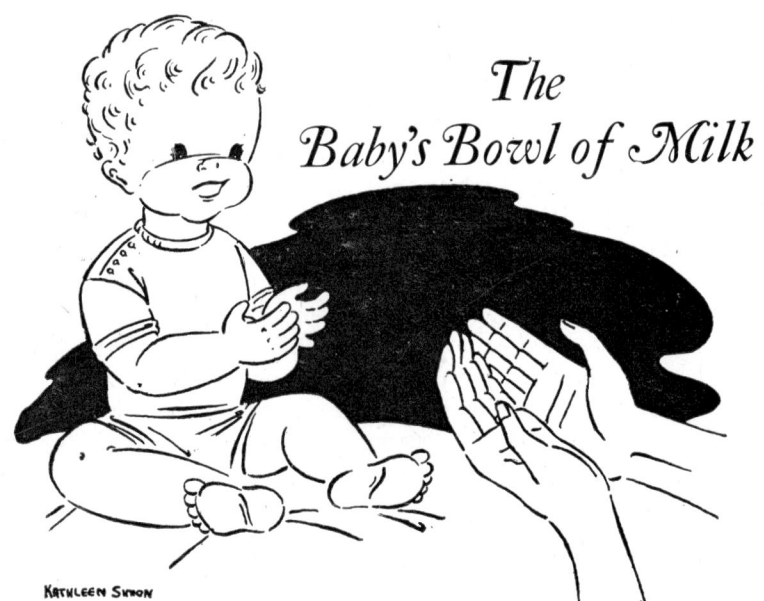

The Baby's Bowl of Milk

This is the baby's bowl of milk,
Sweet and good and white,
   (two hands cupped together)

This is baby's little cup
To drink from every night.
   (one hand rounded)

This is baby's cookie, round;
   (make circle with thumb and first finger)

See him take a bite.
   (separate thumb and first finger)

Now another drink of milk,
Sweet and good and white.
   (drink from right hand)

KATHLEEN SIXON

The Little Mice Are Playing

The little mice are playing,
    Playing, playing —
    (tap fingers of right hand on table)

The little mice are playing,
    Out behind the barn.
The old gray cat comes creeping,
    Creeping, creeping —
    (rest left hand on table with thumb under the first finger)

The old gray cat comes creeping,
    Out behind the barn.
    (thumb slowly moves up to the first finger)

The little mice all scamper,
    Scamper, scamper —
    (tap fingers of right hand running away)

The little mice all scamper,
    Out behind the barn.

Little Robin Redbreast

Little Robin Redbreast sat upon a rail.
    (middle fingers closed, thumb and little finger representing head and tail)

Niddle, Noddle went his head
    (move thumb)

and Wiggle, Waggle went his tail.
    (move little finger)

The Beehive

This is the beehive,
    (hands clasped with fingers inside)

Where are the bees!
Hidden away where nobody sees.
Soon they come creeping out of the hive.
    (turn hands over and release one finger at a time)

One! Two! Three! Four! Five! Buzz!

The Days of the Week

Sunday, the very first day of the week,
We all go to church in clothes clean and neat.
    (hands folded on lap)

Monday's for washing, as everyone knows.
    (motion as if washing on washboard)

And Tuesday's the day that we iron the clothes.
    (right hand horizontal as if ironing)

Wednesday's the day that the mending is done.
    (move right hand back and forth as if sewing)

And Thursday's the day that the calling's begun.
    (motion as if putting on hat for calling)

Friday's for cleaning, dust rugs, and shake.
    (motion as if beating rugs and shaking)

And Saturday's always the day that we bake.
    (motion as if stirring a cake)

There's work for each day, as you can well see,
And work should give pleasure to you and to me.

Visiting Little Playmates

A little boy lived in this house.
　　(Right hand clasped with thumb hidden by fingers)
A little girl lived in this house.
　　(Left hand clasped with thumb hidden by fingers)
The little boy came out of his house.
　　(Release thumb of right hand)
He looked up and down the street.
　　(Move thumb slowly in a circle twice)
He did not see anyone; so he went back into his house.
　　(Clasp thumb under fingers on right hand)
The little girl came out of her house.
　　(Release thumb of left hand)
She looked up and down the street.
　　(Move thumb slowly in a circle twice)
She did not see anyone; so she went back into her house.
　　(Clasp thumb under fingers on left hand)
The next day the little boy came out of his house and looked all around.
　　(Release thumb of right hand and move slowly in a circle)
And the little girl came out of her house and looked all around.
　　(Release thumb of left hand and move slowly in a circle)
They saw each other,
　　(Thumbs pointed toward one another)
Walked across the street, and shook hands
　　(Thumbs come toward each other and meet)
Then the little boy went back into his house.
　　(Clasp thumb of right hand under fingers)
And the little girl went back into her house.
　　(Clasp thumb of left hand under fingers)

Two Little Blackbirds

There were two blackbirds sitting on a hill,
　　(Little pieces of paper perched on forefingers)
One named Jack, the other named Jill.
Fly away, Jack; fly away, Jill.
　　(Fingers soar gently in the air)
Come again, Jack; come again, Jill.
　　(Fingers fly back)

Santa Claus

Down the chimney dear Santa Claus crept
　　(Cup left hand and put first finger of right hand into it)
Into the room where the children slept
　　(Place three fingers of right hand on palm of left hand)
He saw their stockings hung in a line,
　　(Three fingers suspended on left hand)
And he filled them with candies and goodies,
　　(Motion as tho filling stockings)
Altho he counted them—one! two! three!
　　(Indicate by counting fingers)
The baby's stocking, he could not see.
"Ho! ho!" said Santa Claus, "that won't do;"
So he popped her present right into her shoe.
　　(Cup left hand and put first finger of right hand into it)

BE YOUR FAMILY FIRE CHIEF

You can be the Fire Chief in your family. Do you want to know how? Get to know Sparky Dog and Smokey Bear, and they will tell you. Sparky will help you keep fires from starting at home. Smokey will help you keep fires from starting outdoors. That is what a good Fire Chief thinks of first: how to stop fires before they start.

Fire can be our friend, if we use it carefully. Fire keeps us warm in winter. Fire cooks our food. Fire makes the power that runs trains, ships, and airplanes. It makes some of the electrical energy that runs big machines in factories. If we did not have fire, we could not live in nice homes and have the fun we like.

But fire can be our enemy, if we are careless with it. It can burn up our houses and even whole towns. It can ruin fields and forests. Brave firemen and forest rangers work hard to fight fires. They work even harder to keep fires from starting, and that is where you can help.

Here is Sparky in his fireman's hat. ➡ ➡ ➡ ➡ ➡ ➡ ➡ ➡ ➡ ➡

He looks serious because he knows FIRE PREVENTION is a serious business. Sparky uses his fireman's pike to pull down burning walls. But he would rather PREVENT fires than fight them.

Sparky says:
Don't play with matches! Mother keeps matches out of reach of little children.

Sparky says:
Tell your family not to smoke in bed! Lots of fires are started because someone fell asleep with a lighted cigarette or cigar in his hand.

Sparky says:

Don't let junk pile up around your house! Check your attic and basement, your garage or barn for old rags, paint cans, furniture, papers and magazines. All these give fire a place to start. Ask your parents if you can help them on cleanup day.

Sparky says:

Check your kitchen for fire safety! Spilled grease on the stove and cans of grease near the stove catch fire easily. Kitchen curtains should not be near the stove.

Sparky says:

Use electricity carefully! Make sure that no one in your family plugs too many wires into one wall outlet. Overloading the wall outlets can cause a fire.

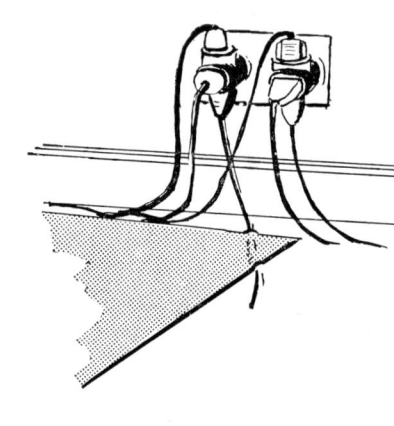

Sparky says:

Talk to your local fireman! Find out what to do in case a fire does start in your home. Learn how to call your local fire department.

Would you like to know Sparky better?
Write to: SPARKY'S FIRE DEPARTMENT
BOSTON 1, MASSACHUSETTS

Here is Smokey Bear, the Famous Forest Ranger

He and the little cubs are begging you to help prevent forest fires. Smokey uses his shovel to clear away brush from forest fires. He also uses it to clear the ground around his campfire. Smokey and his woodland friends need forests. You need forests, too. You live in a TREE HOUSE! It is made of wood from trees. Even if your house is made of stone or brick, wood from trees is used in it. Most of your furniture is made of wood or wood products. So are your books and drawing paper, and your pencils. So are most of your toys. Even the clothes you wear may be made of wood products.

Smokey says:

Don't play with matches! And tell everyone in your family *never* to throw away a match without breaking it in two and feeling the burnt end to see that it is not hot.

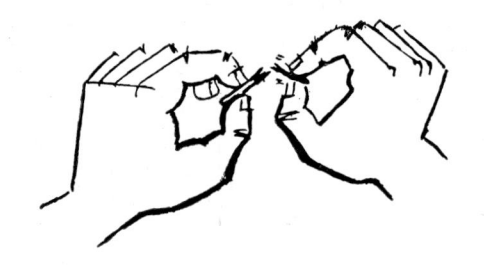

Smokey says:

Be careful with your campfire! Build the fire where it cannot spread. Before you leave it, pour water over it until every spark is drowned.

Smokey says:

NEVER throw lighted cigarettes out of car windows! Tell your parents to crush out their cigarettes in the car ashtray. If they smoke outside the car, tell them to crush out their cigarettes in a safe place.

Smokey says:

Put out sparks that fly from a fire.

Smokey says:

If you see a fire start in the woods, tell somebody at once!

Would you like to know Smokey better? Write to:

**SMOKEY BEAR HEADQUARTERS
WASHINGTON 25, D. C.**

TEACHER

At school you will meet a new friend, your teacher. She likes little children and she can show you how to do so many things.

New Friends at School
By Vernice Keenan

When you go to school you will sit at a table or at a desk. You will have crayons and paper so that you can draw big pictures.

Steve is drawing a picture of a boat. Sally is making a house with a big red chimney.

The teacher is saying, "Good work, children!"

PRINCIPAL

Anne and Miss Martin are very good friends. They are both happy about the fine work Anne does in school.

Miss Martin is the principal. She is a very important person in the school. She is like a leader or a director or a manager. She helps the children, and she helps the teachers, too.

In many schools the principal is a man.

Have you met the principal of your school?

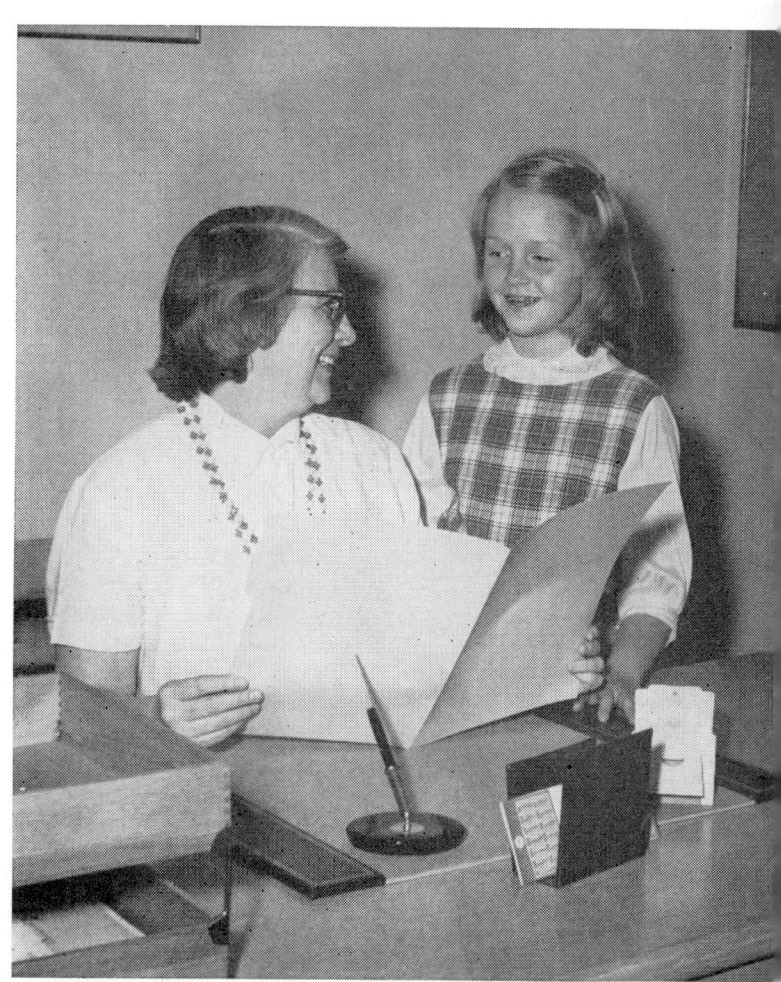

SCHOOL NURSE

Timmy is not feeling well today. He has a stomach ache and his throat hurts. The school nurse is going to take his temperature.

Perhaps he should be in his warm bed at home. The school nurse will call his mother and she will come to school to get him.

The school nurse takes good care of little children. She is our friend. She is almost like a mother.

OTHER CHILDREN

At school you will make many new friends your own age. You will play with them. John and Susan are playing in a ship. The children made the ship from big blocks. They can make other things, too.

BUS DRIVER

Some children walk to school. Others, whose homes are a long way from the school, ride on a school bus.

The bus driver is our friend. He helps little children get on and off his big yellow bus, and he drives very carefully along the roads and through the streets. He wants the children to get to school safely.

We must sit still in our seats on the bus and talk in quiet voices so that we can help the bus driver get us to school safely.

CUSTODIAN →

The custodian in the school is a good friend because he keeps our school building clean and comfortable.

The school is warm, and yet has plenty of fresh, clean air so that we can keep healthy.

The floors are clean, and the windows shine.

The custodian works very hard. He is an important person in your school. You will want to help him by being clean and orderly.

What is this custodian doing?

COOKS

If you go to school where you have to stay for lunch, there will probably be a lunchroom or a cafeteria.

The ladies who work here are our noontime friends. They know what little children like to eat and how to prepare it so that it is just right. They help you with your trays and dishes.

Joey has a sandwich and Terry has some tomato juice. What else do you think they will have for lunch?

What do you like to eat at noon?

↓

← SCHOOL SECRETARY

The school secretary is a very busy person. She works in the school office, answering the telephone and helping people who come to the school on business.

If you cannot go to school, perhaps the school secretary will call Mother on the telephone to find out if you are ill.

When new children come to our school, the school secretary is just about the first person they meet. She helps them find their room, and tells them their teacher's name.

She has a nice smile and a happy voice.

COAT ROOM →

When you go to school, the teacher will show you where to keep your coat and cap.

You will probably have your own special hook in the coat room. Each day you will put your outdoor clothing on your hook.

In the winter there will be boots and mittens, too.

It is a good idea for Mother to sew a tape with your name printed on it on all your clothing. Then you will not get your things mixed up with another child's.

Can you hang your clothes neatly?

MY WEATHER BOOK

MY WEATHER REPORT

Look in the newspaper at home.
Daddy will help you find the weather report.
What kind of a day will tomorrow be?
Will it snow?
Will it rain?
Will the sun shine?
Will it be cold?
What kind of clothes must you wear?

Look in the radio program listings.
When will the next weather report be broadcast?
Look in the television program listings.
When can you see the weather man on television?

In the morning, listen to the weather report on the radio. What is the temperature? Set your thermometer at the right temperature by pulling the ribbon up or down. Mother or Teacher can make you a ribbon thermometer.

Dear Mother,
Please make a ribbon thermometer. Use a ruler to draw the Fahrenheit thermometer scale on a shirt cardboard. Make a slit at top and bottom. Sew a white ribbon and a red ribbon together and insert in the slits, then sew other ends together in back. This makes and endless belt which can be moved up and down. The red ribbon represents the column of fluid in the thermometer.

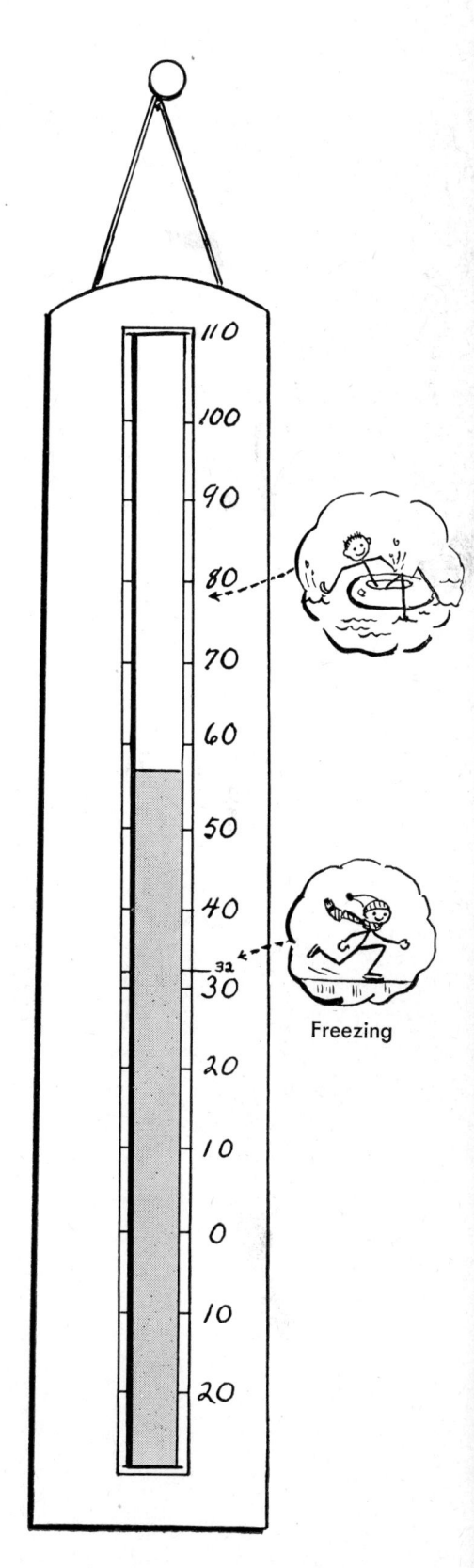

WINTER

> The weather is cold in winter,
> We must dress warmly or freeze.
> We cannot go bare in the winter
> Like the apple and maple trees.

Why do trees take off their leaves for winter? What sports do we enjoy in winter? What clothing do you wear in winter but not in summer?

> Most of the birds have departed—
> The robin, the wren, and the jay.
> It's weeks since the warblers started.
> We must feed the birds that stay.

Why do many birds go south? Why must we feed those that stay?

> The pure white snow blankets the world,
> Beneath it the spring flowers sleep.
> It hides the den where the bear lies curled
> And the trails where the field mice creep.

Some animals, like the bear, hibernate in winter. They sleep until spring. Do you know some animals that stay awake all winter?

SUMMER

> In summer the weather is warm,
> Our clothing is lightweight and cool.
> We like to go visit the farm
> And we like to splash in the pool.

We keep cool in summer by giving off moisture. This is called perspiring. A horse perspires all over, just as a person does. Many animals cannot cool off as easily as we do. A dog perspires only on the soles of its feet. A rabbit perspires only around its lips.

> The leaves grow thick on the trees,
> The flowers bloom in the park.
> Butterflies flutter past buzzing bees,
> The fireflies light up after dark.

Leaves do important work in the summer. They make food for trees and other plants. Bees gather nectar to make honey. They repay the flowers for the nectar by carrying pollen, which makes seeds grow. Seeds make new flowers.

> The fields wear blankets of yellow and green,
> The birds have come back to nest.
> Of all the seasons that you have seen
> Which one do you like best?

Farmers grow wheat in the summer. Bread is made from wheat. What other important crops do farmers grow? What is your favorite bird? What color are its eggs? (See BIRDS in Book Two.) The four seasons are spring, summer, autumn, and winter.

THE RAIN PLAY

By Renald G. Moorcraft
Nature Specialist, Tangley Oaks Educational Center

The Cast

Rain
Cloud
1st Child
2nd Child
3rd Child
Other Children
Wind
Sun
Air
Rain Crow

Rain, Cloud, Wind, Sun, Air, and Rain Crow are identified by cardboard placards they wear on strings around their necks.

Sun wears a large yellow placard cut in a circle, like this

Cloud wears a placard shaped like this

Rain Crow wears a placard shaped like a bird

Rain's placard may be a square of cardboard with raindrops drawn on it, like this

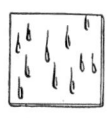

Wind's placard looks like a cloud going someplace in a hurry

Air wears a balloon-shaped placard with his name on it

RAIN: Please, Cloud, let me go! I want to visit Mother Earth. I want to help her fruits and flowers grow. I want to make her fields and forests green. I want to be water for people to drink and wash with, water for fish to live in.

CLOUD: All right, I know Mother Earth will be glad to see you. She always needs our help. (Releases RAIN's hand.)

(RAIN dances toward EARTH.)

CHILDREN: Rain, rain, go away! You will only spoil our play. Rain, rain, you're no good! Stay out of our neighborhood!

1ST CHILD: We hereby form the Children's Anti-Rain Association. We will make it stop raining and never start again.

(RAIN, hurt, stops, then dances back to CLOUD.)

CLOUD: What is the matter, Rain? Why aren't you helping Mother Earth?

RAIN: Mother Earth's children don't want me. They told me to go away. They don't like me!

CLOUD: Don't want you? You, who have helped them so much? What would they do without you? (Takes RAIN's hand.) Come, we will teach these children a lesson. Wind, please push me over the sea.

WIND: But I've just brought you from the sea! We came here to help Mother Earth! Why do you want to go back?

CLOUD: Mother Earth's children have hurt your brother, Rain. They told him to go away. They said he was no good.

WIND: No good? They are very foolish children or they would know how good he is. I will help you teach these children a lesson. But I cannot move you myself. I must ask help from our father, the Sun. Without his help, I cannot move. O, Sun! Please move Air out of my way! I want to push Cloud back to sea.

117

SUN: Back to sea? I brought Cloud here to help Mother Earth by making Rain fall. Why does Cloud want to go back to sea?

WIND: Mother Earth's children have hurt your son, Rain. They told him to go away. They said he was no good.

SUN: No good? My son, Rain? Don't these foolish children know that Mother Earth would be a desert without him? I will teach them a lesson! Air, come here! (SUN shines on AIR. AIR moves from side of WIND toward SUN. WIND moves over and pushes CLOUD over SEA. SUN shines on EARTH.)

CHILDREN: Hooray, the sun is shining!
　　　　　The rain has gone away!
　　　　　The wind and clouds have vanished!
　　　　　The world is bright and gay!

1ST CHILD: We don't like the rain!

2ND CHILD: We don't like the clouds! They make the world dark and gloomy.

3RD CHILD: We don't like the wind! It blows rain and dust in our faces.

SUN: They don't like any of my children!

CHILDREN: We hope the rain and clouds and wind never come back! We hope every day will be sunny and bright!

SUN: I will give them what they ask for. My own children can play at sea for a while.

(SUN shines on CLOUD. CLOUD dances toward SUN, releases RAIN's hand. RAIN dances down to SEA. SUN shines on SEA. RAIN dances back to CLOUD. SUN shines on AIR. AIR dances toward SUN from side of WIND. WIND dances with CLOUD and RAIN over SEA. Repeat weather dance two or three times. If this is too difficult, all except SUN join hands and dance in front of SUN.)

CHILDREN: Oh, it is so hot! It is too hot to play! Oh, for a cool wind! Oh, for a cloud to hide the burning sun! Oh, for a cool refreshing rain!

SUN: They are learning!

1ST CHILD: It hasn't rained for weeks.

2ND CHILD: We haven't even seen a cloud.

3RD CHILD: And we haven't had even a little breeze.

CHILDREN: The hot sun shines day after day! The flowers are wilting. The plants in the fields are dying. The little creatures cannot find water to drink. The heat is making people sick. The sun is turning the world into a desert.

1ST CHILD: I don't like the sun!

CHORUS: I don't like it either! Nor me! I wish it would stop shining.

SUN: Now they don't like *me*! These foolish children still have to learn!

1ST CHILD: Do you remember when we told the rain to go away?

2ND CHILD: Yes. It is our fault. We told it to go away. We didn't know how much we need it.

3RD CHILD: Let's call it back again!

CHILDREN: Rain, rain, come again. Rain, rain, come again! Rain, Rain, come again!

1ST CHILD: It's no use. There is no rain to hear us.

2ND CHILD: Oh, look, there is a rain crow! Let us ask it to find the rain and make it come back.

CHILDREN: Rain crow! Rain crow! Rain crow!

RAIN CROW: Hello, children. What can I do for you?

1ST CHILD: A long time ago we told the rain to go away. Now we are sorry. The sun is turning the world into a desert. We need the rain to make the earth fresh and green again. Will you please find the rain and ask it to come back?

RAIN CROW: Well, I'll try. I think I know where Rain is.

(RAIN CROW flies over to RAIN. Gestures between RAIN CROW and RAIN. RAIN CROW flies back to CHILDREN.)

RAIN CROW: Rain says he can't come unless Cloud brings him. He says you don't like Cloud because she hides the sun.

3RD CHILD: Oh, we like Cloud now! Please ask her to come.

(RAIN CROW flies to CLOUD, gestures with CLOUD, then flies back to CHILDREN.)

RAIN CROW: Cloud says she can't come unless Wind pushes her. She says you don't like Wind because it blows rain and dust in your faces.

3RD CHILD: Oh, we like Wind now. Please ask Wind to bring Cloud to us.

(RAIN CROW flies to WIND, holds conversation, returns to CHILDREN.)

RAIN CROW: Wind says he can't come unless the sun lets him.

1ST CHILD: The sun? What has the sun to do with the wind?

RAIN CROW: The sun warms the air and makes it rise. That makes room for the wind to move.

2ND CHILD: Why, the sun does everything! The sun moves the air so the wind can push the clouds that bring us rain!

RAIN CROW: That's right. Don't you know the sun is the father of the weather? He makes the clouds by warming the sea. He makes the wind by warming the air. He makes the rain by pushing the clouds so high.

CHILDREN: The sun is the father of the weather. He makes the clouds and rain and wind. He also warms the earth. We love the sun. We love them all—the sun, the wind, the clouds, the rain! We love the whole weather family!

SUN (Smiling): They have learned their lesson! I thought they would!

(SUN shines on AIR. AIR dances toward SUN. WIND dances CLOUD and RAIN to above CHILDREN. SUN shines on CLOUD. CLOUD and RAIN dance toward SUN. CLOUD releases RAIN's hand. RAIN dances down to CHILDREN.)

CHILDREN: Look, there's a cloud! Oh, feel that cool wind! Oh, it's raining! It's raining!

How To Talk on the Telephone

When You Answer the Telephone

1. Pick up the handset. Hold the receiver part of it close against your ear and hold the mouthpiece about an inch in front of your mouth.

2. Say "Hello" or say your telephone number. Speak clearly, but don't shout. Talk into the telephone the way you would talk to someone face to face. Be polite and pleasant.

3. Sometimes the person who calls wants to speak to someone else at your house. Let's pretend you are Janie Allen, and Mr. Wright calls to talk to your Daddy. You and Mr. Wright know each other.

Mr. Wright says "Hello, Janie. May I speak to your Daddy?"

You say "Yes, Mr. Wright. I'll call him." Then you lay the handset down beside the base of the telephone. **Don't put it back in the cradle.** Next, you go find your Daddy and tell him that Mr. Wright wants him on the telephone. Don't stand close to the telephone and yell "Daddy!" That would hurt Mr. Wright's ear.

4. When someone calls you, let the person who called end the talk. Of course, if someone talks on, and on, and **on**, you may have to say "I'm sorry, but I have to stop now. Thank you for calling."

When You Call Someone on the Telephone

1. Try to be sure you are calling the right number.

2. When someone answers, tell your name right away.

3. Perhaps the person who answers the telephone is not the one you are calling. Let's pretend you are Howard Allen and you want to talk to Bill Wright. Bill's mother answers the telephone, and you know her voice.

Mrs. Wright says "Sunnyside 5-3757."

You say "Hello, Mrs. Wright. This is Howard Allen. May I speak to Bill, please?"

4. If Mrs. Wright says "I'm sorry, Howard. Bill isn't in," don't say "Oh" and hang up. Say "Thank you, Mrs. Wright. I'll call again. Goodby."

5. When you call someone, you are supposed to close the conversation when you are through. Then you say "Goodby." And remember: don't talk on, and on, and **on**!

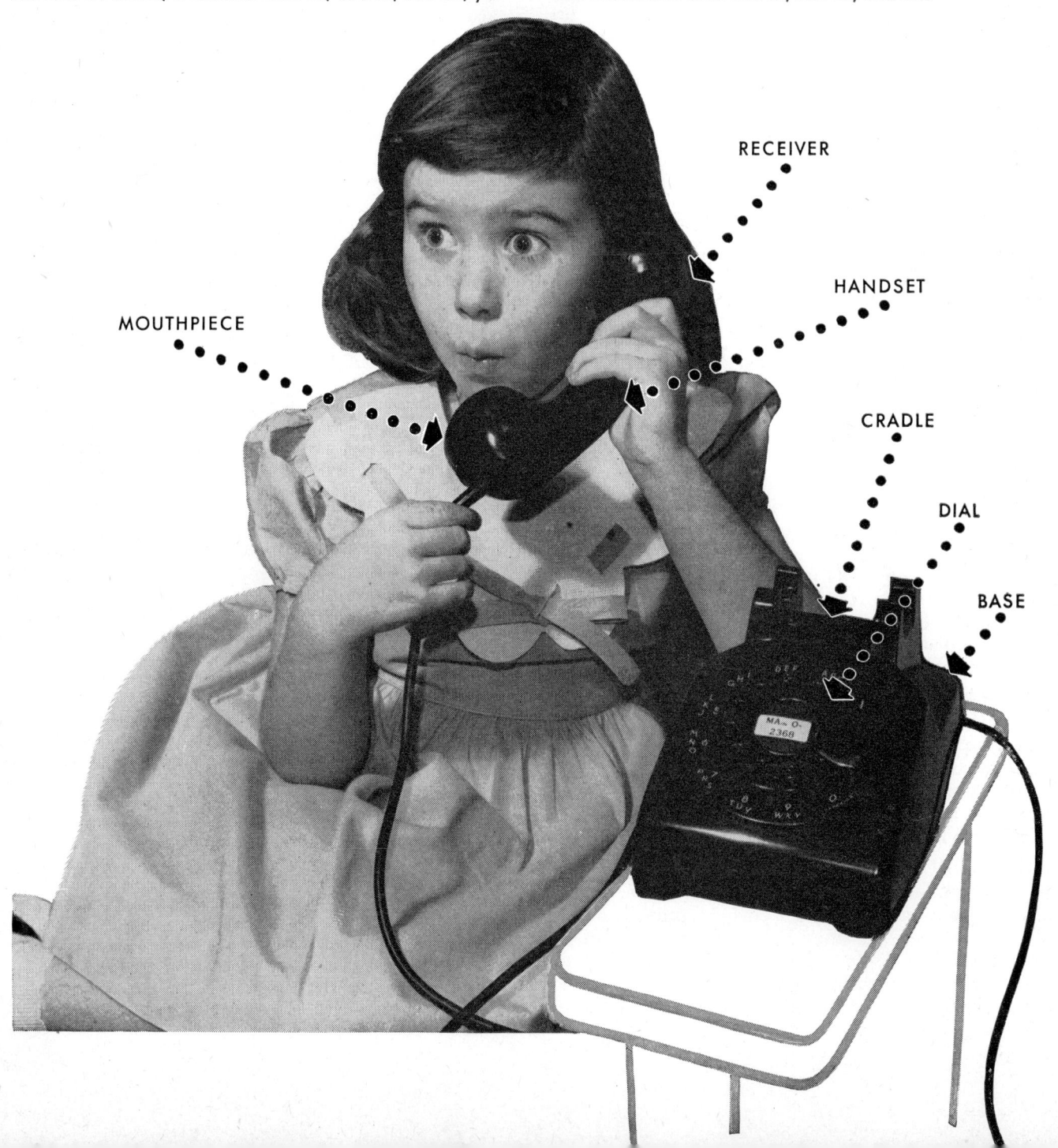

MOUTHPIECE

RECEIVER

HANDSET

CRADLE

DIAL

BASE

Match Each Giant's Picture to His Story

THE COWBOY GIANT was Pecos Bill. At the end of a long hard day on the range, cowboys sat around the campfire back of the chuck wagon and spun tall tales. They liked to tell tales of Pecos Bill, who could whirl a mountain lion around his head with his right hand while he held a full-grown grizzly bear two feet off the ground with his left hand. Pecos Bill could do more work in a day than a whole bunkhouse full of oldtime ranch hands. But what do you know—today, cowboys herd cattle in stripped-down automobiles and airplanes. Pecos Bill never thought of that!

THE GIANT OF THE STEEL MILLS played catch with white-hot ingots of steel. When he was thirsty, he drank from a cup of melted steel. His name was Joe Magarac. When steel workers get tired, they wish they could do their work as easily and as fast as Joe Magarac did. But they are made of flesh and bone, and Joe was made of steel.

THE RAILROAD GIANT could drive a steel drill and lay track faster than any other man alive. He was a big, jolly man carrying a sledge hammer and drill, and his name was John Henry. He had to drill through solid rock to take the railroad tracks across the mountains. One day he dug a two-mile tunnel single-handed. Even men working with modern diesel-powered machinery could not dig a tunnel that fast.

THE GIANT OF THE LUMBER CAMPS could chop down all the trees in ten square miles of forest while an ordinary lumber crew was felling one tree. This giant was Paul Bunyan. He had a tug of war with his Blue Ox, Babe, one day. They pulled so hard that the ground crinkled up and made the Rocky Mountains.

THE GIANT OF THE OILFIELDS, Gib Morgan, was the president of the Hardly Ever Get Oil Company. He drilled wells straight down, sideways, and from underneath up. But he hardly ever struck oil. He struck lots of other things—salt water, sparkling cola drinks, chocolate milk, grape juice, and apple cider. All the time, Gib Morgan laughed at his own failures.

FRIENDLY GIANTS FROM MAKE-BELIEVE LAND

"I'm half man, half horse, and half alligator," roared the frontiersman. "I can outrun, outjump, outfight, and outwork any man alive!"

Of course he exaggerated. He was strong and fearless, but just a boastful man and not a giant.

The frontiersman worked hard. Many people work hard today. When the work is hard and the day is long, men dream of being giants and doing giants' work. A man who had to walk all day to go from one town to another dreamed of being a giant with seven-league boots who could stride swiftly across the country. Another such man dreamed of riding a magic carpet through the air. A lumberjack who worked for hours chopping down a single big tree dreamed of felling an entire forest with one sweep of his ax.

Of such dreams are folk tales made. And our Friendly Giants from Make-Believe Land are the heroes of countless folk tales.

Today we know that the real accomplishments of men are much more important than the fantastic adventures of giants. An airplane can carry us faster than a magic carpet. An atomic-powered ship can go around the world several times without refueling. Television and radio bring pictures and words from far away—instantly. They do these things by the power of whizzing electrons and spinning atoms. Electrons and atoms are among the smallest of all things. But they work like powerful giants. When you turn on a lamp, the giants at the electric power station send you a light to read by. What other modern-day giants can you think of?

Fire-Fightin' Mose Defied the Flames

In New York City a hundred years ago everybody knew Mose, the Bowery boy who followed the fire engines and grew up to be the greatest fire fighter of them all. He didn't fight fires for money, but for the love of it. All firemen were volunteers in those days. But Mose wasn't like the others who, for all their bravery, could be smothered by smoke, scorched by flame, and crushed by falling walls. Not Mose. His lungs dragged in the smoke and blew it out, and Mose didn't even cough. Flames licked at him, and he brushed them away with his left hand while he held the leather fire hose with his right hand until the brass nozzle melted. When a blazing beam fell on Mose's head, he never even felt it, but the beam broke in two.

Some folks say that Mose was eleven feet tall, with hands the size of jersey hams and feet as big as East River barges. He was big, all right, but his feet weren't really *that* big. That story got started when two little boys took one of his boots to use for a boat. They got into it, sure enough, but it was a tight squeeze.

Mose had fire-red hair and wore a fire-red shirt, and the solid brass clamps on his galluses were in the shape of bald eagles. He looked every inch the fireman, and he was boss of the crew of Engine Number 40. The engine was pure white, trimmed with gold. Its name was printed in gold on the side: *Lady Washington*. But everyone called it the *White Ghost* because it slipped through the streets so fast and was always first at a fire. Mose said: "The quicker you get to a fire, the smaller it is. And the smaller it is, the easier it is to put out. But," he always added, "the easiest of all to put out is the fire that never got started!"

One time Mose rode the roof of a dynamite-blasted building clear across the Hudson River and brought it down for a safe landing. And there was the time fire roared down to the water front and threatened the ships in their berths. There was no wind that day, but Mose blew on the sails, and the ships moved out into the safe waters of the bay.

One day Fire-fightin' Mose heard about mountains that spouted smoke and flame and buried whole cities with fire. He went away, and maybe he is still off fighting volcanoes. They haven't needed him in New York lately, with all their brave firemen and new fire-fighting equipment. But, if they ever do, he'll be back, brushing the flames away with his left hand, holding the fire hose with his right, and wading right into the heart of a fire to put it out.

Courtesy Alfred A. Knopf, publisher of *Fire-Fightin' Mose* by Harold W. Felton

Pecos Bill was a rootin' tootin' dream come true

COWBOYS SITTING AROUND the campfire still tell about Pecos Bill. Old Bill was born in Texas. When he was just a little baby, he played with rattlesnakes and grizzly bears. And he was still a baby when he tumbled out of the family wagon as it was crossing the Pecos River. No one noticed he was gone, and Baby Bill was left all alone on the dusty plains. But Bill wasn't a bit afraid, and before long a mother coyote came along and adopted him. Bill lived with the coyotes until he was ten years old. In fact, Bill thought *he* was a coyote, until one day a cowboy found him and told him he was a boy.

The cowboy took Bill back to camp, and the other cowboys named him Pecos Bill, because he'd been found near the Pecos River. They taught him to ride and rope and shoot. Before long, Pecos Bill could out-ride and out-rope and out-shoot just about everybody in Texas— which means in the world. Bill's favorite horse was called Widow-Maker. No one but Bill could stay on his back for ten seconds. But Bill didn't only ride wild horses. One time he broke a mountain lion to the saddle, and another time he rode a cyclone.

Pecos Bill wrestled with grizzly bears and lassoed a railraod train and dug the Rio Grande for an irrigation ditch. When he fought rattlesnakes, he let them have first bite to make things even. He used a rattler for a quirt and wore another one for a hatband. Bill was tough, but he wasn't mean, except with cattle rustlers and other bad men. He did his best to drive the bad men out of the country. There were lots of two-gun men in those days, but Bill was a four-gun man, and the bad men ran at the sight of him.

Pecos Bill died laughing. One day he bumped into a dude from the East. The dude was a pretty silly-looking cuss to begin with, but he didn't show how silly he really was till he started talking. That dude thought a dogie was a dog, instead of a little stray calf! Old Pecos Bill just laughed himself to death.

THE JUNIOR INSTRUCTOR

There'll never be another logger like Paul Bunyan. Some folks would say there'll never be another man like Paul. For one thing, Paul stood about a mile high in his stocking feet. And he used a pine tree to comb his beard. He invented logging, of course; and there are those who claim he invented fishing and hunting, too. And he made the Mississippi River and the Columbia River and Puget Sound and the Rocky Mountains and Old Faithful and a good deal more of the geography of North America. All in all, Paul Bunyan was a fairly unusual fellow.

There's a lot of argument about where Big Paul was born, but that really doesn't make too much difference. There was always enough of Paul to go around. Anyway, he started out in the East and he moved west. He had the greatest bunch of loggers in the world, and he had Babe. Babe was Paul's Blue Ox, the one who was born in the Winter of the Blue Snow. Babe could pull anything he was hitched to. Once he hauled a glacier down from Alaska for Paul, and another time he straightened out a crooked road by pulling at one end of it. Every time Babe needed new shoes, somebody had to dig another iron mine.

Paul Bunyan did everything in a big way. To fry hot cakes for the gang's breakfast, his cook used a griddle a mile wide, and dozens of boys with slabs of bacon tied to their shoes skated around on it to grease it up. The Red River got its name when Paul's ketchup supply fell into it. Paul's clerk, Johnny Ink-Slinger, used a pen attached to a hose that led to a whole barrel of ink.

Paul Bunyan got a million dollars from the King of Sweden, who wanted a place to send a lot of Swedes. Paul cleared North Dakota of trees and then drove all the stumps underground. That turned it into nice farming country.

Paul Bunyan built a continent with a woodsman's axe.

John Hancock Mutual Life Insurance Co.

Stormalong rode the waves and caught the whales.

ALFRED BULLTOP STORMALONG was the greatest sailor who ever lived. In the days of sailing ships, everyone knew about Stormy. He was a New England boy from down Maine way, according to most folks; but there are some who claim that Stormy was navigator for old Chris Columbus when he discovered America, and others say that Stormy rowed the "Mayflower" across the Atlantic, bringing the Pilgrims to Plymouth Rock.

Anyway, Stormalong really came into his own during the years when New England whaling ships were sailing the Seven Seas. Now the ordinary way to catch a whale was to put out from your ship in a whale boat, harpoon the critter, and let him drag you halfway across the ocean until he got tired and quit. But that method was too slow for Stormy. He'd just stand on the deck of his ship, toss a harpoon a couple of miles into the back of the whale, and then haul the whale in, hand over hand, as if he were a sunfish or a bullhead.

The whales got so scared of Stormy that they all hid out at the North Pole, but Stormy followed them up there and caught them anyway. He fought devilfish and tied their arms in knots, and he scared the sea serpents so much that they're still hiding out. Once he trapped a whole mess of pirates by pouring molasses on the deck so that they got stuck like flies on flypaper.

Stormalong was a big man, and he had a big appetite. His favorite drink was whale milk and cider, and he drank it out of a fire hose. He had a big ship, too. The masts were so high they used to knock the stars out of place, and the deck was so long that when it was Wednesday forward it was still Monday aft. Stormy was squeezing her through the English Channel one time, and the white paint scraped off on the English side. That's what made the White Cliffs of Dover. Another time Stormy got careless and rammed into the Isthmus of Panama. Now they call the crack he made the Panama Canal. When Stormy died, it took ten acres of sail cloth to wrap him up, and all the fishes cried. Even the whales felt bad about it.

Joe Magarac's steel muscles are the strength of the land.

STEEL WORKERS ARE CALLED steel men. Joe Magarac, though, was really a steel man. He was made of steel. He worked in the mills in Pittsburgh. Where did he come from? Well, some folks say he was born in Pennsylvania, in a coal car or an ore car or maybe in the middle of a mountain of iron ore. But others say he was born in the Old Country, like lots of the other workers who made American industry great. In the Old Country *magarac* means "donkey," and Joe used to say that he could eat like a donkey and work like a donkey. But he was no donkey, that Joe Magarac. He was a man—a steel man.

Joe Magarac was made of steel. When he thumped on his big chest, it clanked like a steel barrel, and when he got wet, he rusted. But for making steel, there's never been anything like him, before or since. He'd load up the furnace by hand, tossing in armloads of scrap and limestone and coke—tons of it. Then while it heated up to a few thousand degrees, he'd stir it with his big fingers. He'd dip out molten steel in his cupped hands and pour it into molds. And he'd roll it in his hands and squeeze out miles of steel rail and bite off sheets of steel. Joe's steel became girders for tall buildings and tracks for trains. It went into ships and tanks and automobiles and plows and bridges and nails and needles and a thousand other useful products. And Joe's steel was the best steel ever made.

Joe Magarac made steel day and night. He only stopped working to eat. He made steel to build a better country and a better world. Some say that Joe finally hopped into the furnace himself so he could be melted down to make more steel to be used to build more steel mills. But others say that Joe is still around. They say that when there's plenty of steel and plenty of steel workers on hand, Joe lays off and catches up on his sleep. Sometimes he sleeps five years or ten or fifteen. But when there's a need for steel, then Joe wakes up and stretches himself and goes back to the mills. And when Joe gets to work, the steel comes pouring out, shiny and strong, like Joe Magarac himself.

MY PRAYERS

A Child's Grace

God is great and God is good,
And we thank Him for our food;
By His hand we must be fed,
Give us, Lord, our daily bread. Amen.

Now I Lay Me

Now I lay me down to sleep,
I pray You, Lord, my soul to keep;
Your love stay with me through the night
And wake me with the morning light. Amen.

Now I Wake

Now I wake and see the light,
Your love was with me through the night;
To You I speak again and pray
That You will lead me all the day. Amen.

Grace Before a Meal

Be present at our table, Lord,
Be here and everywhere adored. Amen.

In All We Do, In All We Say

Father, we thank You for the night
And for the pleasant morning light,
For rest and food and loving care,
And all that makes the world so fair.

Help us to do the things we should,
To be to others kind and good,
In all we do, in all we say,
To grow more loving every day. Amen.

Good Night

Good night! Good night!
Far flies the light;
But still God's love
Shall flame above,
Making all bright.
    Good night! Good night!

A Child's Grace

Thank you for the world so sweet,
Thank you for the food we eat,
Thank you for the birds that sing,
Thank you, God, for everything.

Plays, Games and Activities

Children must find some outlet for their excess energy. Repression of any natural and healthy impulse is wrong. Any parent who attempts to maintain quiet in the house for the sake of her nerves, pays doubly at the expense of those same nerves, with restless, irritable children. If she has been successful in her efforts for quiet she may have, as her reward, an even worse state of affairs, children thoroughly repressed, lifeless, inattentive and wholly without interest or enthusiasm. Properly directed play will do much to correct these evils and also to develop alertness, quickness of movement and self-control.

"Where shall we play?" is then the next question. And nine cases out of ten the answer should be "Out-of-doors." Hardly a day, barring rainy ones, is too cold and disagreeable for a brisk game of cross-tag.

The mother should by all means participate in the play of the children. The presence of a grown-up adds immensely to the zest and charm of a game. We can all look back upon our own childhood and remember what interest was lent to our play if mother took time to put aside her work-basket and enter into the game as one of us; or if father laid down his paper and suddenly converted into a bogey-man, a bear, or a wicked giant. Besides enhancing the game, the fellowship necessarily existing when the parent enters the game is invaluable to both.

The selfish child is even more in evidence in play than in work. It is he who monopolizes the fun and the action and leaves to his brothers and sisters the "thinking parts." He must be made to see that one does not play a game alone and that a game is not a game unless all participate.

The self-assertive child, however, differs from the selfish child. He has merely reached a necessary stage in his development, and that self-assertion should not be crushed, but rather encouraged.

The slow child must be trained to be alert, keen and resourceful. A game that requires rapid thinking and constant action, such games as basket-ball for the older children and rhythmical, suggestive games for the younger child, can accomplish more for the sluggard than columns of figures or pages of spelling words.

The most important consideration in the presentation of games becomes, "Is the game suited to the faculties of the child?" While it is impossible to fix absolute age limits for certain games, since no two children are alike in their development, yet certain physiological and psychological facts make it possible for a general outline to be followed. Certain interests develop at certain ages, and it is necessary that those interests have a chance to develop. The mother should study the manifestations of the child and determine whether his are the normal interests for a child of his age, and if they are not, special encouragement should be given to the play interests, just as special attention is devoted to a child who is abnormal in his faculties for study. It will be observed that in almost every case the two go hand in hand. The child who is slow to learn is slow to play, and often his intellect can be so awakened in play that he will be noticeably quicker in mental work.

In children between the ages of four and six, there is a predominance of sensory and motor activities. Watch the child as he plays by himself. He is highly imaginative, his interest shifts quickly. At one moment he is an engine puffing and tooting at full speed. In an instant he has become a ferocious animal and his whistle changes into a fierce roar as he scurries along on all fours. The games, then, must involve representation, they must be of short duration, and each child must act often enough to keep him interested. Rules should be few. Rhythm appeals strongly to young children. Repetition is a source of great delight to small children. What seems to the older child a waste of time, in the way of choruses,—"As we go round once more," "As we go round the mulberry bush," etc., is half of the game for the little ones for whom this game is best suited.

From seven to nine is a transition period. The nervous system is developing and bodily growth is rapid. Finer coordinations of motor activity are developing and sense judgments must be formed. The child can take into consideration more points of interest and his games must involve choice,—"Which is safer, this base or that?" Games like Pussy Wants a Corner, Prisoner's Base, etc., appeal to him.

Ten to twelve is the time for storing up of energy and the child is not easily fatigued. More games are played at this age than at any other. Running games have the greatest fascination for children in this age group.

TAP AND RUN

The one who is "It" is blindfolded, or holds his hands tightly over his eyes. Then one of the others tiptoes up and taps "It" on the back. "It" guesses the name of the child and tells what distance the tapper has to run. If "It" guesses right, the tapper has to run the distance "It" calls out, and meanwhile all the others, including "It" will hide. Then the tapper has to find all of the children as in Hide-and-Seek. But if "It" guesses the wrong person, then he has to go as far as he directed the tapper while everyone else runs and hides. Since "It" won't want to run a long way, himself, he will want to be pretty sure who tapped him before he sends him on a long run. The first one caught is "It" for the next game.

SQUIRREL IN THE TREE

Most of the players stand in groups of three, with hands on each other's shoulders, forming hollow trees. In each tree is a player representing a squirrel, and there is also one odd squirrel without a tree. The leader claps his hands, and all of the players must run for other trees. The odd squirrel tries to secure a tree and the one who is left out becomes the odd squirrel for the next time.

DAYS OF THE WEEK

Each player is given the name of a day of the week. One throws a ball against the wall, and calls the name of some day, as Monday. The player named Monday must catch the ball before it touches the floor. If he catches it, he throws the ball.

OATS, PEAS, BEANS AND BARLEY GROW

This is a singing game which is very dramatic. It can be played by any number of children. One is chosen to be the farmer. All the others form a circle about the farmer. They join hands and dance about, singing the song.

Oats, Peas, Beans and Barley Grow

Oats, peas, beans and barley grow, Oats, peas, beans and barley grow, Can you or I or any one know How
Thus the farmer sows his seed, Thus he stands and takes his ease. Stamps his foot and claps his hand, And

CHORUS.

oats, peas, beans and barley grow? Waiting for a partner,
turns around to view the land. Tra la la la la la la,

Waiting for a partner; Open the ring and
Tra la la la la la, Tra la la la la la

choose one in While we all gaily dance and sing,
la la la, Tra la la la la la la la la.

At the end of the first stanza the children stop dancing, and while singing the second stanza they imitate the action which the words suggest. The farmer also performs these actions with the children in the circle. At the chorus, which is sung after the second stanza only, they wait until the farmer chooses a partner at the words "choose one in." Then they all dance around the farmer and his partner until the end of the song. The game is then repeated and the partner becomes the farmer.

OUR GALLANT SHIP

Any number can play. The players join hands and form a circle, each child facing the center. Dancing around, they repeat:

Three times round went our gallant ship,
Three times round went she;
Three times round went our gallant ship,
Then she went to the bottom of the sea.

At the words "bottom of the sea," the children fall. They may repeat until they are weary of falling, and of laughing. This is a game for very young children.

ANIMALS

A child with closed eyes or blindfolded stands in the center with a stick. The others join hands and march around until he taps. He then extends his stick and the one at whom it is pointed must take hold of it and imitate any animal as he is requested, as, "Bark like a dog," "Crow like a rooster," or, "Roar like a lion." If he can be guessed by his voice he must take the blindfolded child's place; if not, the game continues until some one is correctly named.

WHAT IS IT?

Supply a bag containing miscellaneous articles, such as spools, balls, buttons, blocks, etc. Let the children stand in a line with their hands behind them. One of the children chosen places an object drawn from the bag in each child's hand and he must guess what it is by feeling of it without looking at it. The bag may be made of flour sacks or any left-over material.

PLANTING POTATOES

This game is a relay contest. The players are divided into two equal teams. The leader in each team toes a starting line, and his players line up behind him. At a distance of 25 feet from the starting line, and at right angles to it, a row of four circles should be marked on the ground in front of each team. Four stones are used for potatoes and should be placed beside each leader.

At a signal, the leader in each team picks up a potato, runs forward, and places it in the first circle. He returns, gets another potato, places it in the second circle, and so on until all the potatoes have been planted. As soon as he finishes, he runs back and touches the outstretched hand of the next player in his file. The next player in the file immediately runs forward, picks up a potato, and brings it to the starting line. He returns, gets another potato, brings it to the starting line, and so on until they are all gathered at the starting line. The players alternate planting and gathering potatoes until each has had a turn. The team wins whose last player is first to dash over the starting line.

LONDON BRIDGE

Little children love games to which music and rhymes are attached. There are many of these which have been handed down from generation to generation and are still as popular as ever. One of the most popular of these is London Bridge, which is a very ancient game. There are many versions of this. One which is much loved by little children is as follows.

Two taller children are chosen to make the bridge. They join hands and, holding them high, form an arch. The other children form a single line, each one taking hold of the dress or coat of the one in front. They pass under the arch while the two forming the bridge sing the first verse of the song.

At the words "I caught you," the bridge-makers drop arms over the one who happens to be passing through, making a prisoner of him. They take the prisoner off a little distance, singing the *D. C.* as they do so, and he is asked to choose between two articles represented by the bridge-makers, who will have previously decided upon the valuables, which may be a gold watch and a diamond ring. The prisoner belongs to the side represented by the article thus chosen, and he must take his place behind the bridge-maker who is a leader of that side. The song is repeated until all are caught.

Then the two sides line up behind their chosen leaders who have been bridge-makers, grasp each other around the waist and a tug-of-war takes place. Each side tries to pull the leader of the other side across a given mark.

One author tells that this game is supposed to have originated in the ancient custom of offering a sacrifice at the building of a bridge, and that the tug-of-war represents the struggle between the powers of good and evil for the soul of the sacrificial victim.

London Bridge

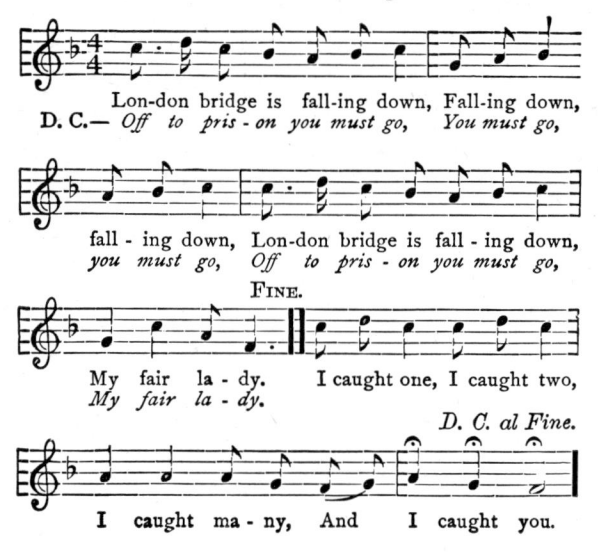

London Bridge Is Ready to Fall on a Marcher.

SUN DIAL

A great circle is drawn on the ground, and it is divided off into twelve equal parts by intersecting lines so it looks like a wheel with spokes. The sections are numbered from one to twelve. One player is blindfolded and placed in the center of the circle. The leader then turns him about so that he will lose his sense of direction. Then he walks around inside the circle while the players count to 12 or repeat the rhyme: "Hickory, Dickory, Dock." At the last count, the player stops suddenly. Then he removes his blindfold and looks at his score. The number of the space in which he stands is his score. If he stops with one foot on a line, or outside of the circle, he scores nothing. Players take turns, and the child who first scores twenty-five or fifty points wins the game. If an even number play, children may pair off and their combined scores may be used to decide the winners. In such a case, the total score should be at least seventy-five or one hundred, since the score will be run up quickly.

PLAYS, GAMES AND ACTIVITIES

STATUES

This game may be played by any number of children. It requires no practice, and can be played anywhere. The statues must stand perfectly still, which is part of the fun; for the statue that laughs or wriggles may have to pay a forfeit.

In playing this game, one child is the exhibitor. The exhibitor takes the other children in turn, or in groups, to be statues. The remaining children form the public, and applaud the exhibition. The children first choose what they wish to represent. Then, at a signal, they strike an attitude that will represent the character they are playing, and hold it motionless until another signal is given. Picking flowers, going to school, the postman, dancing figures; trades, as the carpenter, the blacksmith; famous people of whom you have read; copies of real statues,—all these make suitable subjects, according to the ages of the children, and the number playing the game.

DROP THE HANDKERCHIEF

A child with a handkerchief runs around outside of the ring and drops it behind some one. This child is to pick it up and try to catch the first runner before he gets around to the second child's place. If he is caught he must stand in prison in the center.

No one must tell another that the handkerchief is behind him; but if the first runner gets around and touches him before he starts, he is to go to prison as though he had been caught.

BUZZ

One player starts the game by saying "One," the next says "Two," the next "Three," etc., until the number seven is reached when the word "Buzz" is substituted for it. The next player says "Eight" and so on to a multiple of seven when he must substitute "Buzz." The word "Buzz" is also substituted for any number containing the word "seven," even though it is not a multiple of seven as, seventeen, twenty-seven, etc. When a player says a number instead of "Buzz" or says "Buzz" in the wrong place, or calls out a wrong number he must pay a forfeit and start the game over again by saying "One."

PASS BALL

The players form a ring with the feet placed sufficiently far apart for the ball to roll between them, and each foot touching a neighbor's foot, so that the ball cannot readily pass between players. One stands in the center of the circle, and tries to roll the ball between the feet of a player, who rolls it back with his hands. If it passes between his feet or if he moves his feet so that it cannot pass, he takes the place of the player in the center.

PRISONER'S BASE

Two dens are established twelve feet square and about eighty yards apart. Two smaller dens, close beside each other, are marked at equal distance from the large ones, and a considerable distance in front of a line drawn between them, so as to leave a space in which the game can be played. The two spaces close together are called bases, and are used as prisons, one belonging to each side, and always the prison belongs to the side playing from the den farthest from it.

Sides having been chosen, each side takes possession of its own den. The game consists of a sort of skirmish, any player going out from his den being pursued by a player from the other. When one is caught he is committed to prison, but can be rescued by being touched in the prison by one of his own side, who must necessarily run a somewhat longer distance than his prisoner, who starts to catch him before he reaches base. The side getting the most prisoners wins.

STILL POND

A leader is blindfolded. The others may walk about until he says, "Still pond, no more moving!" after which they must remain perfectly still until some one is caught. Unless the blindfolded one can guess his captive's name he must release him and start again.

FRENCH BLIND MAN'S BUFF

One player is blindfolded, the others form a ring about him. All in the ring are numbered. The one in the center calls two numbers. The players having these numbers change places at once, while the center player tries to catch one. If he succeeds, the one caught takes his place.

FOX TRAIL

This is an old but always popular game. There are several variations of the game, but the following is one easily taught. It is best played in newly fallen snow, which packs easily. Six or more children may play. One is the hunter, the others are foxes. A circle twenty or thirty feet in diameter is tramped in the snow, then straight paths like spokes of a wheel are tramped from the circumference to the center. The number of paths should be less than the number of foxes. At the points where the paths meet the circumference, small circular dens are tramped for the foxes. All the foxes have dens except one who is the Old Fox. The center of the circle where the paths meet is the hunter's goal.

At the beginning of the game each fox is stationed in a den except the Old Fox who must get a den as best he can. The foxes then run from den to den and the hunter tries to tag a fox and the Old Fox tries to secure a den. If a fox is tagged by the hunter they change places. A fox may run on any of the paths or the circumference in any direction, but he may not turn back when once started on a path, and he must run to an intersection before changing his course. The foxes and the hunter must keep to paths already tramped. Only one fox may occupy a den at a time, and no fox may be tagged alone in a den.

THREE DEEP

Any even number of more than twelve children may play this game which especially develops alertness. Two children are chosen, one to be the tagger and one the runner. The other children choose partners and form a double circle, all the children facing the center of the circle. The children in the outside circle stand directly behind their partners. There should be space between each couple large enough to allow the runner to pass through. When all is ready a signal is given and the tagger chases the runner, who, when hard pressed, runs in front of a couple in the circle and stands in front of the inner partner, thus making "three deep." Immediately the outside partner of this three runs as the tagger tries to tag him. He, in turn, may enter the circle and form a three, and the one on the outside, in turn, becomes the runner. If the tagger catches the runner, the runner becomes the tagger and the tagger becomes the runner. No running through the circle is allowed. The excitement increases in proportion to the number of threes formed.

CROSS TAG

The player who is *It* calls out the name of another child, to whom he at once gives chase. At any time during the chase a third player may run between the one who is *It* and the one whom he is chasing; whereupon the chaser must try to catch the new runner. At any time a fourth player may dash between this new runner and the catcher, and he then becomes the object of the chase. This may continue indefinitely until the one who is *It* finally succeeds in tagging the one he is chasing. The one who is tagged then becomes *It* for a new game. Any player may add sport to the game by getting in the way of the chaser without actually crossing between him and the one he is pursuing. Of course, no free player must get so close to the chaser that he touches him, or the chaser may declare him tagged.

Now the Boy Who is It Must Chase the Girl.

BALL AND BASES

Mark a place for home plate and three bases to complete the diamond, as in baseball. Choose sides, which may be called Reds and Blues. Appoint an umpire and a scorer. The first Red player stands at the home plate, the first Blue not less than five paces from him. The Red player strikes the ball with his hand as far as possible in any direction, and runs to the first base, to the second, to the third, and the home plate, if he can, before the Blue has returned the ball to the home plate. He scores as many points as he has run bases before the ball is returned. If the Blue catches the ball, the Red is out. If the runner reaches the third base before the ball is returned to the home plate, he may remain over and try for the home plate when the next one of his side strikes the ball. When all the Reds have played, the Blues have their innings. A game consists of two innings. Some players prefer to use a soft ball.

PLAYS, GAMES AND ACTIVITIES

I PUT MY RIGHT HAND IN

The players form in a circle and sing, suiting the action to the words. At the words "shake, shake, shake," shake the object named toward the inside of the circle, three times. Whirl three times at the last line.

1. I put my right hand in,
   I put my right hand out,
   I give my right hand a shake, shake, shake,
   And I turn myself about.

I Put My Right Hand In

[musical notation: I put my right hand in, I put my right hand out, I give my right hand a shake, shake, shake, And I turn my-self a-bout.]

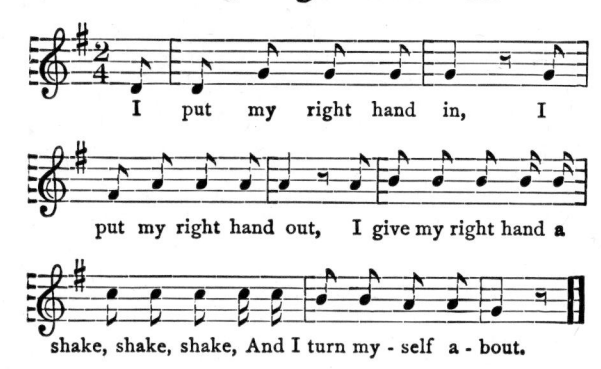

2. I put my left hand in—
3. I put my two hands in—
4. I put my right foot in—
5. I put my left foot in—
6. I put my two feet in—
7. I put my right ear in—
8. I put my left ear in—
9. I put my two ears in—
10. I put my right side in—
11. I put my left side in—
12. I put my head in—

THE FARMER IN THE DELL

Any number may play this game. The children choose one from their number to be the farmer. The other children form a circle around him and, dancing around, sing the song.

1. The farmer in the dell,
   The farmer in the dell,
   Heigh, oh! the derry, oh!
   The farmer in the dell.

The Farmer in the Dell

[musical notation: The farm-er in the dell, The farm-er in the dell, Heigh, oh! the der-ry, oh! The farm-er in the dell.]

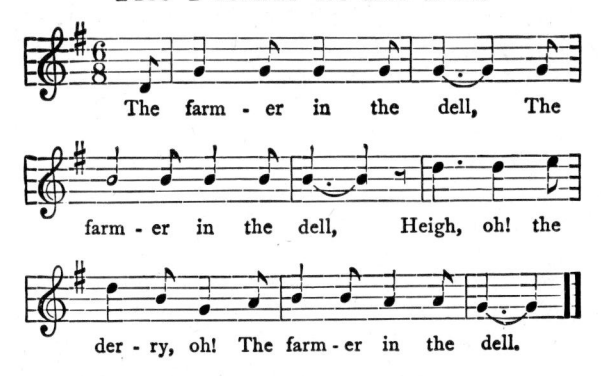

2. The farmer takes a wife,
   The farmer takes a wife,
   Heigh, oh! the derry, oh!
   The farmer takes a wife.
3. The wife takes the child, etc.
4. The child takes the nurse, etc.
5. The nurse takes the dog, etc.
6. The dog takes the cat, etc.
7. The cat takes the rat, etc.
8. The rat takes the cheese, etc.
9. The cheese stands alone, etc.

When the words "The farmer takes a wife" are sung, the farmer points to some child in the circle and that child leaves the circle and stands beside the farmer. At the words, "The wife takes the child," this child points to some other child in the circle and this child takes his stand beside the wife. In turn, the child chooses a nurse, the nurse a dog, etc. At the words "The cheese stands alone," the children within the circle all run back to the circle, leaving the last child chosen as the cheese standing alone in the center. If the game is repeated this child becomes the farmer.

CATCH THE SALMON

The two boys who want to *Catch the Salmon* carry a piece of rope between them, each holding an end. The fish are on one side of a chalk line, across which the catchers must not pass. The catchers carry their rope to this line and try to throw it over any *fish* that comes too near. When they succeed in doing this, the captive must not try to get free with his arms, but he may jump and struggle if he likes. Once across the line, he is on land and must give up.

135

THE MULBERRY BUSH

The game consists in simply suiting the actions to the words of the song, singing and circling to the first verse between the activities.

The activities will be more fun if the children are permitted considerable freedom in acting them out.

Here We Go Round the Mulberry Bush

1. Here we go round the mulberry bush,
   The mulberry bush, the mulberry bush,
   Here we go round the mulberry bush,
   So early in the morning.
2. This is the way we wash our clothes, etc.,
   So early Monday morning.
3. This is the way we iron our clothes, etc.,
   So early Tuesday morning.
4. This is the way we scrub our floors, etc.,
   So early Wednesday morning.
5. This is the way we mend our clothes, etc.,
   So early Thursday morning.
6. This is the way we sweep the house, etc.,
   So early Friday morning.
7. This is the way we bake our bread, etc.,
   So early Saturday morning.
8. This is the way we go to church, etc.,
   So early Sunday morning.

SIMON SAYS "THUMBS UP"

The leader gives the commands:
Simon says, "Thumbs up."
Simon says, "Thumbs down."
Simon says, "Thumbs wiggle waggle," sometimes giving the order without Simon's permission, as:

"Thumbs up."
"Thumbs down."
"Thumbs wiggle waggle."

The leader follows his own directions, but if any children move thumbs when Simon does not say so, they must drop out of the game.

SIBERIAN MAN HUNT

This game, given in the "Boy Scouts of America," will doubtless be familiar to the Scouts.

One player, of any number who may play, starts out across the snow, seeking a good hiding place. After giving him five or ten, or even more, minutes, as agreed upon, the others, armed with snowballs, proceed to follow him by his tracks. As they approach his hiding place he may shoot at them with his snowballs. Any one of the attacking party who is shot must fall out dead. If the fugitive is hit three times with snowballs by the attacking party he is counted dead.

This game can be played to the best advantage in the fields and woods.

CIRCLE BALL

The players form a ring. One of them throws the ball at another player, who must catch it, and throw it at some other one in the ring. It should be thrown in quick succession and unexpectedly. Variations may be made by bouncing the ball, by clapping the hands before catching it, or ordering the person who fails to catch it to sit down. The game may also be played with the players seated.

The Children's Music

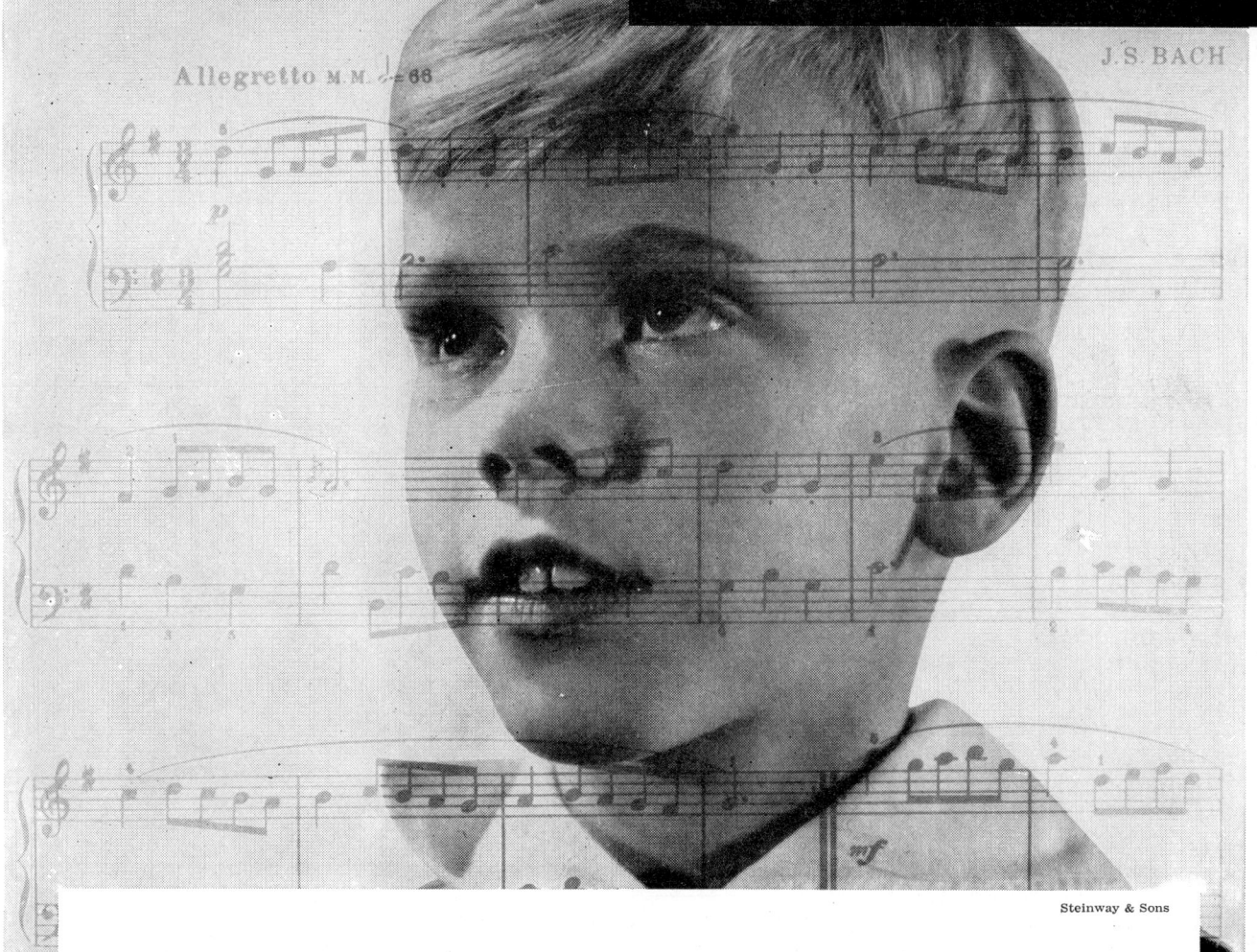

Allegretto M.M. ♩=66

J. S. BACH

Steinway & Sons

Holy Night! Peaceful Night!

FRANZ GRUBER

Slowly

1. Ho - ly night! peace - ful night! Thro' the dark-ness beams a light,
2. Si - lent night! ho - li - est night! Dark-ness flies and all is light!
3. Si - lent night! ho - li - est night! Guid - ing Star, O lend thy light!

Yon - der where they sweet vig - ils keep, O'er the Babe who in si - lent sleep,
Shep - herds hear the an - gels sing: Hal - le - lu - jah! hail the King!
See the East - ern wise men bring Gifts and hom - age to our King!

cresc.   dim.

Rests in heav - en - ly peace. Rests in heav - en - ly peace.
Je - sus the Sav - iour is here! Je - sus the Sav - iour is here!
Je - sus the Sav - iour is here! Je - sus the Sav - iour is here!

137

Home, Sweet Home

Sir HENRY BISHOP

Not too slowly

1. 'Mid pleasures and palaces though we may roam, Be it ever so humble, there's no place like home. A charm from the skies seems to hallow us there, Which seek thro' the world, is ne'er met with elsewhere.

2. An exile from home splendor dazzles in vain, Oh, give me my lowly thatched cottage again! The birds singing gaily that came at my call, Give me them with the peace of mind dearer than all.

Chorus: Home! home! sweet, sweet home There's no place like home, there's no place like home.

3
How sweet 't is to sit 'neath a fond father's smile,
And the cares of a mother to soothe and beguile!
Let others delight mid new pleasures to roam,
But give me, oh, give me the pleasures of home!
Chorus—

4
To thee I'll return, overburdened with care;
The heart's dearest solace will smile on me there;
No more from that cottage again will I roam;
Be it ever so humble, there's no place like home.
Chorus—

Farmyard Song

EDUARD GRIEG

Come out, snow-white lamb-kin, come out, calf and cow, come Puss, with your kit-ten, the sun's shin-ing now, Come out, yel-low duck-ling, come out, dow-ny chick-ling, that scarce-ly can sprawl, come out at my call! Come, pi-geons a-coo-ing, fly out for your woo-ing! The dew's on the grass, come out ere it pass! For soon, too soon the sum-mer it pass-es, and call but Au-tumn, be-hold him!

New and Selected Music

The Birdies' Ball

1. Spring once said to the night-in-gale, "I mean to give you birds a ball, Pray, ma'am, ask the bird-ies all, The birds and bird-ies great and small."
2. Soon they came from bush and tree, Sing-ing sweet their songs of glee, Each one from its cos-y nest, Each one drest in its Sun-day best.
3. The cuckoo and wren they danced for life, The rav-en waltz'd with the yellow-bird's wife, The awk-ward owl and the bash-ful jay, Wished each other "A very good day."
4. The wood-pecker came from his hole in the tree, And brought his bill to the com-pa-ny; For the cher-ries ripe, and the cher-ries red, 'Twas a very long bill, so the bird-ies said.
5. They danced all day till the sun was low, Till the moth-er birds pre-pared to go; Then one and all, both great and small, Flew to their nests from the bird-ies ball.

CHORUS.

Tra la la la la la, tra la la la la la, Tra la la la la la, tra la la la la la;
Tra la la la la la, tra la la la la la, Tra la la la la la la.

Alphabet Song

Old School Song

A, B, C, D, E, F, G, H, I, J, K, L, M, N, O, P, Q, R, S, and T, U, V, W (double-you,) and X, Y, Z. Hap-py, hap-py shall we be When we've learned our A, B, C.

A Thank-You Song

D. W.
Moderato
DIXIE WILLSON.

Bu-sy bum-ble bee, With your drow-sy song, Flit-ting through the sun-ny-gar-den all day long, Do you nev-er tire, Rain-bow wing-ed fel-low, Car-ry-ing so ma-ny loads of pol-en yel-low, Back and forth from flow'r to hon-ey-hive you go, Bu-zing as you're bu-sy dart-ing to and fro, If per chance you be gath-er-ing for me, I thank you, bum-ble bee.

Lullaby

From the German

1. Sleep, ba - by, sleep, thy fa - ther's mind - ing sheep; Thy moth - er, from the dream-land tree, Shakes down a gold - en dream to thee. Sleep, ba - by, sleep, O! sleep, ba - by, sleep.
2. Sleep, ba - by, sleep, the sky is full of sheep; The star - lets are the lamb - kins small, The moon is watch - ing o - ver all. Sleep, ba - by, sleep, O! sleep, ba - by, sleep.
3. Sleep, ba - by, sleep, go dog and mind the sheep; Yes, go, good dog - gie, far from here And do not wake my ba - by dear. Sleep, ba - by, sleep, O! sleep, ba - by, sleep.

The Bird's Nest

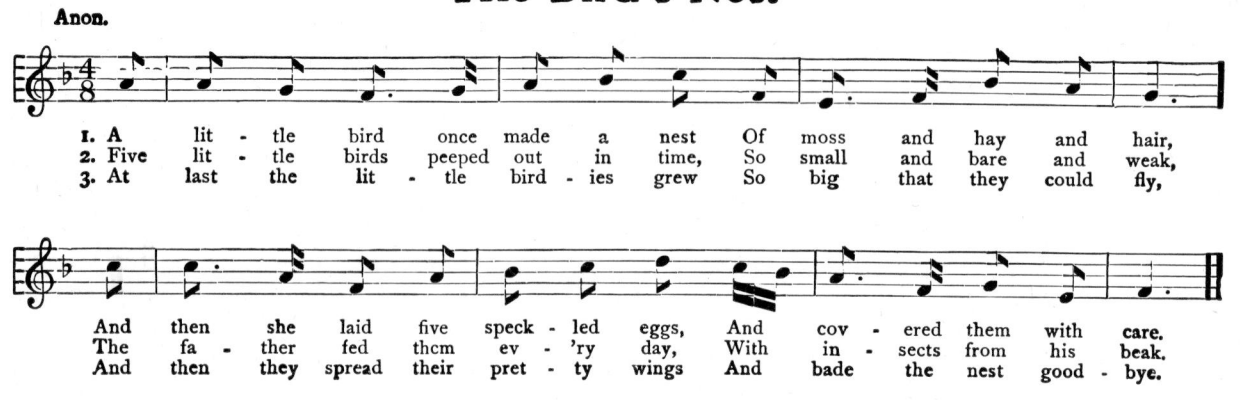

Anon.

1. A lit - tle bird once made a nest Of moss and hay and hair, And then she laid five speck - led eggs, And cov - ered them with care.
2. Five lit - tle birds peeped out in time, So small and bare and weak, The fa - ther fed them ev - 'ry day, With in - sects from his beak.
3. At last the lit - tle bird - ies grew So big that they could fly, And then they spread their pret - ty wings And bade the nest good - bye.

Soap Bubbles

S. G. F.
Sallie G. Fitzgerald

1. Soap bub - bles blue, and red, and gold, Blow as ma - ny as your pipe will hold; See them float so light - ly round, Oh! they burst as they touch the ground.
2. Oh, you air - y fair - y things! You float a - bout as though on wings; Soap bubbles blue, and red, and gold, Blow as many as your pipe will hold.

142

How to Make a Shoe

C. T. Steele
Arr. by Edward A. Parker

1. Wand-'ring up and down one day, I peeped in a win-dow o-ver the way, And put-ting his nee-dle through and through, There sat a cob-bler mak-ing a shoe.
2. See how neat-ly on the last, He draws down the leath-er, mak-ing it fast, And put-ting the waxed-end through and through, Ev-er his head and bod-y work too.
3. Now with ham-mer hear him tap, The shoe is so firm-ly fixed in his lap, And mov-ing his head both up and down, Yet on his face is nev-er a frown.
4. With his awl he makes a hole, First in-to the up-per then through the sole, Then put-ting his pegs in, one or two, Laugh-ing a-way, he ham-mers them through.
5. Now with ham-mer, now with stitch, For this is the cob-bler's way to get rich, He whis-tles and sings, that cob-bler still, Do-ing his work with a mer-ry good will.

Chorus

Rat-a-tap, tap, Tick-a-tack too, This is the way to make a shoe.
Rat-a-tap, tap, Tick-a-tack too, This is the way to make a shoe.

NEW AND SELECTED MUSIC
An Indian Cradle Song

A. J. Gantvoort
Arr. by Edward A. Parker

1. Swing thee low in thy cra-dle soft, Deep in the dusk-y wood;....
2. Coy-ote howls on the prai-rie cold, Ow-let hoots to.. the tree;.....
3. Fa-ther lies on the fra-grant ground Dream-ing of hunt.. and fight,—...

Swing thee low—.. and swing a-loft, Sleep as a pap-poose should... For
Big moon shines on the lit-tle child, Slum-ber-ing peace-ful-ly...... So
Pine leaves rus-tle with mourn-ful sound All through the sol-emn night;— But

safe in your lit-tle birch-en nest, Qui-et will come, and.. peace and rest, If the
swing thee high in thy lit-tle nest, And swing thee low and.. take the rest That the
lit-tle pap-poose in his birch-en nest Is swing-ing low as he takes his rest, Till the

lit-tle pap-poose.. is good, is good, If the lit-tle pap-poose.. is good.....
night wind is bring-ing to thee, to thee, That the night wind is bring-ing to thee......
sun brings the morn-ing light, the light, Till the sun brings the morn-ing light.....

144

NEW AND SELECTED MUSIC

Falling Leaves

L. G.
Laurene Gardner

Quietly.

1. Fall - ing, fall - ing, soft and slow, How they flut - ter, light - ly blow;
2. See the pret - ty car - pet bright, Gay it looks in warm sun - light.
3. How they rus - tle when we walk, Just as though they joined our talk;

Red leaves, brown leaves, cir - cling round, Now they're qui - et on the ground.
Yel - low, red, and green, and brown, Still they're fall - ing, fall - ing down.
Will they qui - et grow and sleep When the snow falls soft and deep?

rit.

Winter Sports

Laurene Gardner

Gaily

1. How we love the snap - py win - ter days, Frost - y air and jol - ly hap - py plays.
2. Let us frol - ic on our way to school Good, clean sport, o - bey - ing ev - 'ry rule.
3. Then a snow fort we will make, One quick charge, the en - emy's line to break.
4. Now the school - bell rings out loud and clear, Sol - diers we, o - bey - ing with a cheer.

We can skate and we can slide, And we can have a fine sleigh ride.
Here come the snow balls thick and fast, We will run and dodge till they whiz past.
Back to the fort, we have won the fight, Let us sing and cheer with all our might.
We will work with all our might, Showing we can stu - dy as well as fight.

The Kitty and the Mouse

S. G. F.
Sallie G. Fitzgerald

1. There was a lit-tle kit-ty with great green eyes, And paws as soft as silk, She sat by the fire and dozed all day And purred when she drank her milk; But Oh, this lit-tle kit-ty with the great green eyes And the purr so soft and low, Had sharp white teeth in her sly lit-tle head, And a claw in each lit-tle toe.

2. A lit-tle gray mouse with sharp black eyes And whisk-ers long and fine, And a tail as long as a la-dy's train Came out one day to dine, But when he saw the kit-ty with the eyes of green, And he heard her purr so low, He said, "I'll not stay this day to dine But back to my home I'll go."

The Snow Fairies

C. T. Steele
Arr. by Edward A. Parker

1. Light-ly trip-ping, gai-ly skip-ping, Come the fair-ies o'er the snow,
And they nev-er stop to tell us Whence they come or where they go;
But when moon-beams light the mead-ow, And we all are safe in bed,
Then the lit-tle snow-flake fair-ies Frol-ic down from o-ver-head.

2. One will try to catch the oth-er; Then they tum-ble to the ground,
Up a-gain in live-ly frol-ic, Chase each oth-er round and round;
Oh, they're jol-ly lit-tle fel-lows! But they can't be seen by day,
When the moon is shin-ing bright-ly, They come out to dance and play!

THE JUNIOR INSTRUCTOR

The Star-Spangled Banner

Francis Scott Key — John Stafford Smith

1. Oh,.. say, can you see, by the dawn's ear-ly light, What so proud-ly we hailed at the twi-light's last gleam-ing, Whose broad stripes and bright stars, thro' the per-il-ous fight, O'er the ram-parts we watched, were so gal-lant-ly stream-ing? And the rock-ets' red glare, the bombs burst-ing in air, Gave.. proof thro' the night that our flag was still there. Oh,.... say, does the star-span-gled ban-ner yet wave O'er the land of the free and the home of the brave?

2. On the shore dim-ly seen thro' the mists of the deep, Where the foe's haught-y host in dread si-lence re-pos-es, What is that which the breeze, o'er the tow-er-ing steep, As it fit-ful-ly blows, half con-ceals, half dis-clos-es? Now it catch-es the gleam of the morn-ing's first beam, In full glo-ry re-flect-ed now shines on the stream; 'Tis the star-span-gled ban-ner; oh, long may it wave O'er the land of the free and the home of the brave!

3. And.. where is that band who so vaunt-ing-ly swore That the hav-oc of war and the bat-tle's con-fus-ion A.... home and a coun-try should leave us no more? Their.. blood has washed out their foul foot-steps' pol-lu-tion, No.... ref-uge could save the.... hire-ling and slave From the ter-ror of flight or the gloom of the grave; And the star-span-gled ban-ner—in tri-umph doth wave O'er the land of the free and the home of the brave.

4. Oh,.. thus be it ev-er when free-men shall stand Be-tween their loved home and wild war's des-o-la-tion; Blest with vic-t'ry and peace, may the heav'n-res-cued land Praise the Pow'r that hath made and pre-served us a na-tion! Then.. con-quer we must, when our cause it is just, And.... this be our mot-to: "In God is our trust!" And the star-span-gled ban-ner in tri-umph shall wave O'er the land of the free and the home of the brave.

CREATIVE OCCUPATIONS

by Miriam Brubaker

IT is the right of every child to play. If we study the young of any form of life we find that play is a perfectly natural and normal state. Watch the old mother cat with her kittens—how they roll, and run, and cuff at one another! Watch the baby chick as he plays with a worm. All life goes through a stage of play. So it is the birthright of every child to have an opportunity to play.

Value of Play

THROUGH play, we find the child developing mentally. He is exploring, investigating, manipulating, and trying out his power over the things in his every-day life. We find that he is developing physically and is learning to co-ordinate his muscles and to use his body with more ease and grace. In working with materials or in his use of toys, the child finds that greater satisfaction comes sometimes by working or playing with others, and so he is gaining in social adjustments in the world in which he must live.

Need for Right Materials

JUST as the adult must have good tools in order to accomplish what he wants to do; so the child should have the right toys and materials to help him develop to his greatest capacity. The tendency to-day is to give children toys that are ready-made, toys which are too perfect, that offer no challenge. Materials that stimulate self-activity and meet the child on his own level of maturity are therefore of greatest importance. Toys and materials that have a "do-with" aspect, and not those which merely amuse and entertain, are cultivating the child's imagination and are leading him to think.

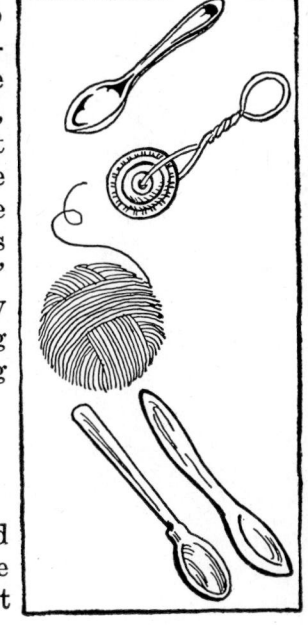

Value of Creative Occupations

THE child who is not provided with materials which encourage creative play or creative work is not using his abilities to the highest degree, but he is slipping into habits of idleness in his thinking as well as in his habits of physical activity. He expects to be entertained rather than to do for himself. If it were not for creative thinking, we could not have the great skyscrapers, the wonderful bridges, and other feats of engineering that we have to-day. The science of aviation would never have reached the stage it is in if it had not been for some people being creative.

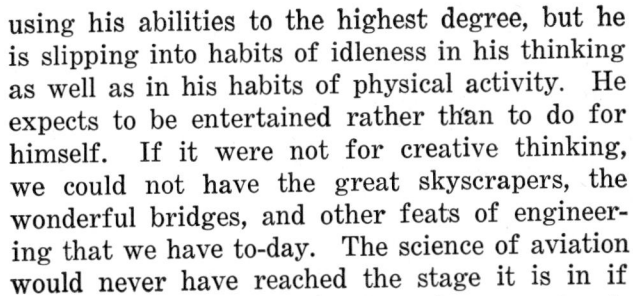

We should give children encouragement in what they create if we are to expect anything from them in the way of new ideas later on.

What the Home Can Provide For the Baby:

THERE are worth-while toys to be found in the shops, but many simple and inexpensive materials are within the reach of the majority of homes, and the mother can easily utilize these things. Even the baby who is not yet able to sit up may be given materials which will put him on his own resources. A string of simple toys strung from one side of his crib to the other will keep him happy and busy for hours. A bright silver spoon, a rattle, a ball made of soft yarn, a wooden doll, or some wooden spools painted gay colors, are some of the articles one might use in this way. A word of caution is needed, perhaps, that these things be far enough from the baby's face so that he is not looking at them with crossed eyes. He will reach out, clutch, feel, hold, and push these interesting objects hanging before him; and as a result, he is gaining control of arms, hands, legs, and back, through his kicking, grasping, and reaching. He is learning the difference between hard and soft, large and small, and is probably gaining some conception of color.

Some parents do not realize how much knowledge a baby gains in this experimental play; and in consequence, they do not provide these simple toys for him that may be found about the home.

149

CREATIVE OCCUPATIONS

For the Baby Who Is at the Stage of Sitting Up:

AT this age the baby is intensely interested in all that is about him. He is beginning to be more observing—and in order to be happy, he must have something to occupy him. What can it be? Any mother is able to provide such miscellaneous utensils as some kitchen spoons, a tin cup, and some tin covers that may be unpleasant to one's ears, but through which the child is learning something about sound and qualities of sound. The fitting and taking apart of clothes pins is a most interesting and worth-while occupation at this age. What could be more fascinating than Mother's coffee percolator; for it is the nicest kind of a puzzle to put together! Boxes with covers, and bottles of various sizes with corks offer opportunity for experimentation. A bottle containing puffed rice which may be poured from one vessel to another is very interesting; and if some of it finds its way to the baby's mouth, no damage is done. Never throw out milk-bottle tops, spools, corks, or little boxes, for your child will revel in these odds and ends, and be occupied for hours.

need any more, some stones or shells, and even bits of yarn or colored string.

Tin cans, provided there are no sharp edges, plus a kitchen spoon or two, will prove excellent utensils for making sand or mud cakes in the backyard. Adhesive tape placed around the top of coffee or cocoa cans safeguards the child from possible cuts. Large homemade wooden blocks about 12 x 12 x 6 inches offer a world of possibilities in construction. Some mothers ask their grocers to save starch boxes and the type of wooden boxes that are used for packing dried fruits. These, with all sides nailed on, make fine hollow blocks. They are large enough for the child to handle easily, and with them he may obtain quick results in building.

A large packing box or two with some boards five or six feet in length and ten inches in width are good incentives for dramatic play. Such boxes may be boats one minute, or a train, an aeroplane, or a house the next minute. Parents will have to swallow their pride in wanting a beautiful and orderly-looking backyard if their children's welfare and happiness are to be considered more important than the view the neighbors may have from their windows.

An excellent piece of climbing apparatus may be made from a carpenter's horse with boards about an inch-and-a-half thick, nailed across

For the Toddler:

THE child who is just beginning to toddle about is at a most investigative stage. He must try out everything and woe unto the parent who does not see that his or her child is given opportunity for this interest in a legitimate way. Otherwise there will be no end to the mischievous acts the youngster will find to do. His nature is to climb, to push, to carry, to pull, and to do a thousand-and-one things each day that show him to be a vigorous and lively human being. Don't thwart and inhibit him but give him materials which satisfy—little baskets or discarded handbags in which to horde and carry such treasures as a clothes pin or two, a bunch of old keys Daddy does not each side. A board one-foot wide, an inch thick, and five or six feet in length, with a cleat across the top to hold it firmly to the top of the "horse," offers an incline for walking up and down. If the board were smooth and varnished or waxed it would prove valuable as a slide.

For the Four-to-Seven Year Olds:

THE desire to create, to make use of the imagination, is almost at its peak at this level. Children of this age, while still interested in the handling of and experimenting with materials are striving toward more pleasing results than did their younger brothers and sisters. We find the kindergarten supply houses offering all kinds of materials which challenge the child to create. The building blocks of various types are highly recommended.

Most homes own a hammer, and that with a few old boxes or boards, and some good nails, will delight any boy, and most girls. Care should be taken that the wood be fairly soft—bass or white pine being of the best type. The nails used should have pretty good-sized heads so that there is a larger surface for the child to strike upon. Above all, the hammer should not be of the "play" variety but a *real* hammer. An adult with all his muscle and skill could not drive nails with a little light-weight toy hammer. The child needs the weight of a real hammer to help drive the nail. The average five-year-old can handle a saw with a good deal of skill, providing some fearful adult is not ever present to nag and warn and make the child miserable with constant remarks about "hurting himself." Children learn only through doing; so we must let them take chances occasionally.

Painting on a blackboard with water is valuable pastime. They are learning to use a brush, and to gain control while using a painting motion. Children delight in "painting with water" and in using it on fences, sidewalks, and walls. This is a foundation step for the use of actual paint, which might well come at the age of five or six. Put an old suit and old shoes on your child. Give him a brush and a can of ten-cent-store paint. Some old boxes, or even some of his play toys, may be the objects of his efforts.

On the following pages, the reader will find suggestive ways to use materials. As clay is one of the most educational and valuable materials because of its creative possibilities, there will be rather an extensive discussion of this material.

The Parent's Part in Creative Occupations

IN inspiring children to be creative, parents have a definite part to play. While children should do as much thinking for themselves as possible and be quite independent in working out problems that confront them in making things, yet the parents should be on the alert to do their part. What is that part? First of all, they need to be in sympathy with the child's efforts. His attempts may be meager, but praise and encouragement, with an occasional suggestion as to the best way to improve his product, or showing possibilities of new features, will carry the child far along his way.

Adults may hold too high standards of the results that children should obtain. This is dangerous. It is well to remember that the process is of greater value and interest to the child than the result; so let the work be his, but let us show our interest in his efforts, and give encouragement and help when needed.

Clay Modeling

Introducing Clay

CLAY is a plastic construction material which offers all of the joy of making mud pies without any of the disadvantages—and the whole family can have fun in using it. It is so pliable that the child can feel his control over it, and derives great satisfaction from altering its form according to his will. Clay is an excellent rainy-day material, as it will hold the attention of even the two-year-old for as long as thirty minutes.

Where to Get Clay

IN some parts of the country, native clay can be secured when excavations are being made for buildings; it may often be had for the asking. It can be purchased wet at any pottery, or in powder form at the various kindergarten supply houses. The latter type must have water added to it, to bring it to a good consistency—the best means for accomplishing this being to knead it with the hands. It should stand several days to allow the water to penetrate every particle, and although it's hard to wait, it will then be in condition to use for a long, long, time. Be careful not to have clay sticky when given to the children as they become hopelessly trapped in it. On the other hand, they cannot be happy with it if it is tough and hard, or crumbly. The purchase price is about eight cents a pound for powdered clay. Five pounds per child is sufficient for home use.

Oily Clay

THE oily variety of clay is not satisfactory as a rule, as it does not become really plastic until it has been handled for some time. Then the child's hands have become tired, and he has become discouraged by the long struggle. Oily clay has a disagreeable odor, and is hard to clean from the floor or furniture.

How to Use Clay

CLAY is not hard to clean from the floor if dropped, but the children should be taught to be reasonably careful in handling it. It is necessary to provide a smooth, hard, surface for using the clay. Sometimes oilcloth covers are made for the work tables, with rubber loops at the corners which slip over the table legs, thereby keeping the cover from slipping. Heavy wrapping paper will do if clipped or thumb-tacked to the table; but if the child has his own work table, there is no reason why the clay should not be used on the bare surface. Some mothers provide a "clay board" (about 12x18 inches) for each child. It is also a good idea to teach the children that all mussy work necessitates wearing some kind of a coverall and that all clay workers wear smocks, or aprons, or overalls to protect their clothing.

Making Things

IN supplying clay to the child, take a piece about the size of a small grapefruit and squeeze it into an irregular wad. A slick, regular piece is not suggestive of the possibilities. The child's first response to clay will be purely experimental—probably that will be the parent's reaction, too. He will poke it, break off little pieces, and roll them into balls, twist and roll long, snaky pieces into shape, pat them, and maybe the toddler will even venture a taste. He may name these creations "cookies" or "balls" or "worms," or he may not make a single comment, but merely revel in his control over this new material. The older child will soon begin to make animals of all kinds, Indians, book-ends, dishes, tiles, and innumerable other things. Then he and the little brother can work together, the one making a pen full of rabbits, and the other supplying clay carrots, apples, and maybe a dish for drinking water. These may be played with

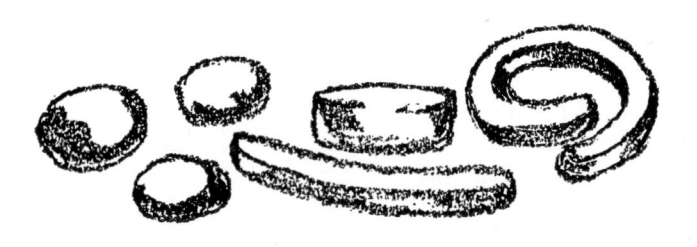

CLAY MODELING

while wet. The older child may be interested in saving his work, but the little one's interest is in "making"—not preserving his article.

The Finished Product

AT first, almost no emphasis should be placed on skill in representing an object, or on fine finish, but instead, it should be placed on the variety of possibilities which clay offers. However, after prolonged use, the child of six will become interested in decorating, painting, or smoothing his products. Impressions and designs may be made with seeds, nail heads, hairpins, and other trinkets. Smoothing may be accomplished while the clay is wet, by dipping the finger tips in water. If allowed to stand for a day or so, the product will become thoroughly dry, and may then be sand-papered to smoothness, or scraped with a pen-knife. It may also be painted to give very realistic and attractive results. The tiger with his black and orange stripes, or the flowered dishes, would delight any child. Thick water color or calcimine is satisfactory for temporary use, but enamel should be used (and the clay should be very dry) if the clay work is to be a permanent thing.

How to Care For Clay

CLAY can always be broken up, dampened, and used again—even after it has been painted. When it has been used, but has not been allowed to become hard, poke holes in the clay with your finger or with a pencil, fill these with water (to restore the original dampness) and place in an air-tight crock or in a galvanized pail with a tight cover. A damp cloth placed over the clay will help to keep it moist until the next time.

When working about the house, or when out for a walk, call your child's attention to the many articles which someone else has made from clay—the tiles in the fireplace, the paper weight, or the panels in some public building.

There are other plastic materials for use with **children of grade age.**

Jumbo drinks from this washtub. He likes to eat peanuts.

These are more expensive than clay, however.

Recipe:
1 cup cornstarch
2 cups salt
Enough water to make a thick paste.
Stir while cooking, and cook until stiff.
Allow this to cool, and cover with a damp cloth until ready to use.
Coloring may be added before cooking or when molded; let dry, then paint with water color.

Permanently-setting clay which does not have to be fired may be purchased at any art store. Some of them are Permoplast, Permodello, Marblex, Sculpto, and Petroplast.

This is an elephant which Jean made with clay. His back is sloping. His head is broad and flat. Jean squeezed out large, floppy ears. She pulled out a trunk that could curl right up to his mouth to feed himself hay and peanuts.

She made thick legs, with almost no feet, and a short, rope-like tail. Meat-skewers or lollipop sticks were put into the legs, to make them strong. The tusks were whittled from matches, after they had been used. No child should be permitted to play with unburned matches.

Jean did not have to paint her elephant, because the clay was just the right color.

She named him Jumbo, in remembrance of the noted circus elephant.

CLAY MODELING

Ted, who was ten-years old, made these candlesticks and this bowl.

These three brown bears were made from fat chunks of clay, and then painted with fresco paint.

One is the Father Bear.

One is the Mother Bear.

Of course, the little one is the Baby Bear.

The Father Bear's pipe

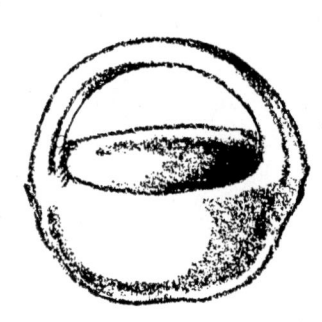

The Mother Bear's basket

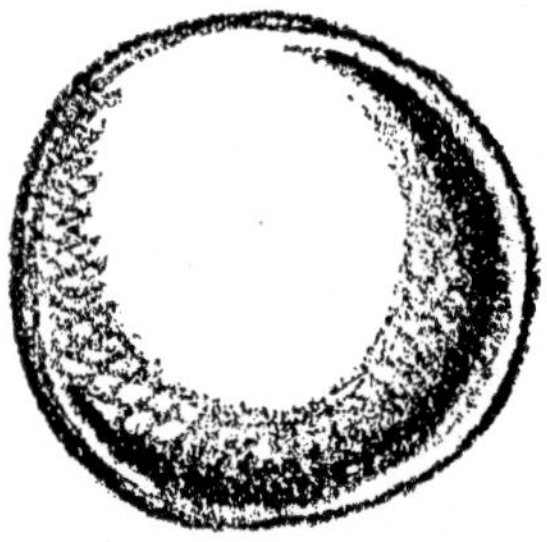

The candlesticks were shaped from a whole piece of clay. Even the handle was pulled out from the big piece so that it would not drop off when dry. (The handle is rather thick so that it will not break easily.) Ted made the hole for the candle by pressing a real candle into the top of the candlestick. That was the best way to get it just the right size.

When the clay was very dry, he spread papers on the table, put on his overalls, and painted the candlesticks with bright-orange enamel. Then the next day, when the enamel was dry, he decorated them with black. The candles are ivory.

The flower bowl matches the candlesticks. It will not hold water, because it has not been fired, but it will hold a little flower pot—or dried berries, such as bittersweet.

Ted gave the candlesticks and the bowl to his mother for her birthday.

The Baby Bear's ball
It is red, white and blue

Clay is the very best material for making—

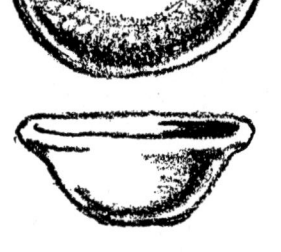

The great big bowl.

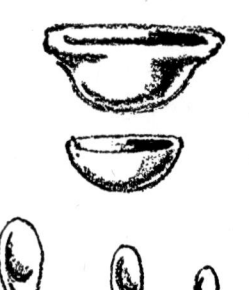

The middle-sized bowl.

The wee, wee bowl.

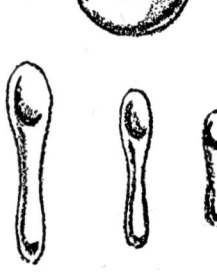

And the spoons!

Sock Dolls

By Betty and Jim

WHEN some of my socks wore out in the toes and heels but were still good in the leg, I used them to make dolls. One of my friends brought some of her socks to my house. We each made a doll for ourselves, and one to send to the children's ward in the hospital. For the dolls we made to give away, we used new socks. This is how we made the sock dolls. We cut off the straight part of the sock, just before it turns to make the heel. We kept the foot of the sock to use for arms, and for a cap.

We cut the straight part of the sock to make legs, and sewed them up. Then we turned the sock and stuffed it with cotton batting, putting the stuffing in at the top.

Then we tied a string around the sock about two inches from the top, to make a neck for the doll. We sewed up the top of the head.

We cut arms from the straight part of the foot, stuffed them, and sewed them to the doll. Then we painted a face with water-color paint. Last of all, we sewed some little buttons down the front and used the toe of the sock for his cap. He was really most attractive. You can make him a sweater from the leg of another sock.

There are many other kinds of dolls to be made from socks or from the legs of cotton or silk stockings. Jim said at first that it was "only girls' work;" but he soon got interested and made a clown doll and a black cat, using two of his own stockings. I dressed the clown doll for him.

The clown doll is made from the leg of a white stocking, just the way that the sock doll is made. His suit is a straight piece of material sewed up, and gathered at the neck and feet. The easiest way to make his sleeves is to cut slits in the sides of his suit, put the sleeves on his arms and sew enough to hold them in the slits. His hat is made from a pie-shaped piece of cloth. Sometimes the eyes, nose, mouth, and hair are embroidered instead of painted.

Toto—the clown.

DOLLS AND DOLL THINGS

Gretchen is made like the other dolls, but her legs are put on separately so that she can sit down. Be careful not to get her arms and legs too short. Her hair is made of yellow worsted, and she is dressed in a blue-and-white striped dress, and white apron. Her shoes are made of paper. Her round eyes are pearl buttons, sewed on with blue thread.

Topsy is made from a black stocking. Her eyes, nose, and mouth are sewed on. Her hair is black yarn.

The cat is made from a white silk stocking. His eyes, mouth, and whiskers are sewed on. His tail is made of strips of stocking, braided and knotted at the end.

Minnehaha is made from a brown silk stocking. She wears a fringed, brown dress. Her hair is black yarn. Her moccasins are made from an old kid glove.

Some day ask Mother for some wrapping paper, and you can make a paper doll and a play house. Perhaps Mother will help you draw a pattern like Figure 1. You can lay the pattern on two thicknesses of heavy wrapping paper and cut out a doll. Then sew the edges with colored yarn, and stuff the doll with cotton. Draw the face with crayons. You can use yellow, or brown, or black yarn for the hair, and dress your doll to represent a Japanese doll or a real baby doll. Crepe paper makes good dresses for a paper doll; but you can use cloth if you prefer.

This pattern may be used on cloth or heavy wrapping paper.

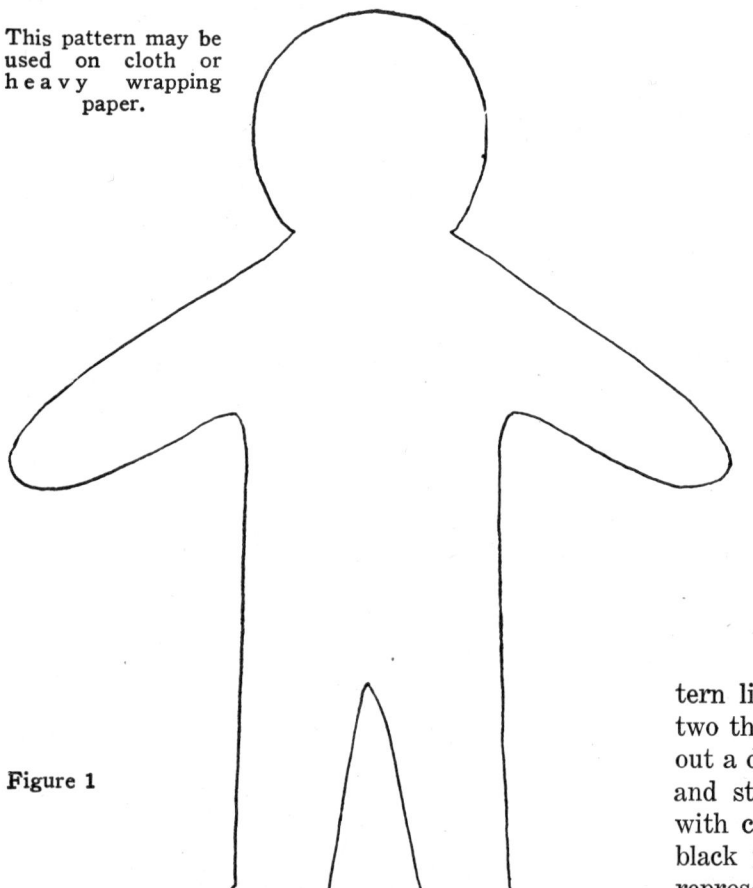

Figure 1

Figure 2

DOLLS AND DOLL THINGS

If you are going to play house with your new dolls, it would be a good idea to have a doll buggy. This is a way to make one quite easily.

Take a shoe box and fasten onto it four cardboard wheels. Figure 4. Large paper fasteners and milk-bottle tops are good for this. Make a handle out of the edge of the lid. You can do this by cutting the entire top out of the lid and then you will have a long strip left for the handle. Figure 5.

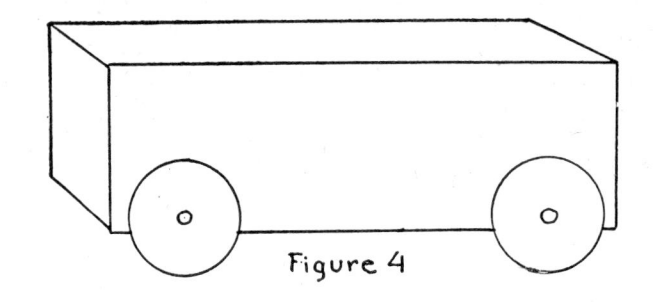

Figure 4

Figure 5

Cut Lid on Dotted Line

Now fasten the handle on with paper fasteners, like Figure 6.

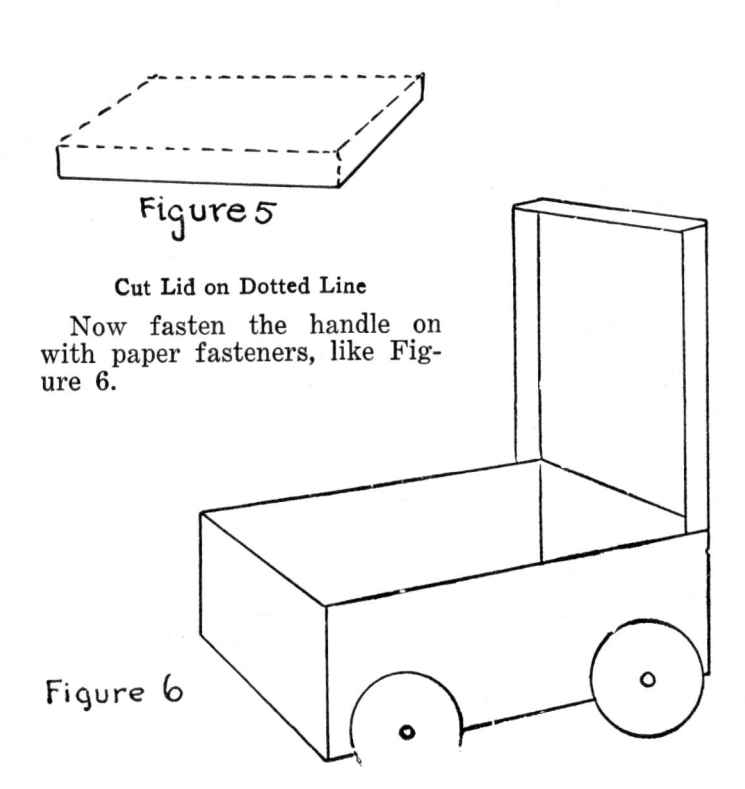

Figure 3

Figure 6

Make a hood out of wrapping paper for your carriage, to keep the sun out of your doll's eyes. Take a piece of paper like Figure 7. It must be long enough to curve from one side of the box to the other. Fold it in the middle and draw the design like Figure 8. Now cut on the line you have made. Then paste the hood to the box. It will then look like Figure 9.

Double and Open

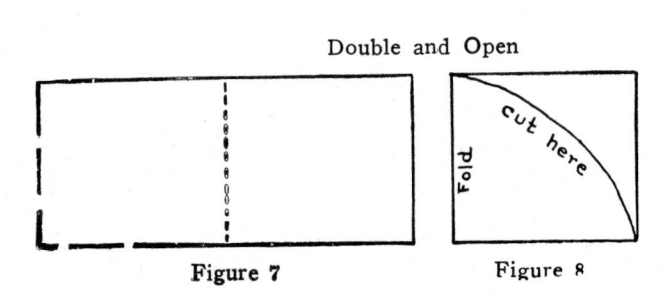

Figure 7   Figure 8

We painted our carriage with bright colors. You can make up any designs you want.

Would you like to make a doll cradle, too? You will have to have two boxes for your cradle. Put the boxes together like Figure 10, and fasten them together with paper fasteners. Can you get someone to help you remove the metal hooks from two thin wood coat hangers? Tack the box to the hangers. You

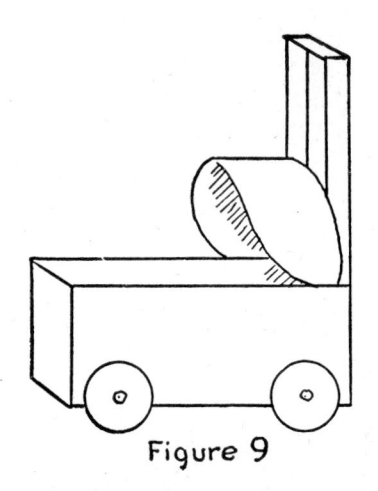

Figure 9

157

DOLLS AND DOLL THINGS

can use them for rockers. Figure 10. If you can't get any coat hangers, you can pretend that yours is a little bed, and it will do just as well.

Figure 10

Figure 11

Figure 12

We made pretty lace curtains to hang around the hood of our cradle, and tied them back at the sides with ribbons. Then we made a mattress to fit the bed, from some flowered material. I stuffed it with cotton and tacked it with bright yarn. I also made some tiny pillows and a tiny comforter for the bed.

If you want a chest for your house, you can make one easily out of another shoe box. It is a handy thing to have in the bedroom, for you can keep the bedding inside of it. All you have to do is to paint your box so that it will look like a chest, and draw a make-believe lock on the front. It is just the right size for your extra comforters, and sheets, and pillows.

Spool Furniture

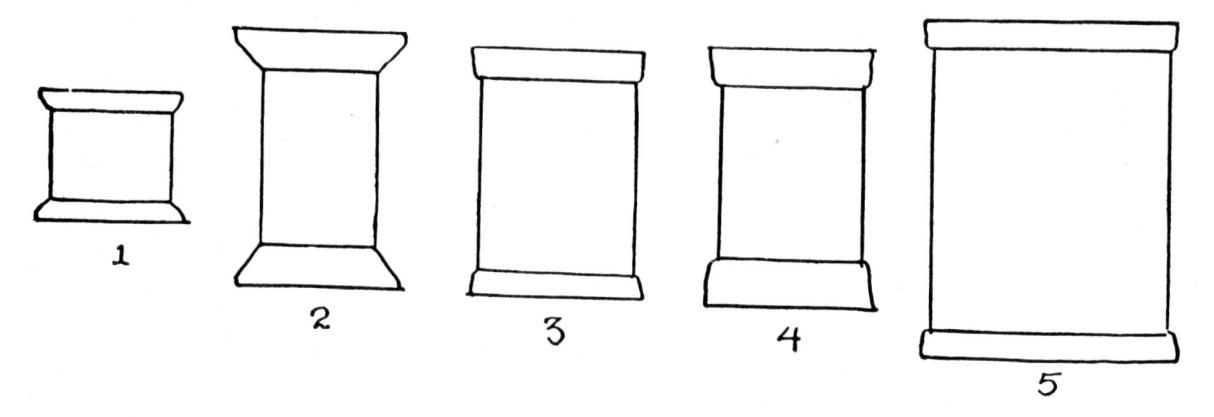

1   2   3   4   5

IT'S easy to make spool furniture for the dolls, and lots of fun! The only materials you need are plenty of empty spools of various sizes, some paper, cardboard, and glue. A pair of scissors, a pencil, and a ruler are useful tools, also.

Two spools shaped like No. 2 make this Italian-Style Library Table.

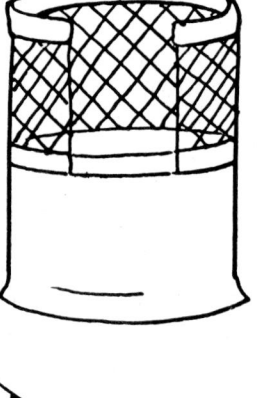

The Chinese-tub chair is made with spool No. 1. The top is a strip of cardboard with the lattice work painted on it, or it may be made from wire netting bound with tape and then tacked into place.

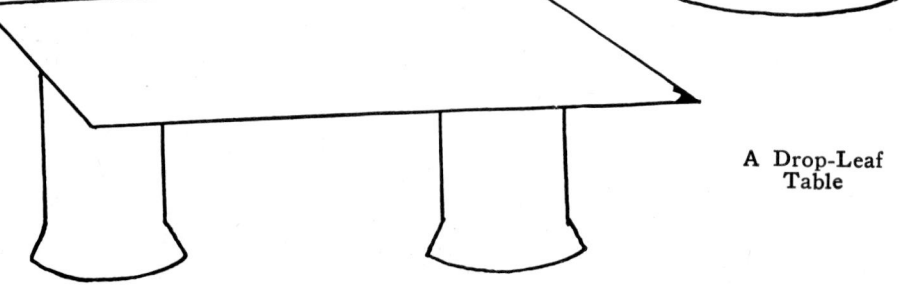

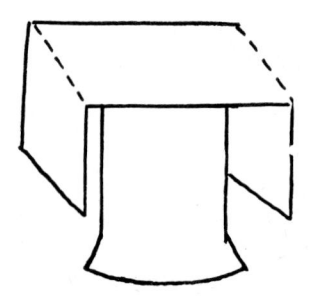

A Drop-Leaf Table

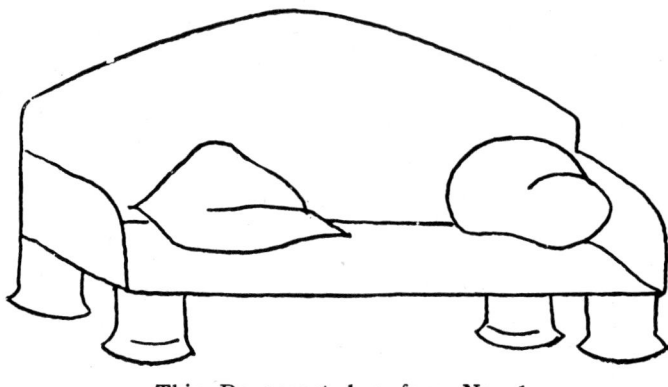

DOLLS AND DOLL THINGS

This Davenport has four No. 1 spools for legs.

The End Table is supported by spool No. 3, cut in two.

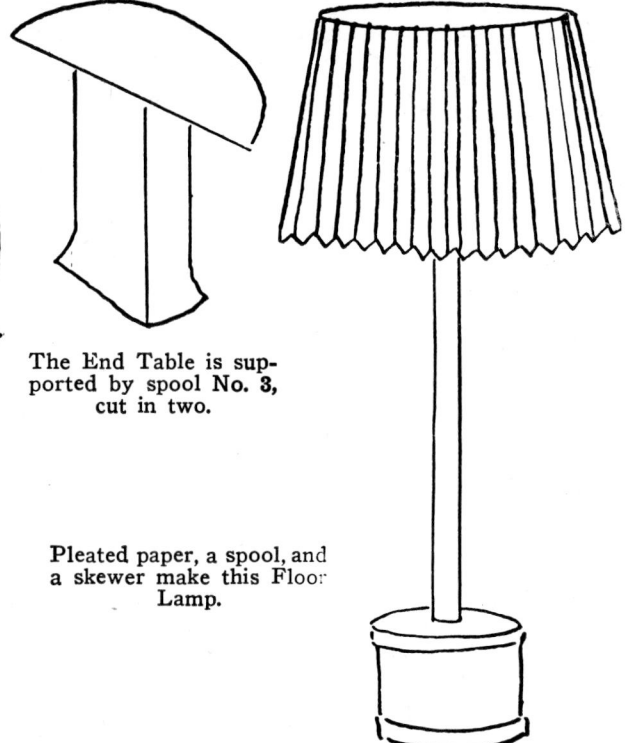

You will want up-to-date furniture, and "period" styles such as Colonial, French, and Italian are very easy to copy. The spools for silk, darning cotton, show-button thread, as well as spools for ordinary cotton thread, you will find handy for the purpose, because then you can make furniture of different heights. Another way to get variety, is to saw a spool up and down through the middle. Half of a spool glued under half a circle of cardboard makes a good end table to place at the end of the doll's davenport.

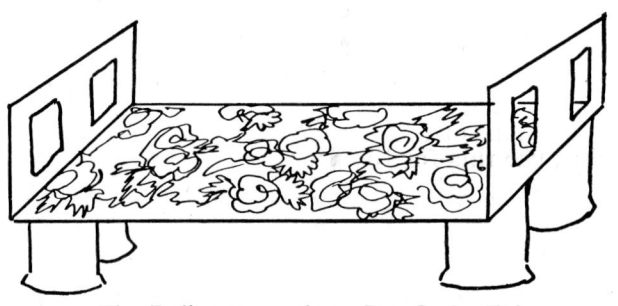

Pleated paper, a spool, and a skewer make this Floor Lamp.

The Dolls may prefer a Day Bed. This one has a cushion of flowered wall paper pasted onto it.

To make the long Italian-style library table, we cut out a long piece of cardboard (the top of a candy box is good) and glue one of your largest spools under each end. It is then ready for the "runner" or table cover. A little drop-leaf table, in Colonial style, is also very easy to make. Take a medium-sized spool for the leg, and cut a long strip of light-weight cardboard. With pencil and ruler, divide this long strip into three sections, making the middle a little larger. Dot lines with the pencil, and then fold down the table leaves at each end, on these dotted lines. The octagonal coffee table is made by cutting a square of cardboard and then cutting off the corners so that it will be an octagon, which means eight-sided.

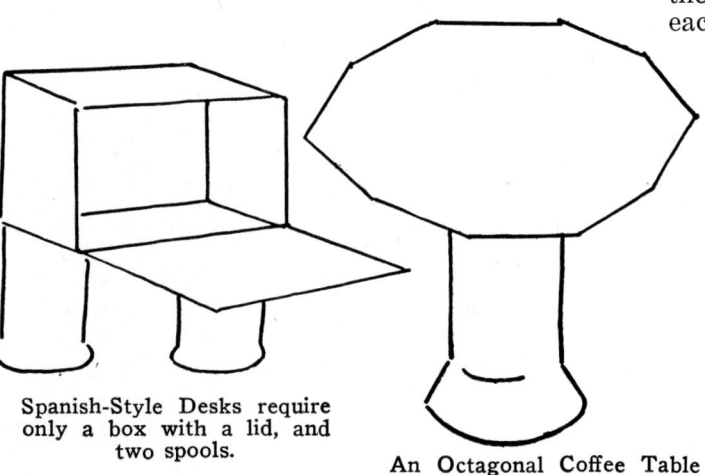

Spanish-Style Desks require only a box with a lid, and two spools.

An Octagonal Coffee Table

The davenport at the top of the page is best made from light-weight cardboard. When cardboard is to be folded, always plan first with a pencil and ruler. You can brace the corners of the davenport by gluing a little piece of paper from the arms to the back. Four small silk spools make the best legs for this piece of furniture. To make it fancy, you can add a pleated valance of tissue paper around the seat, to cover the legs.

A Box with spool legs will make this useful piece. It may be the Doll's Sideboard, Console, or Radio Cabinet.

DOLLS AND DOLL THINGS

The small silk spool is again used for the floor lamp. A wooden skewer, such as comes in a roast of meat, is wedged into the top of a spool and held firmly with glue. If the hole is too big, wind the skewer around and around with string, and then glue it in. The pleated lamp shade stuck on the top is prettiest of all, and it can be tied on with ribbon. Flowered wall paper in a tiny pattern makes a good shade.

You can make a day bed by turning up the ends of a large strip of cardboard. Then cut openings at each end so that it will look like a metal bed with slats. Darning-cotton spools are good for this day bed.

The little rocker is one of the easiest things that can be made, and you'll probably want one for every room. A small silk spool placed sideways so that it will rock, simply has part of a box glued on. Be sure to leave a piece of cardboard at the corner, or the back will not stay up. Let the glue dry for at least two hours.

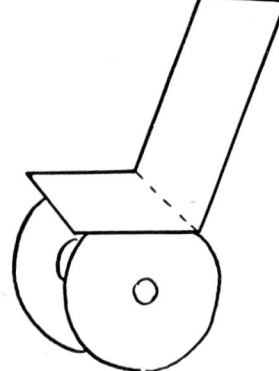

A spool, used sideways, and a piece of cardboard make this Rocking Chair.

Many an up-to-date home has a console or radio cabinet, and the dolls will like the one shown on page 83. It is made from the bottom of a box turned upward. The doors are just drawn on with crayon. Tall spools make good legs for this.

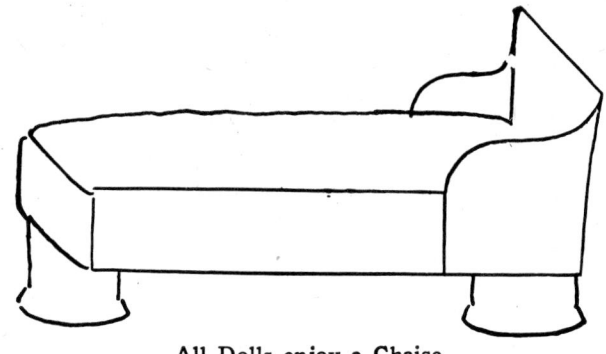

All Dolls enjoy a Chaise Lounge.

The chaise lounge is a box cover with two large spools glued underneath. To make the head and arms, simply cut a piece of paper long enough to curve around the top and make arms. Cut the sides down shorter than the top, as shown in the picture.

A box used sideways with the cover hinged on so that it will drop down like a desk lid, will make the dolls a fine Spanish desk. Two rather tall spools are best for legs, or you may use four if the box needs more support. Then, too, you may be able to find a box with the cover all hinged on. But if you don't, use strong paper, tape, or ribbon for support, and glue the desk lid on.

You can make pretty color schemes by using colored boxes, paper, crayon, or paint. After the furniture is made, you can paste tissue paper on for cushions or table covers. If you have any gilt paint, use this for the floor lamp.

Then you will probably think of other things to make from boxes and cardboard, for the dolls will enjoy a bookcase, fireside bench, or a fern stand.

Spool Dolls

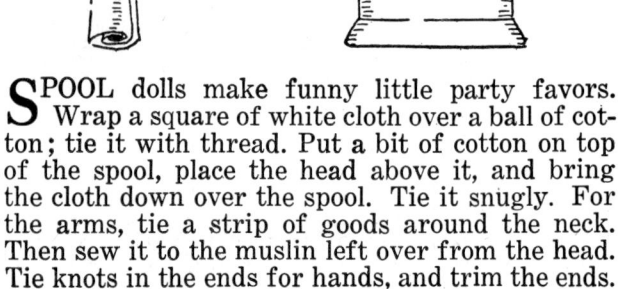

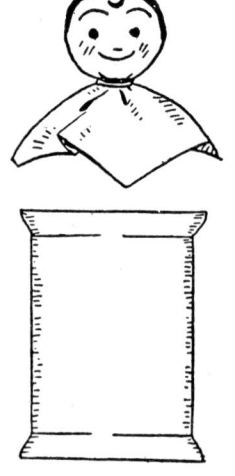

BLACK CAT

SPOOL dolls make funny little party favors. Wrap a square of white cloth over a ball of cotton; tie it with thread. Put a bit of cotton on top of the spool, place the head above it, and bring the cloth down over the spool. Tie it snugly. For the arms, tie a strip of goods around the neck. Then sew it to the muslin left over from the head. Tie knots in the ends for hands, and trim the ends.

The cat is made of black cloth, with features of white paint or thread. (Thread whiskers, of course!) The dresses are made from an oblong or a circle of goods with a slit in the middle for the head to go through, and two slits for armholes. Riddles are written on paper; the paper is rolled tightly, and pushed into the bottom of the spool.

Our Neighborhood Band

ONE afternoon some friends came in to play with us. They wanted to play band; so we thought of ways to make band instruments. I am going to tell you how we made them.

An oatmeal box makes a drum. Cover the box with colored paper and fasten strings across to make it look like a real drum. Pencils may be used for drumsticks.

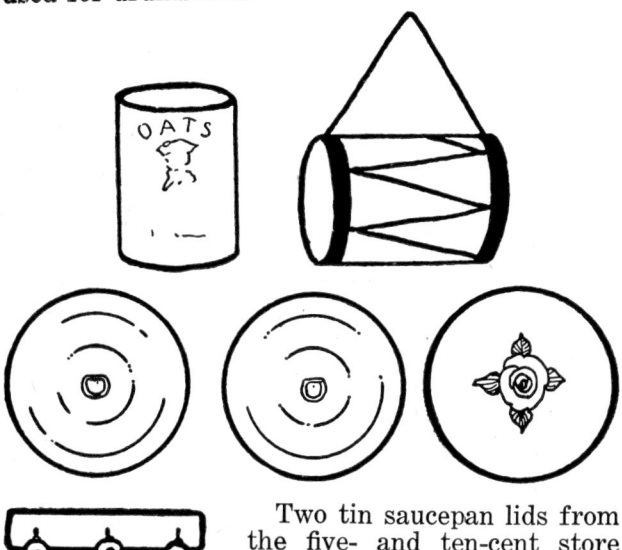

Two tin saucepan lids from the five- and ten-cent store make good cymbals. We painted ours in bright colors, using enamel paint.

The top of a wooden cheese box, or of a round cardboard box, makes a fine tambourine. Make three or five holes in the sides of the box cover, and tie on small bells. Paint a decoration on your tambourine.

Glue coarse sandpaper on two blocks of wood (plain building blocks will do if you have no other wood). This makes a pair of sandpaper blocks to be rubbed together in time to the music.

A box filled with stones or marbles, and with the cover glued on, makes a rattle. Perhaps if there is a baby in your house, he will lend you his rattle.

The instruments do not sound very well if played by themselves; so we asked our big sister to play the piano, and we kept time to that. Sometimes we played we were a soldiers' band and made hats like those in the picture. Of course, one child led our parade and carried an American flag. Other times we played we were a band marching in a circus parade. Do you know that there are phonograph records made especially for use with "toy orchestras?"

A Peep Show and Moving Pictures

ONE rainy day we made a moving picture and a peep show. Both were made from shoe boxes, and it took quite a long time to make them. It was fun to play with them when they were finished. We are holding our peep show in the picture above.

To make the peep show, I removed the corner of the shoe box. Then I cut out almost all of one side and pasted colored tissue paper over the space. This lets in light. The box in the drawing below shows one side cut away. Notice the narrow edge at the front.

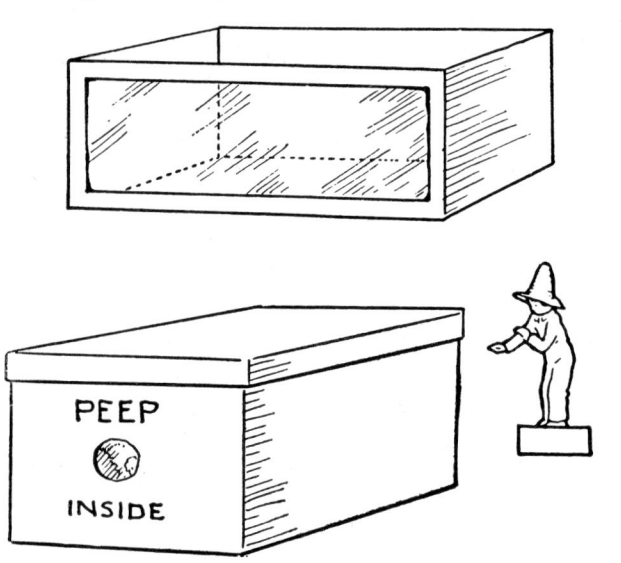

Then I pasted scenery inside my box. The scenery at the far end of the box should look small and far away. Near to the front of the box the trees and houses may be larger. I made paper houses, trees, and people, leaving tiny flaps to paste to the floor of the box. There are so many things that one may make that are easy and very pretty, too.

At the right, above, is one of the little figures I used in my peep show. See the flap on the bottom of his feet. This flap, I folded back and pasted to the floor of my box so that the little boy seemed to be standing up alone. I did the same way with the bushes and rabbit.

Last of all, I cut a window in the front end of the box and put on the cover. When you put your eyes to the hole in the front of the box, the scenery inside looks very pretty. Perhaps you will want to make a scene about your favorite story.

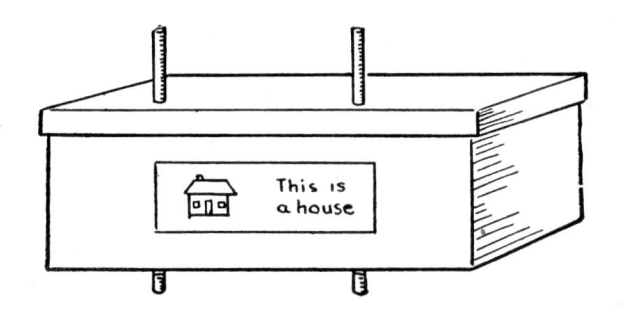

The moving-picture film was made by pasting strips of paper together, and then drawing little pictures on the long strip. We printed a story about the pictures something like the one above. Then we made two holes in a shoe box so that two dowel sticks, or pieces of broom handle, could pass through them. The ends of the film were glued to the sticks. By turning the sticks, it could be made to roll from one stick to the other. We cut a hole in the front of the box large enough to show one picture at a time. Put the dowel sticks far forward in the box so that the box can be put at the edge of a table and the ends of the sticks will not be in the way. We had such fun with our "movie" at home that we decided to make one for school. We had been talking about dairy farms in our class; so we made a film showing all the processes used in the making of cheese. We had to read books and ask Daddy to find out how cheese was made.

Playing Indians

WE often play Indians. We have a wigwam which we put up in the back yard on fine days, and in a corner of our playroom on rainy days. We made our wigwam and our Indian suits ourselves, and you may like to hear how we did it.

We made an inside framework of long sticks, tied together at the top like the drawing in the lower left-hand corner, and we fastened our cover over that. Then we used fresco paint to paint designs on the cover.

The cloth for our wigwam was heavy, unbleached muslin, but old sheets will do just as well. Grain bags sewed together make a substantial tent. We laid the material flat on the floor and cut triangular-shaped pieces which we sewed together. See diagram below.

If the material is large enough, or if you are making a small doll's wigwam, it may be cut all in one piece like the semi-circle at the extreme right. An Indian wigwam has a flap over the smoke hole, but this is more difficult to make; so it is all right to leave the top open as the diagram shows.

Doll's wigwam, cut in one piece. Lay straight side on fold of material.

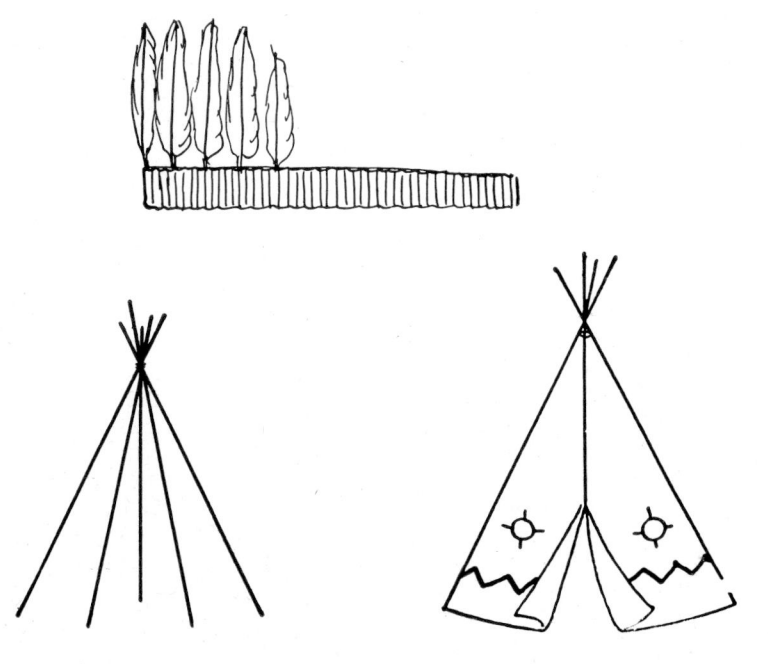

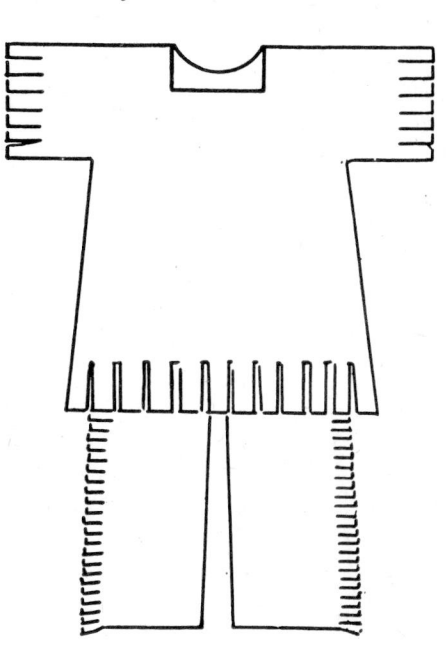

Our Indian suits were made of brown cambric or from a gunny sack. Mother showed us how to make a paper pattern. We used the same pattern for both, but my sister's was a dress, and mine a shirt. It was too difficult for me to make trousers; so I made leggings of cloth, fringed at the sides.

One headdress was a narrow band of cloth, with one feather. Mine was a strip of corrugated paper cut to fit the head, and fastened with a paper fastener. It had chicken or turkey feathers stuck in the holes. Mother helped us dye our feathers with a package of dye we had bought at the drugstore. For a chief's headdress, a strip down the back looks very war-like.

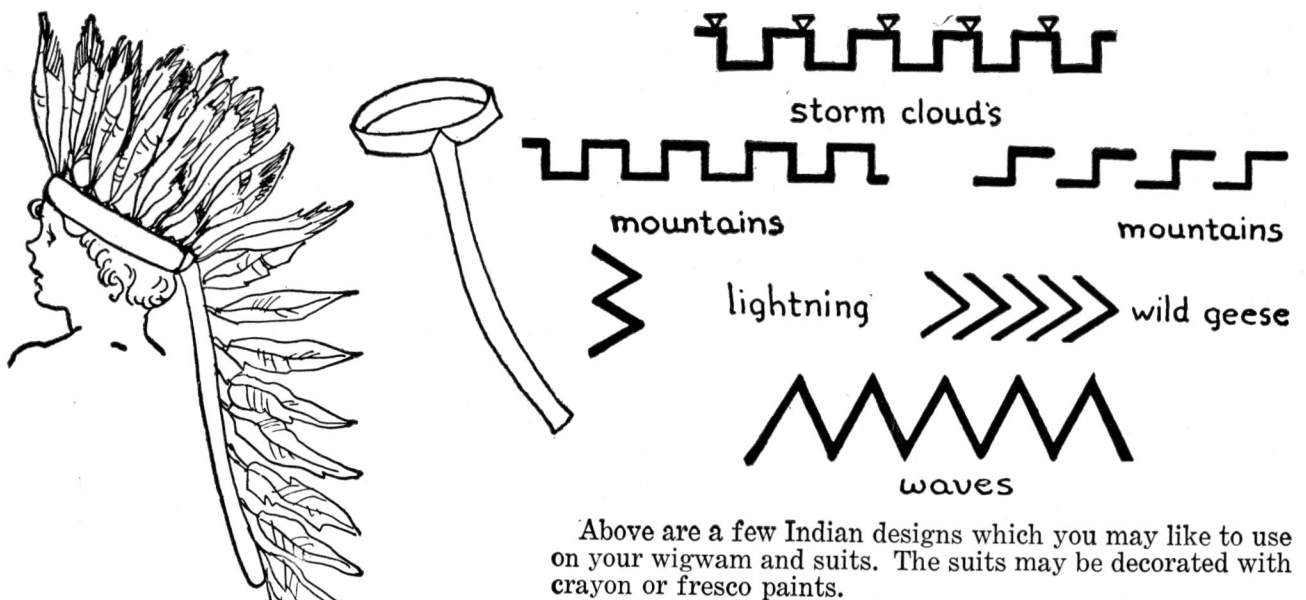

PLAYING INDIANS

storm clouds

mountains   mountains

lightning   wild geese

waves

Above are a few Indian designs which you may like to use on your wigwam and suits. The suits may be decorated with crayon or fresco paints.

The Indians made pictures of the moon and stars, of the sun, and of many strange animals; so you can do this, too. Below are some Indian bird pictures, also a picture of the sun as the Indians would draw it.

We made clay bowls and painted some of the designs shown just below on them. The bird and sun designs were made by Pueblo Indians and Zuni Indians.

"When I am an Indian
With my paint and feathers on,
And I go out on the street,
All the people run."

Dora Buckingham
Songs for Children

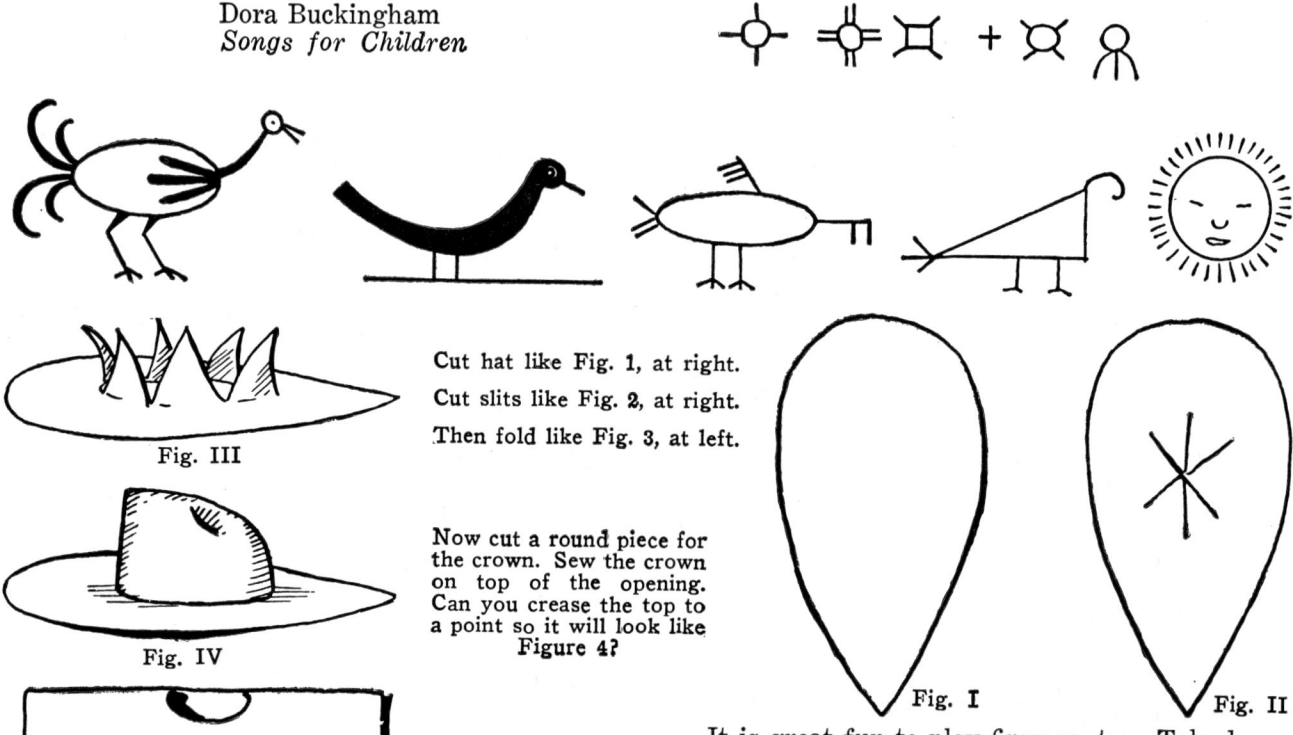

Fig. III

Fig. IV

Fig. V

Cut hat like Fig. 1, at right.
Cut slits like Fig. 2, at right.
Then fold like Fig. 3, at left.

Now cut a round piece for the crown. Sew the crown on top of the opening. Can you crease the top to a point so it will look like Figure 4?

Fig. I   Fig. II

It is great fun to play firemen, too. Take heavy wrapping paper, doubled and glued together, for the hat. See directions above at left.

The fireman's suit can be made of red paper cambric. Your mother will show you how to make a pattern like Figure 5. It is great fun to play firemen, especially if you have a fire engine.

A policeman's or a mailman's cap can be made of a strip of corrugated paper, cut to fit the head and fastened with paper fasteners. The visor of the cap can be made of a square of the corrugated paper fastened to the front; then painted with fresco paints. Corrugated paper for a belt, and silver paper for a star, make a complete uniform.

Games for Juniors to Make

HAVE you ever tried to make games? I will tell you how to make some. The first is the Ring Toss game. Take a thick piece of wood like Figure 1. That will be the standard. Now take a rather thick post about ten-inches long, and fasten it to the middle of the standard like Figure 2. An easy way to do this is to take a long nail and drive it into the center of the standard, first. When you see it just beginning to come through the other side of the board, put your post on the nail so that the nail will be in the very center of the post. Now drive the nail all the way through the post. Then the post will stand up.

Now find some heavy rope, and make rings like Figure 3, by wrapping the ends together with heavy twine, and tying the twine. Make four or five rings. Next paint the post, the standard, and the rings; and your game is finished. Four or five children can play. Take turns throwing the rings onto the post. You can keep a score for everyone who succeeds in getting the ring over the post. A ring over the post counts five.

The second game is called the Giant Game. Find an apple or orange crate. Turn it on its side, with the opening toward you, like Figure 4. Now find a piece of firm cloth the size of the front, for you will want to tack it on to cover the open space on the front of the box. Before you tack the cloth onto the box, draw or paint a giant's head on the cloth. Make the mouth very large. Then cut out the mouth. It will be better if you can bind the edges of the mouth. Sew all around the hole with yarn, to make it very strong. Now tack the cloth onto the open side of the box like Figure 5. Now you will have to saw a little opening in the back of the box. Make it just large enough so that you can reach into the box with your hand. The game is to throw tennis balls into the giant's mouth, and after they are in the box you will have to reach in and get them out again. Each ball that is thrown inside the box counts five, and the first person whose score is twenty-**five** wins.

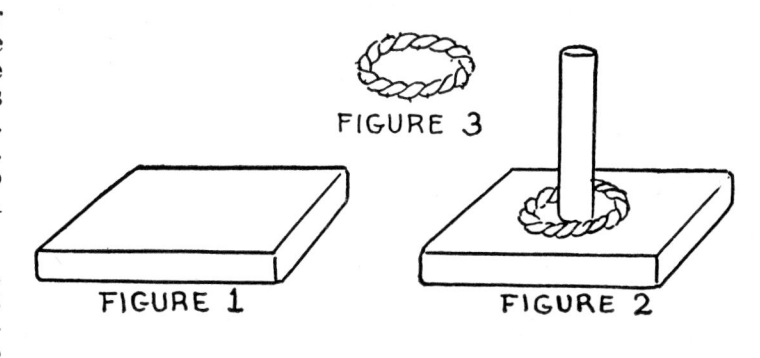

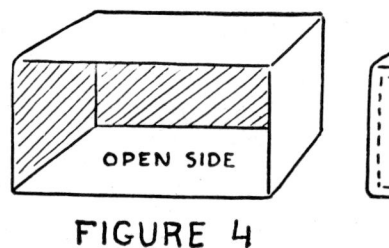

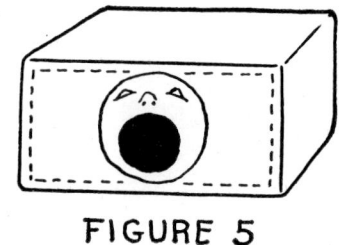

Now you can make several standards like you did for the first game. Make them different heights. Nail berry baskets on top of each post, and paint a number on each basket. Figures 6, 7 and 8. The game is played by standing back at a given distance, and throwing tiny rubber balls into the baskets. A score is made corresponding to the number on the basket. Remember to have only light balls, or your baskets will break. You can get tiny rubber balls at the ten-cent store. Decide what the winning score is to be before you begin to play.

GAMES FOR JUNIORS TO MAKE

The next game is for marbles. Have you some small, light marbles? If you have, you can make a game from an egg carton. A long, narrow egg carton is best, but you can use any kind. Turn the lid of the carton up like Figure 9, and paint a number over each hole. Now stand back away

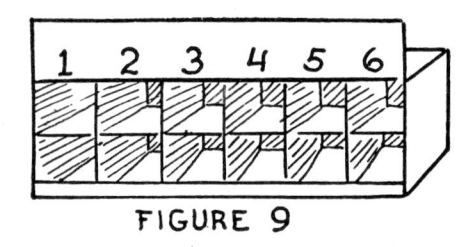

FIGURE 9

from the box and throw a marble into one of the holes. If it goes into a hole just below the number 3, then your score will be 3. If it goes into a hole below the number 6, then your score will be 6. The person who earns the highest score in ten trials wins.

A marble game is made out of a shoe box. Turn the box upside down. Now cut holes like Figure 10 in the bottom of the front side. Do not make them too large. An inch will be wide enough. Now number the holes. Stand back away from the box, and roll the marbles into the holes. If your marble goes into the hole marked 6, your

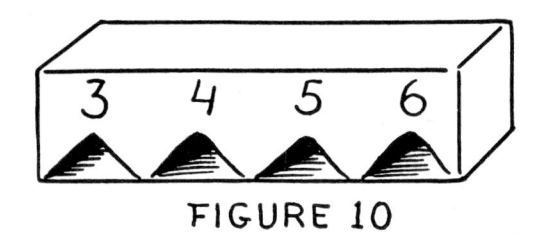

FIGURE 10

score will be 6. If your marble goes into the hole marked 3, your score will be 3. You can make your own rules for winning the game. Perhaps you will want to decide on ten trials, or perhaps you would rather set a number like fifty for the winning score.

A Croquet Set

YOU will enjoy making a croquet set almost as much as you will enjoy playing the game after you have everything ready. We like to play this game in winter when it is storming, or when it is too cold to play out-of-doors. Mother lets us play it on the dining-room table. She puts a thick pad on the table so that we will not scratch the top. A blanket will do if you do not have a table pad.

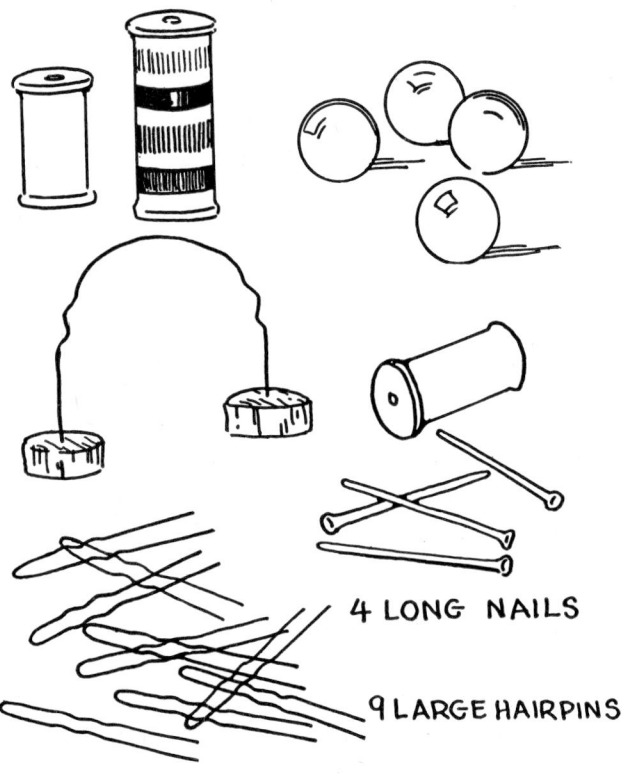

4 LONG NAILS

9 LARGE HAIRPINS

To make this game, you need four small spools, two tall, thin spools like baby ribbon is wound on (perhaps if you speak to the dry-goods man he will save some empty ones for you), four marbles of different colors, eighteen corks (as large as you can get them), nine pieces of wire the length of a long hairpin (long hairpins may be used if it is not easy to get the pieces of wire the right length), and four long, thin nails. Bend a hairpin or wire, as the case may be, into the shape of an arch. Drive each end into a cork. Make all nine arches in the same manner. A mallet may be made by driving one of the long, thin nails into the center of the cylinder of one of the small spools. You need four of these. The mallets are each painted a different color (one to match each marble). The marbles serve as balls. The two slender spools are set up as posts. The "posts" may have bands of the four colors painted on them, or this may be done with crayons.

For playing the game, the same rules apply that you follow when you are playing the game out on your lawn in the summer time.

If you want to play this game on the floor, you can use golf balls and make your mallets from toy hammers, wound with yarn or cloth the color of the marbles. If you do play this game with the golf balls, you will need to make larger arches, and this means that you will need longer pieces of wire for them.

A Book of Surprises

SOME day, when you want to make a new kind of book, try making a surprise book. It is lots of fun. Each page is a surprise. All our friends like to look at the one we made, and some of them have made surprise books of their own.

We folded paper to make pages and fastened them together as we had always done for scrap books. On the first page we drew a picture of a window, and cut it on three sides so that it would open. On the second page we pasted a picture just as large as the window.

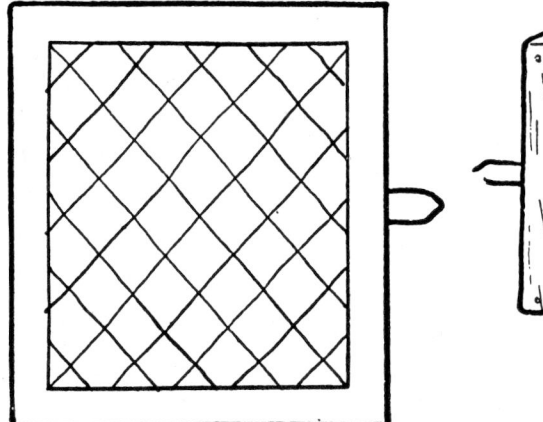

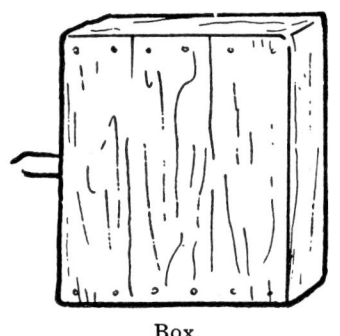

We then pasted the edges of pages one and two together so that the picture could only be seen by opening the window on page one. Paste a little flap on the window, and make a slit in the page to hold the flap; then the window will stay closed. The picture above at the right shows you how the window should open. Of course, we did not make windows all through the book. We drew pictures of other things that can open. It is fun to have the picture underneath be a thing you would least expect to see there.

Window

Box

For instance, when you open the ice box, perhaps you would see a cat or a dog inside. Here are some pictures you can draw. Make your pictures a good deal larger than these if you can.

Book

A surprise book would be nice to send to a little friend who is ill.

Ice Box

Front Door of House

167

Fun With Valentines

IT is fun to play and make your own valentines from scraps of colored paper, lace-paper doilies, paint, and fancy wall paper. Round or square doilies in many sizes may be had from the ten-cent store. Figure 1 is a picture of a lace-doily valentine. The flowers are painted with pink and green water color, and a gold heart is pasted in the center. Then you can make booklets, too, with a design on the cover and a verse on the inside, as in Figure 2.

You can think of other ways to make them, too. Sometimes we like to make funny valentine men, like Figure 3. Or you can make valentine houses out of hearts like Figure 4. It is fun, too, to think up other imaginary things to make out of hearts. You can make many kinds of flowers. Figure 5. Inside your book, you can copy little rhymes, or you can print nicely, *To My Valentine*, or *To Mother* or whatever name you want. We like to put *Guess Who*, sometimes. Then it is like a game.

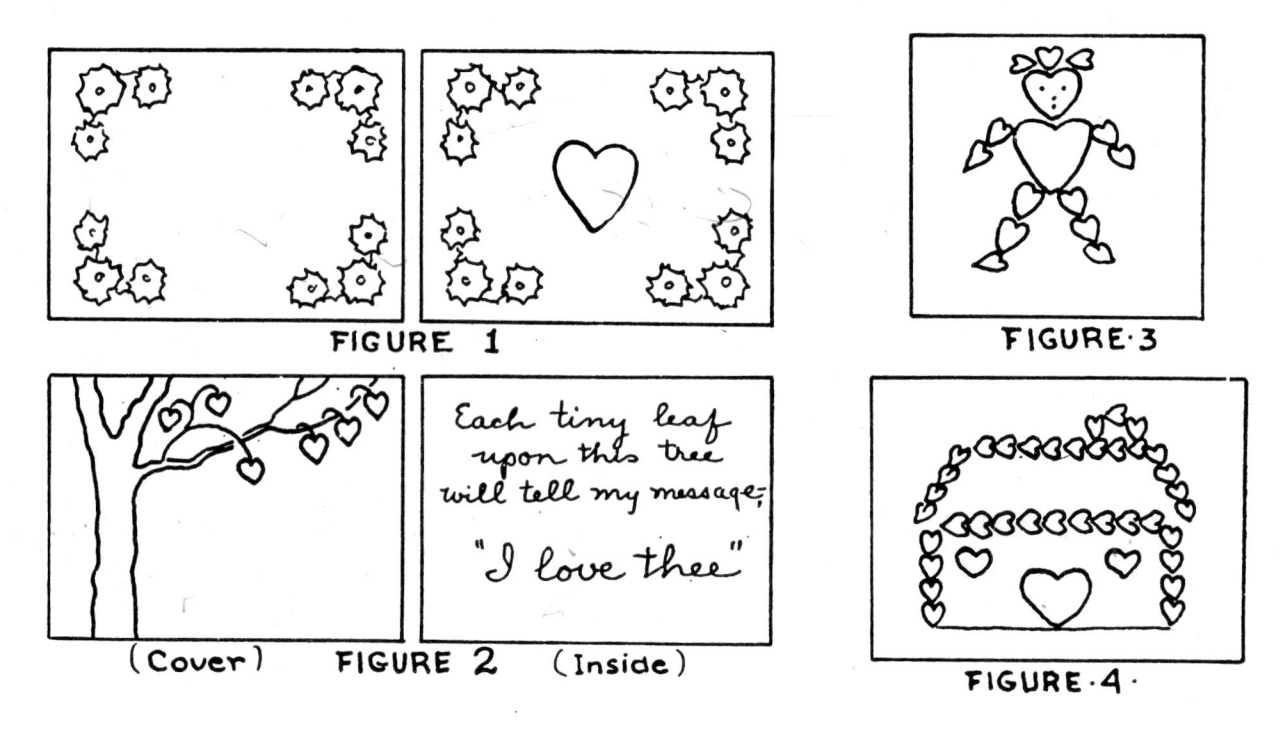

FIGURE 1

(Cover) FIGURE 2 (Inside)

Each tiny leaf upon this tree will tell my message, "I love thee"

FIGURE 3

FIGURE 4

You can make many nice valentines from your colored papers by just cutting hearts of different sizes and pasting one on top of the other on a square background. Sometimes you can make very pretty color combinations by planning carefully which colors look well together.

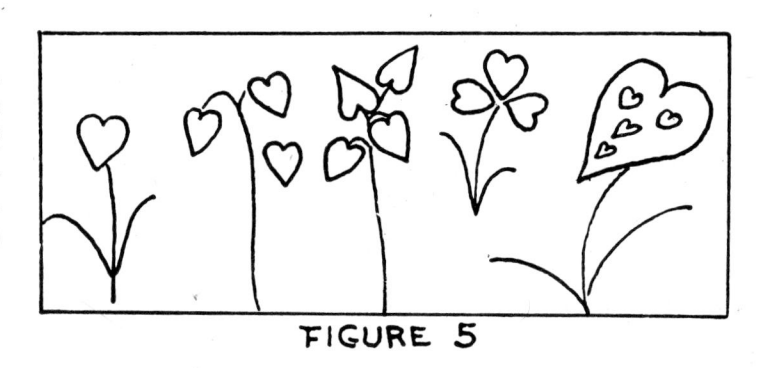

FIGURE 5

The valentine for Mother and Father.

These verses may be used on some of your valentines:

"If you'll be good and kind and true,
 This valentine, I'll send to you."

"Birds and flowers, and sunshine,
 These are for my valentine."

"Within this heart, a message true
 'Oh, Mother, dear, I do love you'."

FUN WITH VALENTINES

For the people that you like best, you can make the valentines pictured.

For your Mother and Father, paste quite a large white paper heart on a colored paper heart. On the white heart, paste flowers cut from wall paper, leaving a space between the flowers. In this space, paste a child cut from a magazine. Do not paste this flat, but fold tiny strips of paper like this. Paste the picture on the strip so that it stands out from the card a little way. See picture at bottom of preceding page.

For your Aunt, who perhaps lives away out in California, try making the window valentine. The window is drawn with crayons on a square of white paper, the flowers are done with crayons, too. The white square is pasted on a colored square. The window is cut so that it will open, and sealed with a heart. Your Aunt will be surprised when she opens the window; for, pasted on the colored square, she will find pictures of her niece or nephew who sent her the valentine.

If your Grandmother and Grandfather live far away, they would like a valentine something like the one at the right-hand, top corner of the page. The door of the cottage opens so that you can put your picture inside.

You could find out the names of children in the hospital and send each one a flower-pot valentine with his own name on it. A strip of cardboard glued on the back will make the valentine stand up.

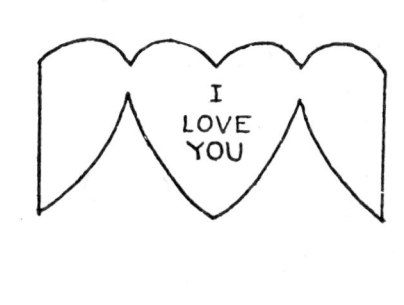

The valentine above is made with a red circle, a silver circle, and a lace-paper circle. Decorations can be cut from magazines or wall paper, and made to stand up, as shown in the suggestion for your Mother's valentine. Sometimes the paper doily can be pasted in just one spot so that it lifts up, to show a verse or picture underneath. This plan of decoration is also pretty on the top of a round cookie or candy box. The other valentine is made from pink bristol board. The top heart is fastened to the other.

The two half hearts shown above fold over the whole one, and are sealed with a small picture or small silver heart. Most people like these valentines that have surprises inside, best of all.

The figure at the right shows three red paper hearts fastened at the bottom with a paper fastener. They open to look like a clover leaf. There may be a message or a little picture on each heart.

May Baskets

MAY baskets should be made before the first day of the month so that bright and early on May-day morning you can go around to your friends' homes and hang your baskets on their door knobs or leave them on the door steps. They are all so surprised and happy when they see the baskets filled with flowers. Then they have to guess where they came from, and who made them. Ring the door bell, and then hide nearby; and when they find the basket, you can see how surprised they are. If they cannot guess who left the basket, come out of your hiding place and tell them who you are.

It is a good plan to save all of your boxes, but the small ones are especially good at Maytime. Just take off the lid and use the bottom of the box for the basket part. Now make a handle from the lid by cutting a strip from it, or from any cardboard. Now fasten your handle to the box, and your basket is ready. May baskets should always be decorated, to be bright and pretty; so here are some suggestions for designs that can be put on with crayon or fresco paints. If you wish, you can paint your basket a solid color and the handle a harmonizing color. Now your basket is ready to be filled with flowers.

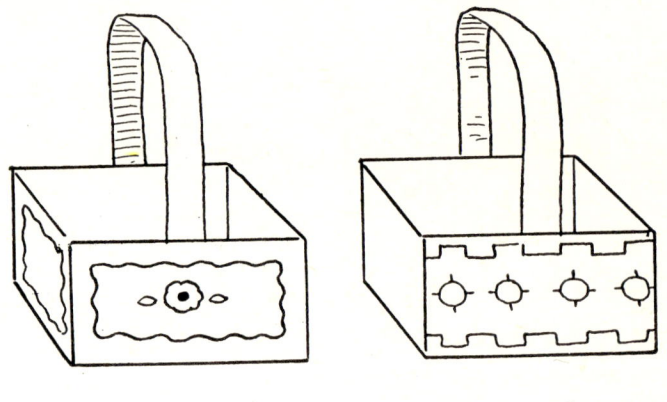

Figure 1.   Figure 2.

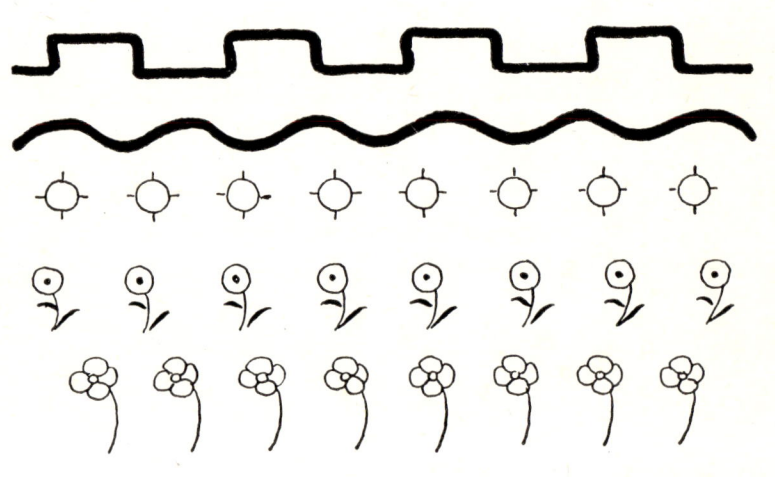

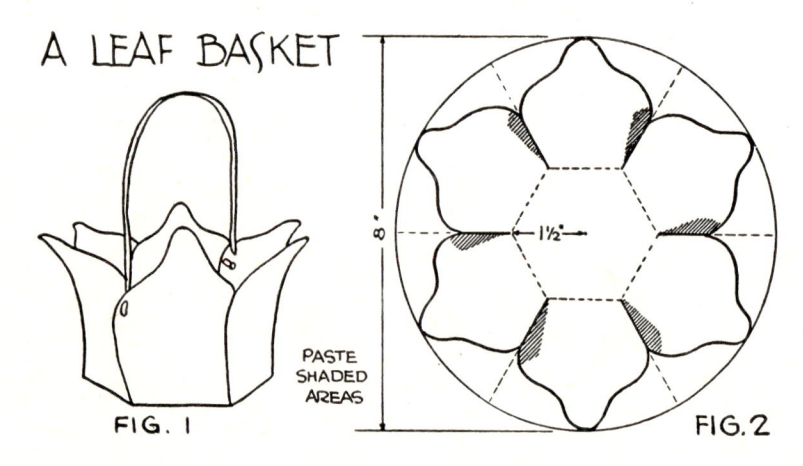

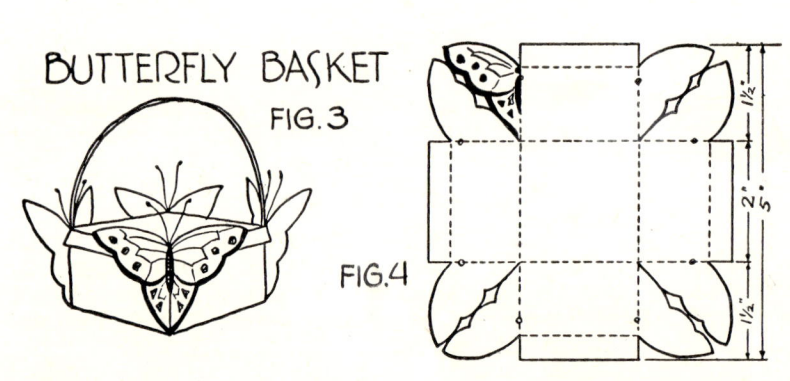

A LEAF BASKET

FIG. 1 — FIG. 2

The green leaf basket is lovely when filled with violets or dogwood. The pattern is made inside of an eight-inch circle. The sides of the hexagon are 1½ inches long and form the bases of the leaves, which are drawn free-hand. Fold on the dotted lines and paste the shaded portion of each leaf; then each is lapped on the outside of the next leaf. Each leaf is curled. The handle is a bit of raffia.

BUTTERFLY BASKET

FIG. 3 — FIG. 4

The butterfly basket, made of tinted paper, is cut out of a five-inch square of paper. It is better to paint the butterflies before folding. The narrow edges and markings on the butterflies' wings, as well as the top edge of each side of the basket, are painted either black or gold. The dotted lines of the square are folded IN and the other dotted lines are folded OUT. Sew the corners together and tie, leaving the ends for antennae. A ribbon of black or gold is used for the handle.

MAY BASKETS

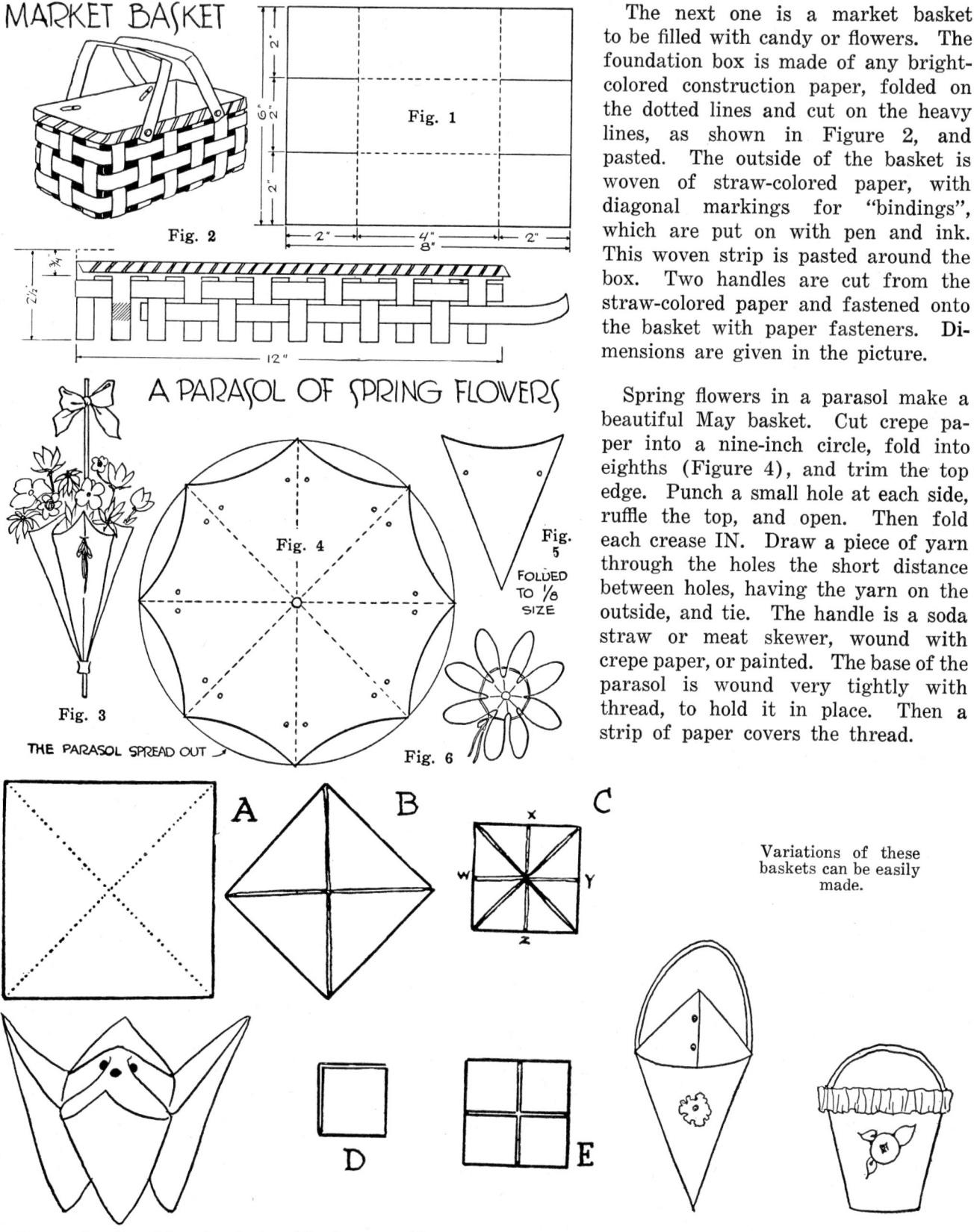

MARKET BASKET

The next one is a market basket to be filled with candy or flowers. The foundation box is made of any bright-colored construction paper, folded on the dotted lines and cut on the heavy lines, as shown in Figure 2, and pasted. The outside of the basket is woven of straw-colored paper, with diagonal markings for "bindings", which are put on with pen and ink. This woven strip is pasted around the box. Two handles are cut from the straw-colored paper and fastened onto the basket with paper fasteners. Dimensions are given in the picture.

A PARASOL OF SPRING FLOWERS

Spring flowers in a parasol make a beautiful May basket. Cut crepe paper into a nine-inch circle, fold into eighths (Figure 4), and trim the top edge. Punch a small hole at each side, ruffle the top, and open. Then fold each crease IN. Draw a piece of yarn through the holes the short distance between holes, having the yarn on the outside, and tie. The handle is a soda straw or meat skewer, wound with crepe paper, or painted. The base of the parasol is wound very tightly with thread, to hold it in place. Then a strip of paper covers the thread.

Variations of these baskets can be easily made.

To make the May basket with four sections, start with a piece of stiff paper, not smaller than nine-inches square. Fold diagonally (Figure A) to find the center; then open, and fold each corner to the center. (Figure B.) Turn this clear over and fold these new corners to the center (Figure C). Now fold up into a small square (Figure D); now unfold back to last square and open the loose corners. (Figure E.) See drawings above.

This basket is made from a triangular piece of construction paper, fastened together with pins or paper fasteners. In the picture, the fasteners show on the inside of the back of the cornucopia basket.

A paper cup may be used as a May basket. A band of gay crepe paper is glued around the top with a piece of the same paper, twisted, to form a handle. Paper fasteners hold the handle on securely.

Party Suggestions

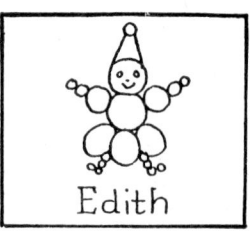

Figure 1 — Please come to our party on June 9, 1928, at 3 O'Clock. Betty and Jim

Figure 2 — Please come to _____

Figure 3 — John

Figure 4 — Edith

DON'T you love to plan parties? Spring is a good time for a party because you can play so many games outside. There is so much more room in the yard than in the house. First, of course, you must plan the invitations. Mother used to buy ours and send them to our friends, but now we like to make our own; for we can work out different ideas. You can get children's letter paper at the ten-cent store. It has pictures on it, and you can do the writing and get your Mother to help you look up the addresses in the telephone book.

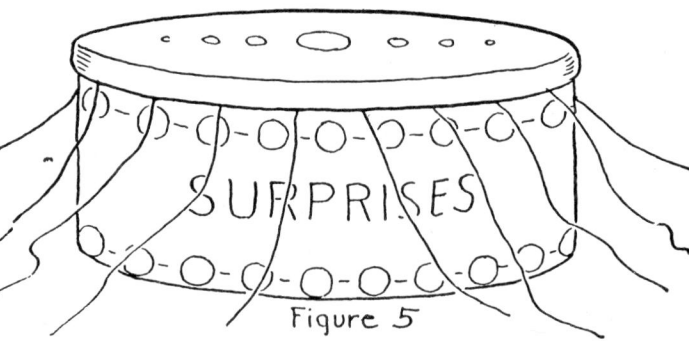

Figure 5 — SURPRISES

Figure 6

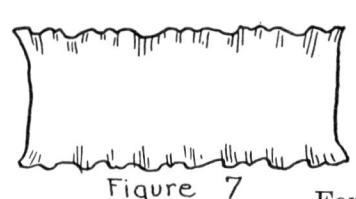

Figure 7

Figure 8

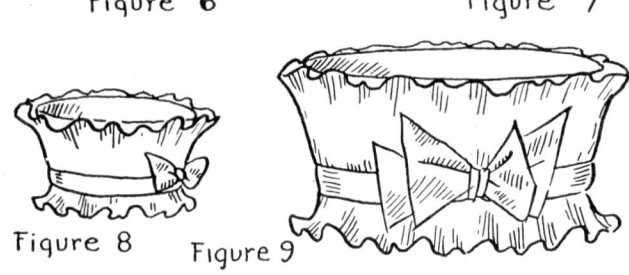

Figure 9

You can also make funny men and ladies on the invitations, out of plain paper. Make your invitations look like little books with the message inside. When the invitations are all sent out, you can then make plans for the party. Plan your table first. You will probably want something for the center. You will like a surprise box. It is such fun to pull your ribbon and see what is on the end of it. We made one Surprise Box out of a hat box (Figure 5). You can make a box quite attractive by using your show-card colors and painting bright designs on it. Have a color scheme for your table by choosing two colors that go well together. Ask Mother if she will help you get some little surprises for each child, at the ten-cent store. Then tie a surprise on the end of each ribbon, and have the ribbon long enough to reach from the inside of the box to a place at the table. Now drop all the surprises in the box and put the lid on carefully.

Next you can make nut cups. Buy some very small paper cups at the ten-cent store. Also buy some crepe paper to match your color scheme. Cut your paper like Figure 6, long enough to fit around the cup. Then pull both edges so that they will look ruffly, like Figure 7. Paste the paper on the cup to look like Figure 8. You can put one of these small cups at each child's place, and fill it with salted nuts. You could make larger cups for the ice cream to match the nut cups.

For place cards, we took oblong pieces of cardboard and folded them in the middle. When we folded them, they would stand on the table. On the front we made a picture of a house. It must have a large door. Cut around three sides of the door. Then you can open it. Now cut a piece of paper just a little larger than the door-opening. Write a name on it, and paste it in the opening so that the name will show from the front when the door is open. When you set the table, be sure that all the little doors are closed; and you will see what fun it is for each child to go about opening the doors until he finds his own name.

When you are in the ten-cent store, get some paper plates. Also buy some paper napkins. You can get your napkins to match your color scheme, or you can buy plain napkins and decorate them yourselves. You might decorate the napkins with "cut-outs."

Now for your plates. With bright show-card colors, paint pretty designs on the plates. You can make your own patterns. You will have to have some little doilies to put on the plates before you serve, but it is pretty to have the plates at each place without the doilies when the guests first see the table. They can match the color scheme, too, and add to the prettiness of the table.

Mother bought us some wafers and animal crackers. We made a frosting of confectioner's sugar and cream, adding our favorite flavoring. We added green vegetable coloring. We spread frosting on a cooky and stuck an animal cracker in it, so that the animal would stand up. We laid a strip of oiled paper around the table just beyond the plates, and on this we set the cookies, making an animal parade.

OUR MAY PARTY

May is one of the nicest months in the year to give a party. So I am going to tell you about some things that we made for our last May party, and maybe you will like to make them, too. We planned a May pole first of all.

Our May pole was made with a wheel on top of the pole (an old bicycle or baby-carriage wheel). When we went around the May pole, the wheel turned with us. Then we could skip and dance around without bothering to see if our ribbons were winding evenly around the pole. We made our ribbons of strips of colored cambric. The wheel was decorated with flowers and leaves, made of tissue paper. We danced to phonograph music.

The boys made elf and gnome costumes of green and brown cambric. Their caps were cut like the picture above. Paste the edges of cap together with fringe at the top. Or the peak of the cap may be pinned over like the picture at the right.

For the wings, take a flat strip of crepe paper or other stiff paper, decorate it, tie in the middle, and fasten to shoulders with small safety pins.

Some of the girls who came to our party made fairy costumes for themselves. They wore white dresses and colored-paper wings —crepe paper is best. Their headbands were narrow strips of colored paper, with flowers painted on; and their wands were sticks wrapped with colored paper.

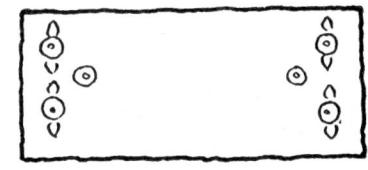

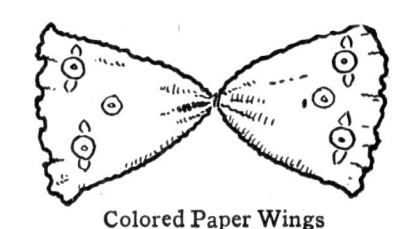

Colored Paper Wings

Costumes for Plays

Fig. 1

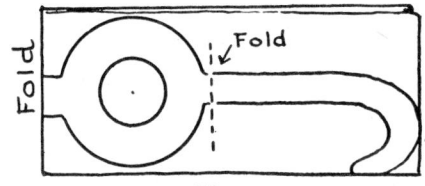

Fig. 2

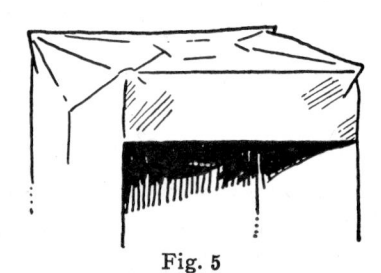

GOGGLES are made by folding stiff paper, drawing the goggles, and cutting around the outside lines. Figures 1 and 2.

For leggings, cut heavy wrapping paper like Figure 3, to fit your legs. Paste strips of cloth along both sides. Place under a weight until dry. Punch holes for laces. Fig. 4.

An aviator's helmet can be made from a large, brown paper bag. Cut out the front. Figures 5 and 6.

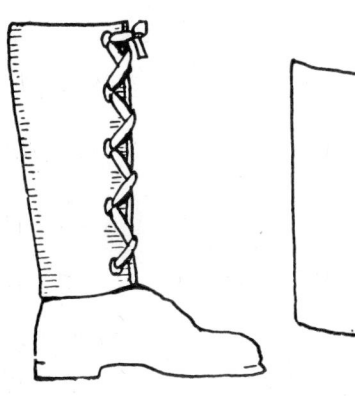

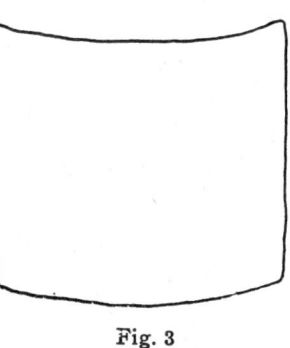

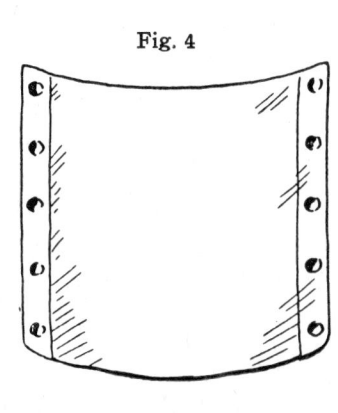

Fig. 4

Fig. 5

Fig. 6

Fig. 3

The two side flaps go over the ears and hang to the shoulders.

173

Plans For Vacation Days
Laura Hassenstein

OUR school is interested in the way we spend our vacation, and so, when we go back to school in September there is an exhibit of all the things that the children in the lower grades have made or collected during the summer. It is most interesting, and there is a prize for the best work. Perhaps the children in your school would like to have an exhibit of summer work. I will tell you some of the things that we did in the summer.

We made bird books, in which we drew pictures of all the birds we saw. We wrote under each bird when and where we saw it, and what it was doing, as well as anything else we could find out about its habits. We made flower books in which we pasted flowers which we had pressed. We pressed them carefully between sheets of newspaper or blotting paper, under a heavy book. Under the flower, we wrote its name and where we found it. Making blue prints of flowers makes an interesting book.

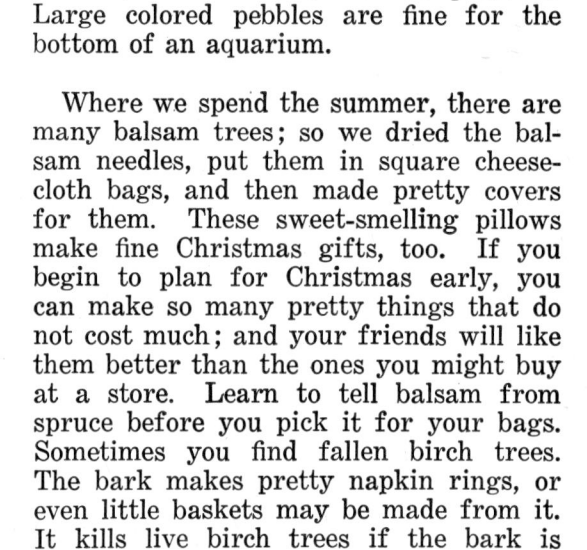

The summer we were at the seashore, we made a fine collection of sea shells, starfishes, sea-urchins, and sea plants. We mounted these on cards. We also collected bright-colored pebbles and used these in clear glass bowls for planting bulbs. These bowls, filled with pretty pebbles, make nice Christmas presents. Large colored pebbles are fine for the bottom of an aquarium.

Where we spend the summer, there are many balsam trees; so we dried the balsam needles, put them in square cheesecloth bags, and then made pretty covers for them. These sweet-smelling pillows make fine Christmas gifts, too. If you begin to plan for Christmas early, you can make so many pretty things that do not cost much; and your friends will like them better than the ones you might buy at a store. Learn to tell balsam from spruce before you pick it for your bags. Sometimes you find fallen birch trees. The bark makes pretty napkin rings, or even little baskets may be made from it. It kills live birch trees if the bark is stripped.

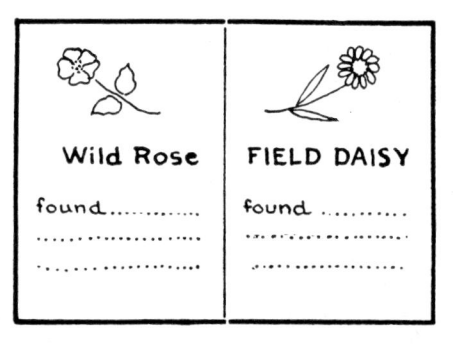

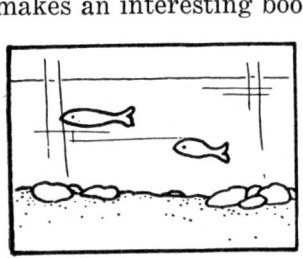

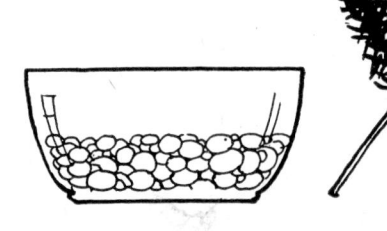

Floating Toys

ONE summer day when it was almost too hot to play, Mother showed us how to make floating toys. When they were finished we sailed them in a large pan of water. It was a nice, cool game for a hot day.

It is fun to make many different kinds of boats. We liked our toys so well that when one of our friends had a birthday party we made some for favors. Using two quite large corks, you can have a canoe with an Indian in it.

First we drew pictures of things that float. We drew them on heavy drawing paper, colored them with our crayons, and cut them out. We left a little flap at the bottom of each. Then we cut a slit in a large, flat cork, and slipped the paper flap into the slit. A flat piece of wood will do almost as well as a cork.

If the corks are small, use two for one toy. Do not make the toys too large, or they will be top-heavy and will not float.

Before you put your toys in water, ask your mother to melt some paraffin wax for you, and quickly dip the toys into the hot paraffin. That will make them waterproof so that the water will not spoil them.

Here are some of the toys that we made. Perhaps you will be able to think of more things that float, and make some different ones.

Use tiny corks for the baby ducks and a larger one for the mother.

After we played with these floating toys, Mother suggested that it would be fun to experiment to find out what things would float and those that would sink. We collected all sorts of things from around the house, such as keys, spools, tin lids, pencils, small glass jars with lids, and some without lids, nails, screws, a screw driver, a celluloid soap dish, a little wooden box, and a lot more things. Sometimes we were surprised; for some things which we thought would float went straight to the bottom. Of course we were careful not to use things that would be spoiled by putting them in water.

We also used some things to eat with which to experiment. We tried putting navy beans, lima beans, prunes, raisins, sugar, and macaroni into some pans of water. Again we had some surprises. Why don't you try this and find out for yourself what will happen?

Hallowe'en Favors

HALLOWE'EN is a gay time for parties, and many things can be made to make it a happy time. Bobbing for apples in a pan of shallow water affords no end of amusement, and trying to eat an apple hung on a string, with your hands behind your back, is quite a task. Even if you open your mouth as wide as you can, it will be hard to get a bite. Getting ready for the party is the most fun.

For our party, the younger children made an orange-and-black paper cap by pasting a band of orange paper to a stiff paper band which fitted around their heads. The top was fringed, gathered together, and tied. A piece of black, fringed paper was tied in with it. Black spots were pasted on the cap. We had crepe and tissue paper, scissors, and paste, and we made our own caps. They were much prettier than the ones that come out of snappers, and it was fun to work together and make them, ourselves.

Some of the older children made cat caps. Mother cut out the pattern of a cat's head, and this pattern was pinned to black crepe paper and cut around. The black crepe paper should be doubled so that there will be two heads. These should be made quite large so that when the edges are sewed or pasted together there will still be room for a child's head. On the front of the cap, paste eyes, nose, and paper whiskers.

I met a little elfman once,
Down where the lilies blow.
I asked him why he was so small
And why he didn't grow.
He slightly frowned, and with his eye,
He looked me through and through,
"I'm quite as big for me," said he,
"As you are big for you."
    John Kendrick Bangs

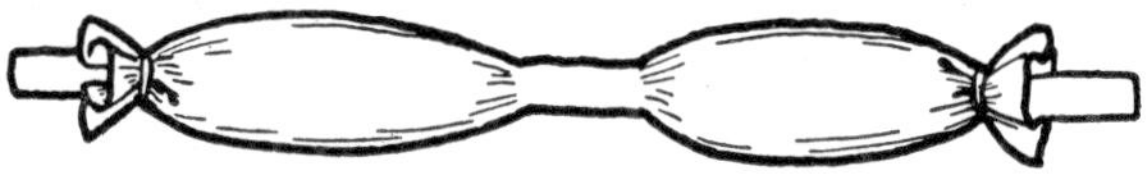

Some of the boys made clown-doll caps. These were made in the same way as the other dolls; but they were tall caps, and they had larger paper frills around their necks. They look even better if puffy sleeves are put on their arms. This may be just a piece of paper, tied in at each wrist.

clown cap

head completed cap arms

We had been very busy before the party, making favors for the table. These were clay pumpkins—about three-inches high. We made eyes, a nose, and a mouth in each, and each had a different expression. The top was made so that it could be lifted off. The pumpkin was painted yellow, and the stem green. A coat of white shellac gives water color paint a good finish and keeps it from peeling off from the clay. In each pumpkin, we made a place for a candle; and when all the little pumpkin lanterns were lighted, the table looked very pretty.

Mother dressed some lollipops in orange and brown crepe paper and hid them all about the yard among the brown leaves, for a surprise. What fun it was to look for them.

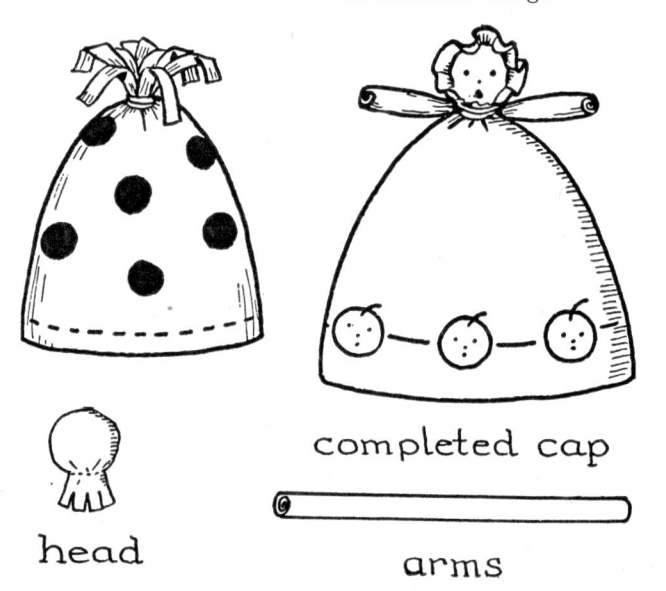

Other children made funny doll caps. These took longer to make than the others, but they were great fun. The skirt was a band of crepe paper about twelve inches high, and long enough to go around a child's head. This was decorated with cut paper made into Hallowe'en designs. Then the edges of the skirt were pasted together. It was gathered at the top and the head slipped in; then tied in. The head is a ball of cotton batting covered with white crepe paper on which features are painted. A crepe-paper hat or bonnet is pasted or sewed to the head. The arms are crepe paper, rolled and sewed to the top of the skirt. Above are pictures to show you just how these caps are made. Remember to be careful to measure carefully, and to use just enough paste.

Thanksgiving

AT Thanksgiving time one way of showing that you are thankful is to give things to other people. If you are glad to be well and strong, perhaps you would like to make things for children who are shut in. Once we sent some of the things below to the *Children's Hospital*, and some we sent to a little friend of ours who cannot walk.

We made several puzzles by pasting a brightly-colored picture on tag board and cutting it into pieces. (The pieces should not be too small).

We made several scrap books. In these we pasted pictures and little stories cut from JUNIOR HOME. One book was a story about two children, with pictures of the house they lived in, the toys they played with, and the things they did. We cut the pictures from magazines, and printed the stories underneath. Another book was a "surprise" book with double pages so that when a "window" or "door" was opened there was a picture underneath. We got some small boxes, decorated them with cut-out pictures, and in each one put "something to do." In the first box we put a bubble pipe, a little bowl, and a piece of soap. This, we sent to our little friend; not to the hospital.

In another box we had crayons and pictures to color. One box was a sewing box. In it were pieces of colored cambric, thread, needles, pins (in a pretty pincushion), thimble, scissors, and a little doll to dress. This went to a little girl in the hospital who could sit up in bed, and she wrote us a letter saying that she made three dresses for the doll.

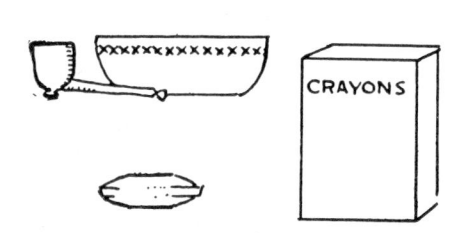

Mother will need table decorations for the Thanksgiving dinner table, and you can make some quite easily. Ask Father to get you some stalks of corn. With a sharp knife, cut them in short lengths, and stick them into balls of clay modeled like pumpkins, and painted a bright orange. Shred a few of the leaves of the husk, press them into the clay, hollow the top, and put in a yellow candle. You will have a very appropriate candlestick.

Turkeys made of potatoes look quite at home on the Thanksgiving dinner table. Get a smooth potato to use for the body. Draw a paper head, cut it out, color with crayons, and insert it into the potato. Find some chicken feathers for the tail. Insert toothpicks or matches for legs, and then put him into a clay standard.

> A pumpkin rolled away
> Before Thanksgiving Day
> Said he, "They'll make
>   a pie of me,
> If I should stay."

> "Gobble, gobble," said the
>   turkey,
> " 'Tis near Thanksgiving
>   Day.
> How'll you treat me?
> Will you eat me?
> Then I'll run away."

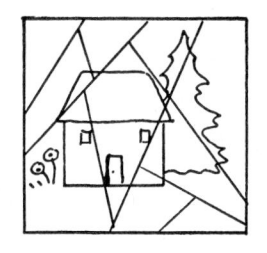

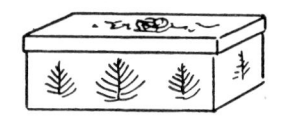

A lemon makes a splendid pig, with cloves for eyes, a curl of brown paper for the tail, and four matches for the legs.

You can make turtles for place cards. Take a half of a walnut shell and paint it green with little brown dots. Paste or glue a whole clove with the ball for the head on the divided half of the walnut shell. Use four cloves for the claws and legs, and another one with the long end out for his tail. Paste the turtle on a card, and he will look ready to walk away.

Of course, Mother will need nut cups. Baskets made of oranges are very appropriate for this harvest-dinner decoration. You will enjoy your dinner very much more for the part you took in making it a festive occasion.

Christmas Gifts

WE are busy all the month before Christmas making Christmas gifts. Everyone likes a gift that has taken time and thought. We make our own Christmas cards, too. We bought five handkerchiefs with colored borders. On each we pinned a card with a little rhyme and a picture of a child, dressed in the same color as the border on the handkerchief. Diagram at right.

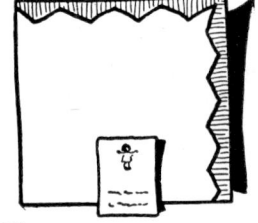

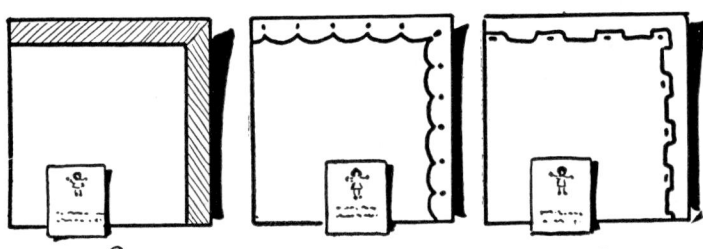

For Mother, we made a telephone pad from a piece of wood. The wood was decorated with crayon and covered with shellac. The pad was put on while the shellac was wet. A screw-eye at the side holds the pencil.

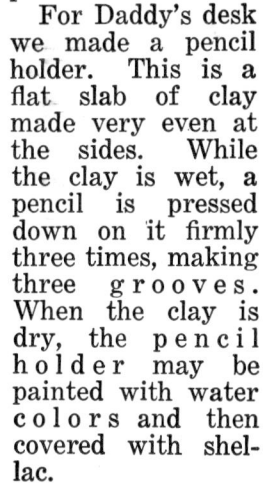

For Daddy's desk we made a pencil holder. This is a flat slab of clay made very even at the sides. While the clay is wet, a pencil is pressed down on it firmly three times, making three grooves. When the clay is dry, the pencil holder may be painted with water colors and then covered with shellac.

For Mother, I made three dusters of cheesecloth, sewed around with bright-colored silkateen. I put crayon designs on them.

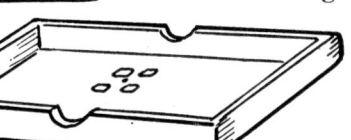

Grandmother is always wanting string to tie up a package; so we made her a string box. This was made from one of those heavy cardboard ice-cream or cream containers. We made a hole in the top for the string, decorated the box, and covered it with shellac.

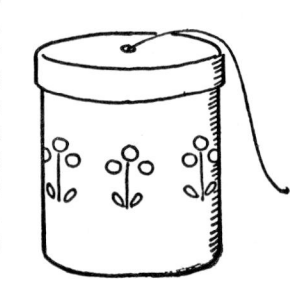

On Monday when you dress in blue,
I hope this handkerchief will do.
On Tuesday when you dress in green,
Please let this handkerchief be seen.
On Wednesday when you dress in pink,
This kerchief will be nice, I think.
On Thursday when in yellow dressed,
Pray use this kerchief, neatly pressed.
On Friday when you go to town,
Here's lavender to match your gown.

I made an inkwell for Daddy which matched the pencil holder. The inkwell is a clay cube, hollowed inside so that it can hold a little tin box or tiny glass cup for the ink. A square cover with a tiny knob completes the inkwell. I painted it green with a little design on each side. If you'd like to make a blotter and a desk pad to go with these, your present will be most complete.

Grandfather smokes; so we made him a very pretty ash tray. It was made of clay, shaped very carefully, with a place on each side so that the cigar could be laid across it. We painted it green with a black design in the bottom, and then we covered it with shellac. The picture of it is below at the left. If your Grandfather does not smoke, make him the same gift as you do for your Father.

For other friends, we made little clay Christmas trees. We painted the pots a soft red, and the trees rather a light green so that the bright-colored balls (also painted) would show well. These make nice paper weights, and most any friend will be glad to have one. Even Daddy would like one of these with his desk set.

We made clay bowls. In some of our bowls we put a little clay flower holder and stuck sprays of bayberry or red Christmas berries into it. These berries do not need water, and our bowls, even when covered with shellac, are not waterproof. Most folks are very particular not to stain their tables or flower stands with water so that it is better to give them bayberry or Christmas berries with the bowls that have flower holders. Then there will be no danger that water will leak through. These cheery gifts will make Christmas last a long time.

This is the way we make our Christmas place cards. Stand a small, clean twig in a marshmallow; print the name of the guest on it with red cake coloring. Stand one at each plate. It is prettier if the twig has berries on it.

Stick Printing

STICK printing is fun, and with a stick-printing outfit, you may decorate many articles that you make from unbleached muslin or other plain material. Stick printing is easy to do, and it looks so well when finished.

Materials needed are:

1. Several different-colored packages of dye intended for boiling.
2. Several saucers with squares of felt, Turkish towelling, or other absorbent material.
3. Sticks or small objects of different shapes—match sticks, corks, and wooden beads.

The top of a Japanese paintbrush is good. Mix the dyes with hot water in pint jars, about half a package to a jar.

Saturate the felt in each saucer with dye, but do not let the dye swim around in the saucer. Decide what combinations of shape and color you need for your design. Press the stick on the felt pad; then press it firmly on the material. It is better to use material that is white or natural color. Then the colors you use will show up.

Here are pictures of some of the ways in which we used stick printing. If the finished design is pressed with a hot iron over a damp cloth, it will not wash out so easily. For stick-printing on paper, use water-color paints instead of dyes.

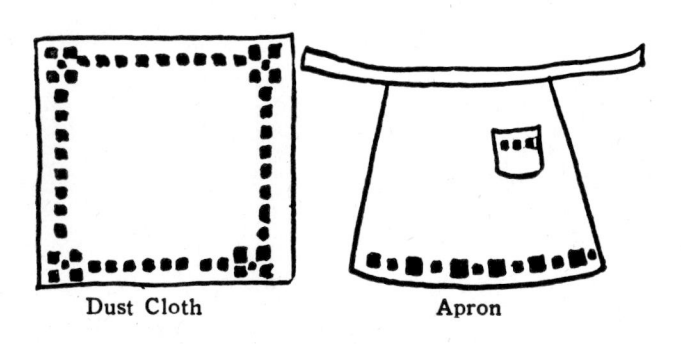

Dust Cloth   Apron

Bureau Scarf

Bag   Doll Dress

Curtains for Doll House

Here are a few interesting designs. Be sure to use colors that look well together, such as orange and black, orange and blue, orange and purple, or green and black. Stems of flowers may be made with the long side of a match stick.

Made with top of Japanese paintbrush and small round stick.

Made with top and side of match. When using the side of the match, lift it quickly and carefully from the cloth in order to get a clear line.

A design like this may be made by cutting the flat surface of a cork with a sharp knife.

Fresco Painting

DON'T you love to paint? Have you ever tried painting large pictures with fresco paints? If not, you would like it. Use large brushes and bright colors. You can buy packages of cold-water fresco or calcimo paint at a paint store.

These paints come in powder form; so you must mix them with cold water. Take a glass jar for each color and mix paint with a little water until your mixture is as thick as thin cream. Use a separate brush for each jar. Large sheets of unprinted newspaper from a newspaper office, or sheets of wrapping paper, are the best material on which to paint. You can buy easels that are especially made for children to use, but a large piece of heavy cardboard or beaver board will do. Stand it on chairs or against the wall, and tack your paper to it.

Sometimes it is fun to paint a very big picture together. Daddy bought us a long piece of beaver board so that we could paint long pictures and make scenery for plays.

Remember:
Always wear an apron or smock when you paint.
Spread newspaper on the floor; your brushes may drip.
(We like to paint out-of-doors.)
Do not let your colors touch each other, or they will run into each other.

"Poster paints" come ready mixed (at a stationery store) and so are easier to use, but they are much more expensive than fresco paints.

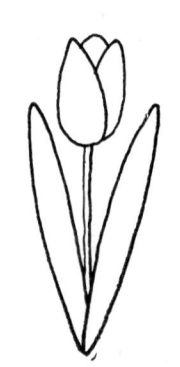

(Easel)

180

The Question Box
By HARRY O. GILLET

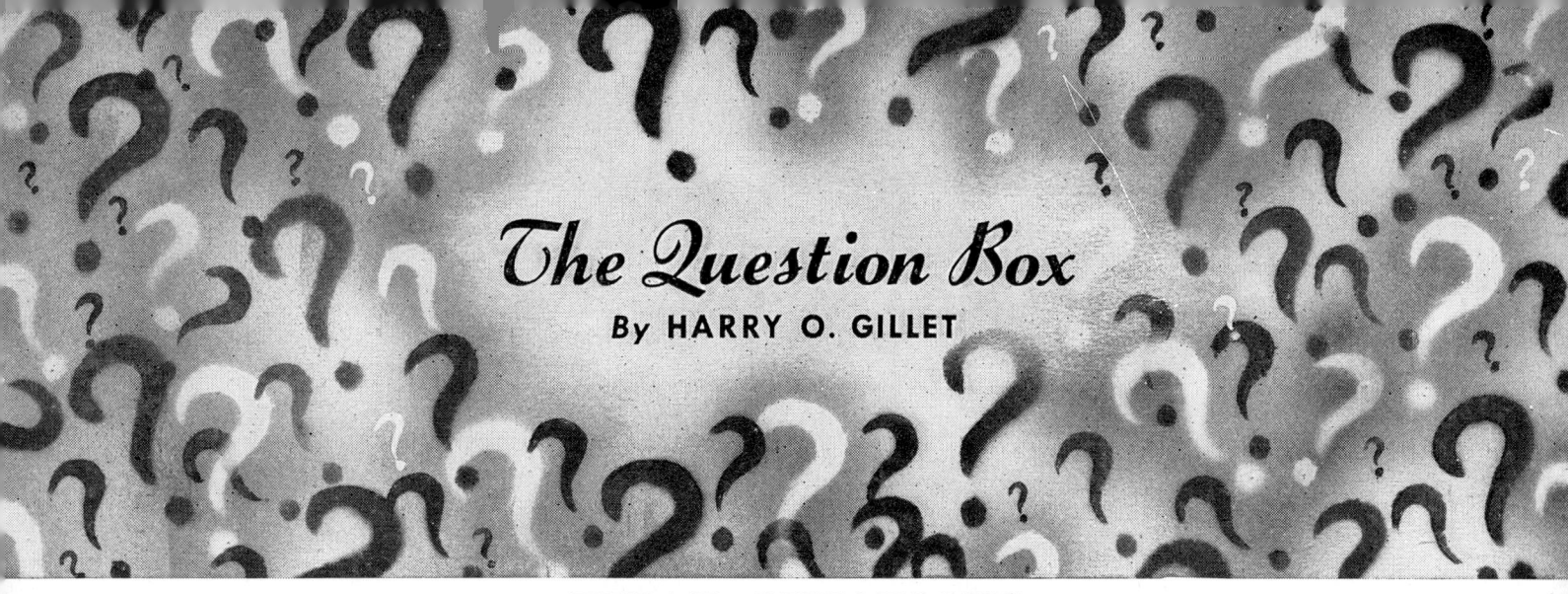

···· WHAT QUESTIONS ····

What is the largest bird?

It is not the goose or the turkey or the eagle. It is the ostrich. We see ostriches in zoos, but the wild ostrich lives in the dry parts of South Africa and in Arabia. It eats the coarse desert plants with some stones for its gizzard. In the gizzard the stones help to grind the food, for the ostrich does not have teeth to grind it. The full-grown ostrich stands seven or even eight feet high, but it is its long neck that makes it stand so tall. The wings are not large enough to let the ostrich fly, for it is a heavy bird. It may weigh as much as 300 pounds. It can run very fast, however—much faster than any horse. The hen ostrich lays eggs as large as a dozen chicken eggs.

The male ostrich has beautiful white plume feathers on its wings and its tail. They can be clipped off and sold. Many tame ostriches are raised for their plumes in the warmest parts of the United States. Visitors go to see them. They like to see an ostrich swallow a whole orange at a time.

What are snakes good for?

Farmers who know about snakes like to have them in fields and near the barns. Snakes eat mice, rats, gophers, and insects. Mice are very harmful on a farm. They eat the farmer's plants in the fields and his corn in the cribs. Rats also are very harmful. They eat the food that belongs to the horses and cows and pigs. Farmers do not kill snakes if they know how useful they are.

Of course, snakes may do harm also. They eat frogs and toads and earthworms and birds' eggs in nests on the ground. Frogs and toads are useful because they eat flies and mosquitoes and many other kinds of insects. Earthworms are useful because they make the soil better for plants. Most snakes in the United States and Canada are not dangerous to people. Only four kinds are poisonous: rattlesnakes, copperheads, water moccasins, and coral snakes. Before you pick up a snake you must be sure it is not of the poisonous kind.

What are mosquitoes good for?

Mosquitoes are pests. They sting us and draw out our blood. The wound itches. We don't like to hear them buzz. We put screens in our windows and doors to keep them out. But out of doors they attack us wherever they can get at our skin, on our faces and arms and legs. Most mosquitoes are just a nuisance, but, in places where people are sick with malaria or yellow fever, there is a kind of mosquito that carries the disease to other people. That is a dangerous kind.

It is only the female mosquito that attacks us. The male mosquito sucks just the juices from plants, but the female likes blood most of all. She pushes in her little sharp-pointed lance, squeezes out a little saliva to keep the blood from clotting, and sucks out the blood until you can see that she is full of it. Blood is food for the mosquito. If we did not slap the mosquito until she is full of blood, the wound would not itch so much, for she would have sucked back the saliva along with the blood.

Are mosquitos good for anything? They are not good for much. Mosquitoes live most of their lives in the water. There they don't look like mosquitoes at all. They haven't any wings or legs. Their name then is wigglers, for they wiggle through the water. They eat decaying particles of plants. Maybe they do some good in the water. But we don't like them when they get wings and fly around and sting us.

What animal is the largest?

Almost everybody thinks the elephant is the largest animal. A big alligator is longer than an elephant, but an alligator does not weigh as much as an elephant. A hippopotamus is very big, and so is a rhinoceros, but neither is as big as an elephant.

People do not guess that a whale is the biggest animal of all. Maybe you thought a whale was a fish. But a fish lays eggs, and a whale does not lay eggs. A mother whale has live babies, just as a mother cat has live kittens. Fish breathe with gills, but a whale breathes with lungs, like a dog or a horse. The whale comes up to the surface to breathe. So a whale is not a fish. One kind of whale weighs as much as fifteen big elephants. This whale is as long as five elephants in a row. It is the largest animal ever on earth.

What does the hen say to her chicks?

The little chicks seem to know what the mother hen is saying when she clucks to them. If she clucks in a certain way they run to her to get something to eat. Probably the hen has scratched up some food. If she clucks in another way, the chicks run to her for another reason. She is saying "DANGER." She has seen a hawk in the sky just ready to swoop down and pick up a chick for his dinner. The little chicks hurry to get under mother's wings away from harm.

Probably the hen doesn't say many kinds of things to her chicks. Hens can't talk as we talk. But the kinds of clucks mean something to her chicks.

What are the sprouts on white potatoes?

Have you noticed that in the spring potatoes that have been stored through the winter have little potato plants growing out of them? We say the potatoes are sprouting. A new plant is growing where each bud or eye was. Look for the buds on a potato. How many buds do you find?

The farmer does not plant potato seeds. He gets pieces of potato ready. He cuts the potato so that each piece will have a bud. He knows that a sprout will grow from each bud. Then he puts each piece by itself in the soil. He plants the pieces in rows. Soon green sprouts will be growing in each row. They will become big plants. Each will yield several new potatoes. That is the way the farmer gets a crop of potatoes.

What does the elephant do with his trunk?

The elephant's trunk is a nose five or six feet long. It reaches down to the ground. It has two nostrils, like our noses. The elephant uses his nose to smell, as well as to breathe. He can smell much better than he can see. If he suspects danger, he will raise his trunk to smell better. Also, he will open his big, flappy ears to hear better.

At the circus we like to see an elephant pick up hay with his trunk and lift it to his mouth. He uses the trunk like an arm, and the end of it like a hand. The African elephant has two knobs on his trunk for fingers; the elephant from India has only one knob for picking up things. But either elephant can pick up as small a thing as a peanut. The trunk is very strong. With it the elephant can lift as heavy a thing as a big log. He can lift a man easily.

The elephant drinks by sucking water halfway up his trunk and then squirting it into his mouth. On a hot day he likes to squirt water over his back. Because his trunk is so important, the elephant is very careful not to let it be injured. He needs it to eat, to drink, to breathe, to smell, and to lift things.

What is a tadpole, or pollywog?

Another name for tadpole is pollywog. A young tadpole is a little frog. Only it isn't a frog yet. It doesn't have any legs and it has a tail. It has hatched from an egg which a mother frog laid in a pond. She laid many other eggs at the same time. So the tadpole has many brothers and sisters.

For a while after a tadpole comes out from its egg, it holds to a twig or a blade of grass in the water. Then it begins to swim around to find things to eat. It eats bits of plants and tiny insects. It eats and eats, and grows and grows. After a few days hind legs will begin to grow out. The legs grow longer and longer, with frog toes. Then the shorter front legs begin to grow out. By this time the tail has become longer and thicker. The tadpole doesn't look much like a frog yet. But in a few weeks after it is born, its long tail begins to get shorter. The gills, like fish gills, that enable it to breathe become covered, and the tadpole is ready to come out on land and breathe with lungs. The long tail has been used up to make the body grow. It is now a frog, no longer a tadpole. It can jump with its long hind legs. It can jump into the water if enemies come near. It can close its nostrils so that it can stay under water a while and not drown.

What is the sun?

If we did not have the sun to warm and light the earth nothing could grow. There would be no plants, for green plants must have light and heat. There would be no animals, either, for animals must have plants to eat, such as grass, or they might eat animals whose food is plants. And without plants or animals for us to eat, we people could not live either. So you see how important the sun is to everybody.

The sun is far, far away from the earth—93 hundred hundred hundred miles. It is round like the

THE QUESTION BOX

earth, but very much larger. It doesn't look so big, for it is so far away. The sun is very hot, but not because anything is burning on it. It never gets cool. Changes from one element on it to another keep it hot.

People used to think that the sun goes around the earth, for it seems to come up in the east in the morning, move across the sky, and go down in the west in the evening. But that is only what it seems to do. What really happens is that the earth is turning all the time and we go around with it. We see the sun when our part of the earth is turned toward it. People living on other parts of the earth see the sun rising when our part is still dark.

What makes a balloon go up?

Did your balloon ever get away from you and go sailing up in the air? What made it go up? Why didn't it fall, like most things? Probably your balloon had hydrogen in it. You can't see hydrogen, for it is invisible, like air. But it is much lighter than air. The heavier air around the balloon moved in under it and pushed it up. After a while the hydrogen leaked out and your balloon came down somewhere else.

Balloons that are large enough to carry people may be filled with helium. This is better than hydrogen, for helium will not burn. Hydrogen will catch fire even from a spark.

What makes an echo?

When you throw a rubber ball against a wall, it bounces back to you. Sound can bounce back, too. When it bounces back you hear an echo. It is the same sound coming back to you. Sometimes you can hear a train whistle, first from the engine and then from a hill. The sound echoes back from the hill. If the hill is near, the echo comes back in a few seconds, for sound travels fast. But if the hill is not near, the echo takes longer. Also, if the hill is far away, the echo is faint, for sound becomes less as it travels. There can be echoes from other things too, such as big buildings. The echo from the wall of a room comes back so soon that it almost mixes with the first sound. If a good many people are talking in a room, all the echoes together are such confused sounds as to annoy us. We call such confused sounds reverberation.

What is your shadow?

Your shadow is a queer thing. You have him and then you don't have him. He may be with you out of doors, but he leaves you when you go into the house. When you go out, he is with you again. At night when you are in a room that has a light, he may be on the wall or the floor. He is never on the ceiling.

Your shadow is where the light cannot shine because you are in the way. The light from the sun or from a lamp cannot shine through you, and so you make a shadow. Your shadow may be long or he may be short. He may be so small that you can hardly find him. How can that be?

The picture shows why your shadow is long in the morning before the sun has risen very far in the sky. In the later afternoon when the sun is again low in the sky, your shadow is long again. Do you see why? And at noon it is almost under you and so small that you can hardly find it.

Ask your mother or your father to read Robert Louis Stevenson's poem about the shadow to you. It is in Volume II.

What is a rainbow?

Have you seen a rainbow in the sky after a shower? It is curved like a bow and has colors in it. If the rainbow is bright you can see a band of red which shades into a band of orange, then yellow, green, blue, indigo, violet.

What makes the colors? The sun has to be on the other side of the sky and shining toward the rainbow part of the sky, to make the rainbow. The sun is shining on the little drops of water in the sky. It is shining into the drops also, and it becomes the different colors as it goes through, just as drops of dew on the grass show different colors when the sun shines into them. The back sides of the drops act like little mirrors and reflect the light through the drops again. The sunlight, with its different colors caused by going into the drops and out of them, comes to our eyes, and we see a rainbow.

What makes rain?

Rain comes down from the clouds. How does the water get up into the clouds? Water on the earth disappears. Puddles dry up. The wet road becomes dry. We hang out wet clothes and the water goes out of them. We say the water evaporates. It goes up into the air as water that we cannot see. But it is water just the same. It is water vapor. A great deal of water vapor is rising from oceans, lakes, and streams, from the ground and from all kinds of plants growing in the ground.

All this vapor goes up into the air. It is carried up and up by warm air. As the water vapor rises it becomes cooler. Then it becomes tiny droplets of water. We say it condenses. The droplets make a cloud. That is what a cloud is—condensed water vapor in drops. The wind carries clouds along. If the clouds get cold enough, the drops become larger. They may become large enough and heavy enough to fall. Then it rains.

What are shooting stars?

Shooting stars are not real stars. They are pieces of rock, or rock with iron and nickel in it. We call them meteors. Millions of them are dropping to all parts of the earth every day. They are of all sizes. Most of them are as small as grains of sand or tiny pebbles. A few are large enough to weigh tons. We do not know where they are coming from, but in space beyond the earth and its atmosphere there must be great numbers of these stones. Those that get near enough to the earth are pulled in by gravity. When they reach the air around the earth friction with the air makes them so hot that they shine with a bright light. Most of them burn up in the air and so do not reach the ground. The larger ones that reach the ground are called meteorites. Many museums have meterorites to show to people.

What is that bright star in the west?

Sometimes when we look at the western sky after sunset we see a star that is so bright we want to know its name. Probably the bright star is Venus.

Men who study the stars tell us that Venus is a planet, not like the millions of real stars in the sky. Our sun is a real star. Venus is a member of the sun's family. Our earth is another member of the sun's family. There are nine planets. They all shine because they reflect light from the sun. The real stars shine with their own light.

If we are up before sunrise we may sometimes see Venus as a bright star in the east. Then Venus is called a morning star. Sometime during the night we may see other planets in the sky, especially Jupiter, Mars, and Saturn.

What makes the wind blow?

When we blow out a candle, we make a little wind with our lungs and mouth. An electric fan makes a wind, but not a big one like the wind out of doors. What is wind? It is just air moving. Usually we can feel it moving. Or we may see the dust or the smoke it carries along with it. We may see it moving the leaves on the trees and the flowers in the garden. We cannot see the wind itself, for wind is just air.

What makes the wind out of doors? It is heavier air pushing lighter air. Usually cooler air is heavier and warmer air is lighter. So the cooler air pushes the warmer air. The warmer air may rise, because the cooler air pushes in under it and makes it rise. The cooler air does not have to be cold, but just a little cooler, to push in under the warmer air. This pushing makes wind, for wind is only moving air.

Wind can change in direction. It may blow from the east and be an east wind, and then gradually it may change to a south wind or a west wind or a north wind. It may blow hard enough to push down branches of trees, or it may blow so softly that we can hardly feel it. It can push sailboats over the water and make windmills pump water. It can make us more comfortable on a hot day.

What is an atom?

When we see an iron nail or a silver spoon, it looks solid, and it is solid, in a way. But people who know tell us that the nail and the spoon are made of many, many tiny particles called atoms. They are so small that nobody has ever seen them separately even with the best magnifying glasses. An atom is not solid. It is made of two parts, a very tiny central part and an outer part. The outer part is made of one or many particles that are moving around the inner part, but not very close to it.

Everything on earth is made of atoms: rocks, soil, water, air, and all kinds of plants and animals, even people. There is one kind of atom for the oxygen we breathe and another kind for the mercury in the thermometer. The number of particles in the outer part is different for each kind of atom. There are ninety-eight or more different kinds of atoms. Atoms of different kinds are combined to make such things as water and gasoline and salt and almost everything else.

What is a volcano?

A volcano in action is a wonderful sight. It is a mountain that looks as if it were afire, but it is not really burning. Hot gases that seem like fire and smoke are coming out of a big hole at the top or on a side. At night they make the sky red above. There is a sound of explosions in the earth. Hot rocks may be shooting high in the air and falling down to make the mountain higher. Often a stream of melted rock called lava flows down the mountain. It is so hot that it sets fire to trees and houses. When it gets cool it is hard rock.

Volcanoes start deep in the earth in places where it is very hot and where steam and lava can force their way to the surface. They are active for a while, and then they become cold and quiet. Many mountains were once active volcanoes. They are made of the rocks that were shot out and the lava that cooled as it flowed down. Some volcanoes that are active now are in Alaska, Hawaii, the Philippine Islands, and Mexico.

What is lightning?

Lightning is electricity. Some clouds have electricity in them. We call it a charge of electricity. The charge becomes more and more powerful when moist, warm air is rising into a cloud. The warm air gets cooler as it rises, and the moisture becomes raindrops. Finally the charge is so powerful that it jumps to another cloud which has an electrical charge of another kind in it. The two kinds of electrical charges are called a positive and a negative charge. The electricity may jump between the cloud and the earth if the cloud and the earth have different kinds of electrical charges in them. The lightning makes a very bright streak in the air as it jumps.

What does a postman do?

The postman brought Nell a birthday gift from her grandmother, who lives in a city over a hundred miles away. Now Nell has written a letter to thank her. On the envelope she has written the name and address. It is ready to go to the corner mailbox. There will be many other letters in the mailbox, all going to different people in different places. Nell wonders how each will get to the right place.

Nell's mother explains what happens. A mailman will take all the letters to the post office. Another man will read each address. He will put Nell's letter in a mailbag which will go on a train or plane to the post office in grandmother's city. There will be many other letters in the bag. A mailman will read each address. He will give Nell's letter to the postman who carries letters to grandmother's street. Mother explains that letters do not get mixed up, because each mailman knows just what to do.

What makes thunder?

After lightning comes the crash or the rumble of thunder. If the lightning is near by, the thunder is a loud crash. If the lightning is far away, the thunder is not so loud when it reaches our ears, for sound grows dimmer as it travels. Sometimes we see lightning between distant clouds without hearing the thunder, because it is so far away.

Lightning causes the thunder by heating the air through which it passes. This heating causes the air to expand (swell) quickly, and sets up strong vibrations of the air. These vibrations are sound. Then the air contracts (shrinks), and this contracting makes new sound vibrations. Thunder cannot hurt us, even though it is so loud.

What is it like on the moon?

Nobody has ever been on the moon to see what it is like, but men who have studied it through telescopes know a great deal about it. They tell us that on the sunny side of the moon it is very warm, and on the dark side it is very cold. There is no air to breathe anywhere on the moon, and no water. There are no trees or even grass. The moon looks as if there had been many volcanoes on it. Some of the old volcanic mountains and craters are very large.

If people could be on the moon they would see the earth like a big moon. They could jump much higher and throw a rock much farther than on the earth, for everything weighs less there. But why should anybody ever want to live on the moon, even if he could?

What is an escalator?

Do you have stairs in your home? Many stores have stairs too. If the store is on several floors it has elevators. But some stores have something very different from elevators to take people up and down. It is a moving stair, a stair that climbs up or down. Its name is escalator. One escalator is going up all the time and one escalator is going down all the time. If you want to go up, you get on the first step, and that step moves up to be the second step and then the third step and so on to the top. Then you get off. You are on the second floor. Another escalator will take you farther up. If you want to go down, you get on the top step of a "going down" escalator, and this step moves down, and again down, until you are at the bottom. Then you get off. The escalators are stairs that move up or down all the time. Sometimes an escalator is full of people, one on each step. It is fun to ride up or down on an escalator.

THE JUNIOR INSTRUCTOR

···· WHY QUESTIONS ····

Why do we put air in a tire?

If we had solid rubber tires the road would seem very rough. Instead, we have hollow tires filled with air. The air in the tires makes the rough road seem smooth.

Air is like a cushion. We can squeeze it and it comes right back into shape, like our pillow or the cushion on a chair. When the air-filled tire hits an uneven place in the road, the roughness squeezes the air at that point, and the pressure goes through all the air in the tire. The air is elastic. It takes up the jars and they do not get to us in the car or on the bicycle. The air absorbs the shocks.

We must not put too much air in the tire, for then the air isn't as good a cushion and we feel the shocks of the uneven road too much.

Why do postage stamps have different colors?

When we want to mail a letter we put a postage stamp on the envelope. Also, we put stamps on packages to go by parcel post. There are stamps for one cent, two cents, three cents, and so forth. The stamps for each amount are printed in a different color. Also, the amount is printed on the stamps.

The man at the post office must look at each envelope or package to see whether the right stamp is on it. He knows each kind of stamp by its color, and so he does not have to look at the printing on it. The color helps us too, for we know what color goes with each amount.

Why do machines have to be oiled?

You have seen the man at the gasoline station putting oil in the car. Without oil the motor would not run very long. The moving parts would rub against each other so hard that they would get very hot and wear themselves out. The oil gets between the parts that move next to each other and keeps them from rubbing too hard. So the parts last a long time.

A watch is a machine. It has wheels that fit into each other. The jeweler puts a little oil in the watch to keep the wheels from wearing out. You know a good many machines. They all require oil: the bicycle, the vacuum cleaner, the kind of clock that you have to wind, the tractor, the diesel motor of the streamliner, the airplane motors, the engine of a boat, and many others.

Why does glass crack?

Did you ever make the mistake of pouring boiling water into a cold milk bottle or a cold drinking glass? The glass cracked with a snap. It was ruined and had to be thrown away. What made it crack?

Glass, like many other things, gets bigger (expands) when it becomes warmer. When you poured the hot water into the cold milk bottle, the glass expanded fast. But it expanded much faster on the inside of the bottle than on the outside. Heat does not go through glass very fast. The unequal swelling (expansion) made the glass pull apart, or crack. A thick bottle is more likely to crack than a thin bottle. A thick drinking glass is more likely to crack than a thin glass.

If you pour cold water into a very hot milk bottle, the bottle will crack. The hot glass is expanded, and when it is cooled it becomes smaller (contracts). The unequal contraction of the thick glass causes it to crack. The safe thing to do is to let the glass get hotter or colder gradually. Then it will not crack.

Why does a bottle break when water freezes in it?

Have you seen bottles broken because water froze in them? This is what happens: When water freezes, it swells. Because the ice is hard, it cannot swell out at the top. It pushes so hard when it swells that it breaks the bottle.

If milk in the bottle freezes, it pushes hard too, but the milk bottle is very strong. It does not break easily. The milk pushes out at the top. Besides, milk does not freeze as solid as water.

In places where it gets very cold in winter, we must not let water freeze in the water pipes in the car. The pipes would break. It costs a great deal if the pipes have to be replaced. So we put alcohol

THE QUESTION BOX

into the water, for alcohol and water do not freeze until the weather is much colder. Or we may take the water out of the pipes and put in antifreeze instead.

Why can we see our breath out of doors on a cold day?

We don't really see the air in our breath when we are out of doors on a cold day. We see the water in it. The water is in tiny drops, like the water in fog or cloud.

There is always water in the air. It has evaporated from seas and lakes and streams and plants. It evaporates from the ground all the time. It is water vapor. But we do not see this water in the air unless it has become cooled enough to form little drops. Then it is fog or cloud. If the drops are larger, the water is mist or rain.

The air that we breathe out has a good deal of water in it. But it is warm air and water vapor until it leaves our noses. When it goes out into the cold the water forms tiny drops like fog or cloud. Almost immediately this little cloud evaporates and the air is clear again.

Why does our heart beat faster when we run?

You know that the heart is constantly pumping blood to all parts of the body. It carries oxygen and digested food. The heart pumps blood to the lungs, where it gets the oxygen. It pumps the blood with its oxygen to the muscles and everywhere else in the body.

When we run our leg muscles and foot muscles have to work harder. They need more oxygen and more digested food. We have to breathe faster to supply more oxygen. The muscles must have more blood flowing through them. The heart has to beat faster to pump the blood faster. After we stop running or jumping or exercising, the heart can beat more slowly, and we do not have to breathe so fast.

Why does hair turn gray?

When we are children our hair is not gray. It may be black or brown or golden or flaxen. It may be a color that we call red, though it is not really red. When we are grown up, the color may slowly go out of it, and it becomes gray.

The color in our hair is in little specks in the hollow inside of each hair. The specks grow in as the hair forms in the skin on the head. When some grown-up people are still young, the color specks form less and less, and their hair begins to get gray. Some people do not have gray hair until they are much older. We cannot tell how old a person is by his hair.

Why doesn't the sun shine at night?

The sun does shine at night. But is not shining on our side of the earth, and so we cannot see it. The people on the other side of the earth are seeing it. The sun seems to come up in our sky in the morning and go down out of sight in the evening, but it is the turning of the earth that makes it seem that way. The sun is shining all the time.

Why does smoke go up?

Why doesn't it go down the chimney? Why does it always go up the chimney? You have seen it coming out at the top, not at the bottom. And you have seen the smoke going up from a bonfire, not sideways, unless the wind pushes it sideways.

To know why smoke goes up, you must know first what smoke is. Smoke is mostly air that the fire has made hot. It has tiny particles of partly burned coal or wood or dry leaves in it. That is why we can see the smoke. We cannot see hot air, but we see the smoke in it.

The hot air goes up the chimney or up from the bonfire because it is lighter than the cold air. The cold air is heavier, and so it goes in around the fire, and pushes the hot air up. The hot air carries the tiny particles of partly burned coal or wood or dried leaves up with it. And so we can see the smoke going up.

Why does the woodpecker tap tap on a tree?

Often it is a dead tree or a dead limb on a tree or an old post. Dead wood is likely to have boring insects and worms in it. The woodpecker wants to eat them. So he pecks hard with his strong, sharp bill and finally reaches the insect and pulls it out. The end of his bill is uneven, so as to keep the insect or worm from getting away. He swallows his food alive.

The tree may be alive, but with some diseased places in it. The borers are making them worse and harming the tree generally. The woodpecker is a sort of tree surgeon without knowing it.

The woodpecker can walk up and down a tree trunk and not fall off. He can hold tight while he is pecking. His sharp claws dig into the wood and his strong tail presses against the wood. He holds on without thinking about it.

Why do we put water in the car?

Everybody knows we must put gasoline in the car, for it is gasoline that makes the car go. But why must the car have water also?

The motor becomes very hot as the gasoline explodes in it. If it becomes too hot it will not work. It will be ruined. So we put water in the motor, around the cylinders where the gasoline is exploding. Some of the heat goes into the water. The water does not stay still. A pump keeps it moving. It goes in a pipe to a radiator in the front of the car. A big fan turning fast pushes air from outside the car around the radiator pipes. The air takes some of the heat from the water and makes the water cooler. Then this cooler water goes back to the motor and takes more heat from the cylinders. We must always have enough water in the motor and the pipes if we want the motor to work well.

Why does a parachute let people drop safely?

If an airplane is in trouble very high in the air, and a man has to jump out, he wants to have a parachute attached to him to help him land safely. A parachute is like a very large umbrella with ropes instead of a handle. You know that if you try to run when you are holding an open umbrella behind you the umbrella seems to be holding you back. You are slowed down. It takes a good deal of your strength to move so much air out of the way.

Soon after the jumper leaves the plane, he pulls a cord which opens the great parachute. It fills with air. Immediately he falls more slowly. The air under the parachute has to be pushed aside, and doing this uses up much of the pull of gravity. The man will almost float down with the parachute, and will land safely.

Why do leaves on many kinds of trees change color in the autumn?

All trees have green leaves in the summer, but in the autumn the leaves on some trees turn red or brown or yellow or purple before they fall off.

Some trees are evergreen. Their leaves are green in the summer and also in the winter. Probably you know some of these trees. Do you have pines or hemlocks or live oaks where you live?

But many other kinds of trees and bushes have green leaves in the summer and let the leaves fall to the ground in the autumn. Do you have poplars or maples or elms where you live? On these trees and many other kinds of trees the leaves change from green to some other color before they fall.

What happens to the green color and where do the new colors come from? You must know first what makes the leaf green. It is called chlorophyl (clō'-rō-fil). It is the substance by which the leaf can take something from the air and combine it with water to make food for the tree or bush. Without chlorophyl a tree could not grow. Now, at the end of the summer, when the leaves are about ready to fall off, the chlorophyl disappears, for the tree has no use for it any more. When the chlorophyl is gone, the green color is gone, and the other color of the leaves shows. It is red or brown or yellow or purple. This autumn color was in the leaves all the time, but during the summer it did not show through the green.

Why does the robin have to pull to get the worm out?

The robin in the picture has seen the worm come out a little way. The robin grabs it in its bill and pulls and pulls. But the worm holds on. The worm can swell out the part of its body that is still in the hole. Also, the worm has little bristles or stiff hairs that it can stick out to fasten itself in the hole. But the robin keeps pulling and tugging. Finally the worm is too tired to hold on any longer. Then the robin eats the worm or carries it home for its hungry babies to eat.

Why do we have an eclipse?

Once in a long time the newspapers will tell us that, at a certain time on a certain day, the sun will be in eclipse. That means the sun will get dark, or seem to get dark, in the daytime. It will get dark first on one side and gradually all the way across, or sometimes only part of the way across. After a while the sun will begin to get light again, first on the side that got dark first, and soon it will be bright again all the way across. The eclipse will be over.

For many years people could only guess why there was an eclipse. Most people guessed wrong. Then men who studied the sun and the moon and the earth through the year learned that we have an eclipse of the sun when the moon in traveling around the earth gets between the earth and the sun. Then, of course, we cannot see the sun until the moon has moved away. The sun is shining all the time, but the moon has cut off our view of it. You will want to see an eclipse of the sun some time.

An eclipse of the moon may occur, too. Then the moon gets dark, first on one side, and then gradually all the way across, or part of the way across. Soon it begins to get light again, first on the side that got dark first. An eclipse of the moon occurs when the earth gets between the sun and the moon. Then the light from the sun cannot shine on the moon, and so the moon gets dark. The moon cannot shine unless the sun is shining on it. The moon just reflects the light of the sun. It has no light of its own.

Why do we have policemen?

Do you have a policeman at the corner near the school to see that children get across the street safely? That is just one of the many things policemen do. They help old and feeble people also to get across the street. They don't let cars go too fast. They answer people's questions about where to go. If there is an accident and people are hurt, a policeman comes soon to help. He knows the laws, and he arrests people who disobey them. The policeman is a good man for a person in danger or in trouble to know.

Why does a squirrel hide nuts?

A squirrel does not need to be told by his mother that winter is coming. Then he will not find much to eat on trees and bushes. He may not even know about winter if he is a young squirrel. But he hides nuts just the same. His instinct tells him to do it. He does other things too, because his instinct tells him. He does not need to be shown how to climb a tree or crack a nut. Knowing what to do without having learned is instinct.

Squirrels hide nuts in all sorts of places—in the ground, in holes in trees, in attics (if they can get in), and in wide cracks. Then they seem to forget some of the places. In winter they hunt around and around. Sometimes the nuts the squirrels have hidden in the ground sprout and become trees.

Why do rosebushes and thistles have prickles?

Many animals have ways of protecting themselves from their enemies. Some can bite, some can kick, and others have horns. Porcupines have needles. Skunks give off a bad odor. A few snakes and some insects have a poisonous bite. Birds fly. Many animals run away or get into their holes.

But plants cannot get away. They have to stay where they are. Some plants have ways of protecting themselves. Rosebushes and thistles and some trees and bushes have prickles or thorns. Cactus plants have needles or thorns. Animals like cattle and horses and sheep that eat plants stay away from plants with strong prickles. The prickles protect the plants.

Why are houseflies dangerous?

A housefly is a dirty insect. The female fly lays her eggs in filth, which may be manure or garbage. The eggs hatch in filth. The larvae (maggots) grow there, and when they are ready to fly they carry some of the dirt with them.

The fly can hardly help carrying it, for its six feet have sticky pads, and the part of the mouth that touches food is sticky. The fly brings the dangerous bacteria with it when it comes to our table and lights on our food.

We use screens, fly paper, and poison in our fight with flies. Also we swat them. But the best way is to keep filth away from them. Then they cannot grow, for the maggots must have something to eat. We must keep our garbage in covered cans and we must put something on manure so that flies will not like it.

Why should we like toads?

We should be glad to have a big toad in our garden. Of course, he is not pretty. His eyes seem to stick out from his head. His skin is unpleasant to touch. On his skin are little lumps that look like warts. But they are not warts, and we do not get warts by touching them. He seems to do nothing all day but sit, unless he becomes afraid and hops away.

A toad is really of much use in our garden. He eats hundreds of insects that are enemies of our garden plants. Beetles, slugs, cutworms, moths, and plant lice are his food. He eats flies and mosquitoes too. A toad does not need to hop around to find them. He chooses a cool, damp place and waits for an insect to come to him. Then out shoots his long, sticky tongue. The insect is caught, popped into the big mouth, and swallowed. The toad's tongue is fastened at the front of the mouth and folded back. So it can go away out, and the insect seldom escapes. We should not harm toads, for they are very useful.

Why does wood float and silver sink?

Why does a piece of wood float and a silver spoon sink in the water? Anything floats if it is lighter than the water it takes the place of. If you put a piece of wood into a pan of water, the wood pushes some of the water aside. If the wood is light in weight, like pine, as compared with water, it floats high. If the wood is heavier, it floats low and almost sinks. Ebony wood is so heavy that it does sink. Balsa wood is so light that you can hardly hold a big piece of it under the water. Iron, copper, lead, silver, and gold are all very heavy as compared with water, and so they sink.

A piece of rubber sinks, but a tire inner tube full of air will not sink. The tube with air in it weighs much less than the water it pushes aside. The tube is a good thing to play with when you are in the water. It is so light that it even holds you up.

Why doesn't a bird fall off its perch when it sleeps?

A canary bird can stay on its perch all night without falling off, even if it is sound asleep. So can a chicken. Forest birds do not fall off branches and twigs. How do they stay on while they are asleep?

When a bird is on the ground, its feet are spread out. But they curl around a perch or a branch and hold the bird tight. The bird does not have to think about holding on. When it squats down to go to sleep, the muscles in its legs pull the toes and claws tight around the branch, and it cannot fall.

· · · · HOW QUESTIONS · · · ·

How do the baby birds learn to fly?

Baby birds grow fast. They soon get so big that the nest is full. A baby old enough to fly may be standing on the edge of the nest. The mother or father is flying near by. The baby may open its wings but it seems not to know yet that it can use its wings. It may jump down to a branch, or it may fall down. Then it may move its wings enough to be off its feet. It tries again and again, and soon it is flying. The young bird does not have to be taught how to move its wings. That ability comes from an instinct that all flying birds have. They just use their wings and soon they are flying.

How high can a bird fly?

A bird flies by fanning his wings against the air. It must have air to fan its wings against or it cannot fly. So, if it tries to fly too high, it finds itself in trouble. The air gets thinner and thinner. There finally isn't enough air to push its wings against.

Some birds can fly higher than other birds. They have big wings. But even these birds could never fly many miles up into the air. They are sometimes so high, however, that we can hardly see them.

How do we hear?

We hear different kinds of sounds: piano music, singing, talking, an explosion, thunder, a footstep, the telephone bell. You can think of many others. How do we hear these sounds?

Something must come to our ears. What is sound and how does it come to our ears?

Sound is movement back and forth of particles of air. If we tap a window pane, it moves in and out very rapidly, but so little that we cannot see it move. We say it is vibrating. The vibrating glass makes the air particles next to it vibrate. The vibration travels to our ears in air waves, which are somewhat like the little waves on the pond when we throw in a pebble. There is a membrane (ear drum) in our ears. The air waves make it vibrate. After nerves have done their part, the brain tells us that we are hearing the sounds.

Sound can travel through many other things also, but it is usually air waves that bring the sound to our ears.

How can we tell east and west?

Wherever we are we like to know which way is east and which way is west. An easy way to tell is to notice where the sun rises. That way is east. Where the sun sets is west. You see that east and west are opposite directions. If you raise your arms sideways, and one arm points east, the other points west.

How about north and south? To think how to know these directions is not so easy. But here is a good rule: Stand with your right arm pointing east and your left arm pointing west; then the direction in front of you is north and the direction behind you is south.

When you study maps in school, you must remember that the top part of the map is north and the bottom part is south, and that the right-hand part is east and the left-hand part is west.

How do we know the earth is round?

If we could get away up far from the earth and could look down on it, we could see that the earth is almost round, like a ball. But we know in other ways that the earth is round, and not flat as it seems to us. Ships are going around the world all the time. Many airplanes have gone around the world. When the earth gets between the sun and the moon, the earth's shadow on the moon shows that the earth is round. A long time ago people thought the earth was flat, and that they would fall off when they reached the ends of it.

How does a chick grow in the egg?

Have you seen little chicks coming out of the egg shells? The hen has been sitting on the eggs for twenty-one days. She has kept them warm. Or the eggs have been in the warm incubator for twenty-one days.

At first the eggs were like the egg you have for breakfast. They had yellow yolks and the part we call the white. But the heat of the mother's body started a tiny spot in each egg to grow. It grew and grew. It got bigger and bigger. It used up the yolk and the white. For some time after it began to grow it didn't look at all like a chick. But later legs and wings and feathers grew on its body. Finally it was a chick, strong enough to pick a hole in the shell and then to break the shell and come out. A great deal had happened in the egg in twenty-one days.

How did the salt get into the sea water?

The sea water is very salty. We cannot drink it because it is so salty. Where did all this salt come from?

There is a little salt in the ground. When rain water sinks into the ground it dissolves some of the salt out and carries it to rivers and lakes. We cannot taste the salt in river water and lake water, for there is not enough in it to taste. We call this water fresh water. All the time rivers are taking fresh water to the sea. Sea water has no place to flow to. It just evaporates. But salt cannot evaporate. And so what was just a little salt in the water becomes more and more, and the water gets saltier and saltier. Also, the rivers are bringing in a little more salt all the time. Now the sea water has a great deal of salt in it.

How does a vacuum cleaner work?

Have you heard the vacuum cleaner making a humming noise? The noise comes partly from the motor which is working the air pump. Another sound comes from the wind by which the rug is being cleaned. The pump is making the wind. The pump is sucking the air into the cleaner from the rug. It is this air, or wind, which picks up the dust and dirt from the rug and carries them to the big bag. You can feel the air going into the cleaner if you put your hand on the rug near where the cleaner is sucking.

How does a spider make a web?

Probably you have seen several kinds of spiders. You have seen garden spiders, house spiders, and grass spiders. This story is about the garden spider and her web.

The picture shows a spider waiting in the middle of the web for an insect to get caught in it. She has made the web strong so that the wind will not be likely to destroy it and it will hold her and her victims. She may have started at the end of a branch of a shrub. From it she spun a thread which caught on another branch. She walked along this bridge and spun another thread from the middle to another branch, and so on. Soon she had made the spokes of her web. Then she began at the middle to make the cross threads from spoke to spoke. Later she made stronger, more sticky cross threads. In the center she spun threads across and across, for that was where she was to stay.

When a fly or other insect flies against the web, the sticky threads hold it until the spider can sting it and make it helpless. Then she sucks the juices out of it, and lets the hard parts drop. Spiders destroy many harmful insects in our garden.

How do animals go to sleep?

We see how cats and dogs go to sleep. They just lie down and close their eyes, as we do. Cows lie down, but horses can sleep standing up. Sometimes horses lie down, too. Birds go to sleep on twigs of trees and bushes without falling off. They can hold on tight without trying to hold on. They don't stand on the twig. They squat down, and their leg muscles fold the toes and claws around the twig.

Some animals and birds sleep during the day and are awake during the night. Owls do their hunting after it gets dark. The owl listens carefully for the sound of a mouse, sees it move, and swoops down without a noise to grab the mouse. Many insects, also, are quiet during the day and come out at night. The bat sleeps all day in as dark a place as he can find. He hangs head down as he sleeps. At night he flies around and catches insects.

Some animals, like bears, sleep through the cold winter, day and night. We say they hibernate. Frogs and snakes that live where it gets cold hibernate in the ground or under stones.

How does a caterpillar become a butterfly?

The big orange and brown Monarch butterfly you see in the fall was once a caterpillar. But first it was a little green egg on a milkweed leaf. It hatched into a tiny caterpillar, which ate and ate the milkweed leaves, and grew bigger and bigger. It was then in the larva stage. As a growing caterpillar it had to shed its skin several times. Finally it attached itself to the plant and its skin became like a bag and hard. There it stayed for ten to fourteen days while great changes were taking place. It was then in the chrysalis or pupa stage. When it broke out of this covering, it was a beautiful butterfly, becoming larger as it came out. The female was soon ready to lay eggs.

Many flying insects go through these four stages in their development: egg, larva or caterpillar, pupa or chrysalis, and butterfly or moth.

How does a draft cool you?

A draft is a breeze or wind that isn't too strong. It may be a wind out of doors or a wind from a fan. If you sit or stand in a draft when you are warm and sweating, you will soon feel cooler. Of course, you must not let the draft cool you too quickly. That would be bad.

How does a draft cool you? Have you ever put your hand in warm water and then waved it in the air? Did you notice that your hand felt cool until it got dry? It was the evaporation of the water on your hand that made the coolness. We say water evaporates when it changes from liquid water into water that we cannot see in the air. Evaporation always makes coolness.

When you are sweating, water is coming out on your skin. Then a draft makes this water evaporate faster, because the draft is blowing off the moist air from the skin and bringing in new air to the skin. More water then can evaporate into the new air.

How does the weather man tell what the weather will be?

Every day we want to know what the weather will be the next day. We listen to the radio report, or we read the newspaper, or we look at the weather map in school. The report tells whether it will rain or be cloudy or clear, what the temperature will be, and what kind of wind we shall have. How can the weather man find out?

In the United States and Canada there are weather men at many places. They make records. At a certain hour each day they telegraph the records to central stations. The records tell the temperatures and the amounts of rainfall of the day before, the present direction and rate of wind and the air pressure, whether it is clear or cloudy or raining, and the temperature.

At the central weather stations men put this information on big maps. The information comes from several hundred places, including places in Alaska, the West Indies islands and certain islands in the Pacific Ocean, Mexico, and even ships at sea.

The men at the maps have studied a great deal about weather. From the information they have put on the maps they can tell much about what kind of weather a place will have in the next twenty-four hours or longer. Usually the weather men are right. Sometimes they are wrong, because the conditions that make the weather have changed.

How do the firemen know there is a fire?

Every city has a fire station, where the hose truck, the pumper, the ladder truck, and the chemical engine are kept. Day and night some firemen are in the station ready to go to fires. Many cities have several fire stations.

Suddenly the telephone may ring. There is a fire. The voice tells where it is, and the men are ready in an instant. Often it is not the telephone that tells them where there is a fire. It is a signal bell and an indicator on the wall. Somebody near the fire has hurried to a red signal box and pulled down a handle. Electricity goes through the wires to the station. The indicator on the wall shows just where that signal box is. The firemen rush to that box and soon they see where the fire is.

How does water put out a fire?

If you want to make something catch fire, like coal or wood or paper, you must make it very hot. When you put a piece of paper into the match flame, the paper begins to burn because the flame is hot. If you put water on the burning paper, the paper will stop burning, because it will no longer be hot enough to burn. Water cannot get hot enough to keep the paper burning. Firemen try to put out a fire by putting water on it. Boy Scouts and Girl Scouts are very careful to put plenty of water on their camp fires before they leave them.

Another reason why water puts out a fire is that it may keep the oxygen of the air from getting to the fire. If you put a burning stick into water, the fire goes out quickly. Wood and coal and paper and other things must be where oxygen is or they cannot burn.

How does a compass work?

A compass points north and south. We use it to show directions. We can make a needle into a compass. We must stroke the needle with one end of a magnet. We must stroke it from eye to point or from point to eye, but not both ways. Then, if we tie a fine thread around the middle of the needle and hold the needle up by the thread, one end of the needle will point to the north and the other end will point to the south. But we must not hold the needle up near the magnet or a stove or a car or anything made of iron, for then one end of the needle will move away from north and point toward the iron. Boy Scouts and Girl Scouts use compasses which they can buy at stores. These compasses have needles balanced on a pivot. The Scouts use them in the woods to find their directions. Pilots on boats and planes also use compasses. When they see which way is north, they know also which way is south, and then they can tell which way is east or west.

How does a thermometer work?

The tube in a thermometer has mercury in it. Sometimes it has red alcohol in it instead. When the mercury or alcohol gets warmer it swells and needs more room. So it moves up the tube. When the mercury or alcohol gets cooler it needs less room and goes down the tube.

There are numbers on the thermometer. These are put on to show how warm or how cold it is. We like our rooms to be not too warm or too cold. We like the top of the mercury or alcohol to be at about 70. We say the temperature then is 70 degrees. When mother puts a health thermometer under your tongue, she wants it to show between 98 and 99 degrees.

How does the bat avoid bumping its head?

The bat flies around in the dusk or the darkness to catch insects in the air. But it does not hit a house or a tree, for it suddenly dodges aside and avoids a bump.

The bat has a wonderful way of knowing that something is ahead. As it flies, it makes a constant cry or hum, too high pitched for a person's ear to hear it. This hum sets up vibrations in the air. They bounce back from the obstacle to the bat's ears, and the bat's wings change the flight instantly.

How does a snake crawl?

A snake doesn't have legs, but some snakes can crawl along the ground very fast. We can watch a snake crawl and still not find out how it does it.

A skeleton of a snake shows many ribs. They are all attached to the backbone. Muscles attach each rib to the rib before and the rib behind. The muscles can move the under parts of the ribs. The tips of the ribs move the crosswise scales on the snake's under side. So the muscles move in order, and the scales push the snake along. Usually the snake does not crawl straight ahead, but in curves from side to side.

···· WHERE QUESTIONS ····

Where does salt go in water?

If you put a spoonful of salt into a glass of warm water, the salt disappears. You cannot see it. But you can taste it. It is still there. Why cannot you see it?

You will find out why, if you let the glass of salty water stand uncovered for a day or two. You will begin to see the salt again. It will be sticking to the glass.

Salt dissolves in water. When the water becomes less by evaporation, the salt begins to come out and you can see it again. Only a certain amount of water at a certain temperature will hold a certain amount of dissolved salt. When all the water has gone from the glass, all the salt will be left and you can see it again.

Where are the highest mountains?

Every continent except Australia has high mountains. The highest in North America is Mount McKinley, Alaska (20,257 ft.). Canada's highest is Mount Logan (19,850 ft.). The highest in the United States outside Alaska is Mount Whitney in California (14,495 ft.). The highest mountain in the world is Mount Everest, in Asia; it is 29,002 ft. high. Africa has Mount Kilimanjaro (19,587 ft.), and South America has Mount Aconcagua (22,835 ft.). Europe has Mont Blanc (15,781 ft.).

When you are older and study maps, you can see where the high mountains are.

Where are the stars in the daytime?

At night, if it isn't cloudy, we see thousands of stars in the sky. But in the daytime they seem to be gone, for we cannot see them. They are there in the sky, just as they are at night. The reason we cannot see them is that the light from the sun is much brighter than the light from the stars.

Where do sponges come from?

Do you use a sponge in your house? You may use it in the bathroom or to wash woodwork and windows. Many people use a sponge to wash the car. We like to squeeze out the dirty suds and let our sponge fill with clean suds.

The sponge came from the ocean, where the water was warm and not too deep. It grew there. It was alive. The sponge we use is only the skeleton. In the ocean it was full of small, jelly-like animals. The skeleton was around them, not in them. It was attached to something solid, such as a stone or a shell. The animals got their food and oxygen from the water that flowed in the skeleton around them. What we know as a sponge, then, is only what is left after the animals have died and been removed. They died when they were taken out of the water.

In your home you may have sponges that never were alive. They are not real sponges. They are made of rubber or plastic.

Where do diamonds come from?

Diamonds come from mines. Some mines are very deep. The best mines are in one region in South Africa. The diamonds are in a kind of blue rock. Men must take out a good deal of rock to find a single good diamond. When a diamond is found it does not look like the diamonds we see. It does not sparkle. It has to be ground very carefully by men who know how. This kind of grinding is called cutting. When the cutting is finished, the diamonds are sent to stores to be placed in rings and other jewelry.

Where does the wood go when it burns?

A tree makes wood as it grows. This is how it makes wood: The green leaves take in carbon dioxide from the air and water that comes up from the ground through the roots. We cannot see the carbon dioxide. It is invisible, like the air. When the sunlight shines on the leaves, they change the carbon dioxide and the water into food for the tree. Then the tree makes wood from the food.

When wood burns, just the opposite takes place. The wood combines with the oxygen of the air and becomes carbon dioxide and water again. We cannot see this water, for it is like evaporated water. The ash that is left is mostly the mineral which the roots took out of the ground along with the water.

THE QUESTION BOX

Where do the Eskimos live?

The Eskimos are cold-weather people. They live mostly in the far northern part of North America, scattered in small groups in Alaska, northern Canada, and Greenland. It is a land of long, cold winters. The summers are so short that vegetables and fruits and grains like wheat, corn, and oats cannot grow. The people have to live on meat and fish. Traders bring in a few things like guns, needles, strong thread, knives, and cooking utensils to exchange for furs. The Eskimos kill seals, walruses, whales, and polar bears. They catch fish through a hole in the ice. They are ready to spear a seal which comes to the hole to breathe. Also, they hunt caribou when these animals come north in the summer to eat the moss and other small plants.

Only in the southern part of Eskimoland are there trees of any size. In the far north, trees cannot grow high. An old birch tree may be only three feet tall. The Eskimos can get driftwood from the beaches. Their homes are usually like tents, but are made of furs on a framework of whalebone and wood. The people can make good houses of snow, if necessary. But it is the fur clothing that keeps them warm. A little bowl of stone makes a stove and furnishes a little light. The oil comes from the animals killed for food and furs.

Where does gasoline come from?

Gasoline comes from oil that was in the ground. The oil in the ground is not thin and clear like gasoline. It is yellow or greenish or dark brown. We call it petroleum. Usually it lies away down in the earth. We find it only in certain regions of the earth. Men use machines to drill round holes down to where the oil is. The petroleum comes up, or machines pump it up. It goes in pipes to where it is made into gasoline and other things like kerosene, oil for diesel engines and for heating homes, and oil to lubricate machines. Finally trains or trucks bring the gasoline to the filling stations where we buy it to make our cars and trucks and tractors go.

Where does coal come from?

Coal comes from down in the earth. Sometimes it is a long way down and sometimes not very far down. Coal isn't everywhere in the earth, but only at certain places. Men dig down to where the coal is. Usually it is between layers of rock. The place where the men get the coal is called a mine, and the men are called miners. It is dark down in the mine, and the miners have little lamps on their caps.

The miners often have to blast the coal to get it loose. Then they send it up in an elevator to a building where it is put through machines which break the bigger pieces. After it is washed and sorted into small pieces and medium-sized pieces, it is put into railroad cars to go to the cities.

Where does electricity come from?

We use electricity to light our homes and sometimes to toast our bread, make our coffee, wash our clothes, and do many other things. Where does the electricity come from?

We know it comes into the house on wires. The wires are on poles. If we follow the wires far enough we come to buildings with big machines. The electricity comes from these machines. These machines are called generators. Some generators work by water power, and some work by steam power. Water power comes from a river which has a dam to make a higher pond of water. Then the water can go down a pipe to make the machines work. Steam power comes from burning coal or oil. Trains bring the coal from the mines. Sometimes trains bring the oil in tank cars, and sometimes the oil comes a long way in pipes.

Where did dinosaurs live?

Millions of years ago dinosaurs lived on every one of these continents—North America, South America, Europe, Asia, Africa, and Australia. They were reptiles, like the alligators, snakes, and turtles that live on earth today. Some dinosaurs were very small. Others were the largest land animals that have ever lived. These big dinosaurs were much larger than elephants. Dinosaurs of one type grew to a length of more than eighty-five feet. They had heavy bodies, strong legs, long tails, and long necks. Their heads were small, and their brains were tiny. While some of the smallest dinosaurs were flesh eaters, like lions and tigers, the largest dinosaurs lived on plants which grew in the swamps where they made their homes.

Long before man appeared on the earth all the dinosaurs had disappeared. Perhaps they died when the temperature became cooler, killing the plants upon which they fed. We know about dinosaurs today because their skeletons have been found in many parts of the world. When we see these skeletons in our museums, we may feel thankful that such huge beasts no longer roam the earth.

Where do frogs stay in the cold winter?

In the autumn when the water in their ponds and streams becomes cold, the frogs have to get ready for winter. Frogs cannot keep warm through the winter like sparrows and foxes and squirrels. They are cold blooded. That means they are always as cold as the air or the water around them. Of course, in the summer they are as warm as the air or the water around them. In the winter they are so cold they are stiff.

Before the weather gets too cold in the autumn, the frogs seem to sense what they must do. They cannot think as we think, but they know what to do without having to learn. They burrow down into the mud and slowly lose feeling. Their hearts beat very slowly. They are still alive, but they do not need to eat. We say they are hibernating. In the spring, when the water gets warmer, they slowly become active again and come out from the mud. They have not suffered at all in the cold winter.

Where did the earthworm come from?

Early on a warm morning just after a rain we may see earthworms on the sidewalk. Where did they come from? Some people think they must have come down in the rain. But these people are wrong. Earthworms never come down in the rain.

The earthworms came up from the ground. They came up in the night. That is when they come out to eat tiny pieces of old leaves and grass. Then they go back into the ground before the sun can shine on them long. They cannot live long in bright sunlight. Sometimes they have crawled onto sidewalks and do not get back to the ground. Then we see them.

Where do monkeys live?

Most monkeys live where the climate is very warm. They are found on tropical islands, in southern Asia, in Africa, and in Central and South America. The only monkeys in North America are those housed in zoos or kept as pets. The only wild monkeys found in Europe are those living at Gibraltar. Australia has no wild monkeys at all. In Asia monkeys are found living as far north as Tibet and Japan, but monkeys usually make their homes in much warmer lands. Many of them live in dense jungles, spending most of their time high in the trees. When they swing from branch to branch in search of fruit and other food, they use their long arms to pull their bodies along. And when they walk, they travel on all fours. Thus their hands serve as an extra pair of feet. But their feet also double as hands, for a monkey's feet can grasp and hold objects just as his hands can. Some monkeys can also grip tree branches and other objects with their long tails. With so many ways of holding on, the monkey is in little danger of falling from his lofty perch. Not all monkeys live in trees, however. The doglike baboon spends all his time on the ground. This member of the monkey family makes his home in a cave and he often can be heard quarreling with his neighbors.

Where does rubber come from?

Rubber comes from trees, but not the trees we see where we live. Rubber trees grow where it is hot and wet all the time. Rubber is made from the sap of these trees. Men make a cut in the trees in such a way as to let the sap flow out slowly into something to hold it. This sap is thin, not thick like molasses. But it is not as thin as water. A man dips a long stick into it and holds it over a fire. He dips the stick into the sap many times. The rubber forms on the stick. It becomes like a ball of crude rubber. Then the man takes it off and puts it with other balls. Finally there is enough to sell. This rubber goes on ships and railroads to factories where other things are put with it to become the rubber that we know. Some of the rubber nowadays is made from chemicals and not from sap. We call this rubber synthetic rubber.

SPACE TAXIS will carry people and supplies between the earth and a space station. Great power will be needed to drive the taxis into space, for the earth will pull back on them. The closer things are to the earth, the more the earth pulls them. When they get far enough away, the earth stops pulling them. This makes them light and easy to move.

Near the earth, too, it is hard for objects to push through the air at high speed. Air pulls on moving objects, just as water pulls on your hand when you move your hand in a pool. The farther you get from the earth, the less air there is. Up in space there is no air at all to push through.

Now you know two important things about space ships. It will be hard to get them into space. It will be easy to move them in space.

SPACE SHIPS

These men are construction workers, like the men you see building houses. They are not on earth, but floating in space. They are making a space station in space. They have joined two space ships together. Now they are building the space station around them. Space taxis are bringing supplies to them. The men must carry tanks of air to breathe, for there is no air in space.

Why do we need a space station? Because it will be easier to make flights into space from a space station than from the earth. When a space ship starts from a space station, it will not have to pull away from the earth, and it will not have to push against air. Its fuel supply will carry it much farther.

Here is the space station. The space taxis near it show you how large it is. It is big enough to be a small city. Thousands of people live in it. It has hotels, restaurants, stores, laundries, and barber shops, like a city. It also has landing fields, hangars, fueling stations, and repair shops for the space taxis. From a space station like this, it would be possible to send a space ship on a journey to the moon.

SPACE SHIPS

The moon is about 240,000 miles from the earth. This is about ten times the distance around the earth. But an unmanned rocket could reach the moon much faster than it could travel around the earth ten times. Going to the moon, it would not have to pull against the earth or push through air. In fact, as it neared the moon, the moon would pull on it. One type of rocket could reach the moon in about ten hours. The moon may have large deposits of minerals that will be mined.

MOON 240,000 MILES

EXOSPHERE 500 MILES

IONOSPHERE 200-300 MILES

STRATOSPHERE 20 MILES

TROPOSPHERE 7 MILES

Someday men may travel to the moon. A space ship could land on the moon and send out explorers. You will see that this space ship is not streamlined like the space taxis. It does not have to be, for it does not go through air. We streamline things only to make it easier for them to push through air.

This explorer is carrying air in tanks on his back. There is no air on the moon. The explorer is also heavily armored. The armor is to protect him from the meteors that fall on the moon.

From the control room of the space ship, other members of the party watch the explorer set up a testing device on the dry, dusty surface of the moon. Below them, a hydraulic elevator smoothly lowers a second explorer to the ground. He has just passed through the air lock, which keeps the artificial atmosphere from leaking out of the space ship. At the top of the space ship are antennae for radar, radio, and television communication with earth. The operators may be seen in the room just below the antennae.